ILLUSTRATING NATURE

Right-brain Art in a Left-brain World

Available through Nature Works Press:

BOOKS – NATURAL HISTORY

The Redrock Canyon Explorer (for all ages) – a complete and fascinating guide for exploring nature in the American Southwest

Wild Babies, a Nature Sketchbook – bobcats, black bears, redtail hawks, gray squirrels, big-eared bats and black-tail deer in their natural habitat

Beaver Year – a year in the life of a beaver colony

Elephant Seal Beach (formerly **Elephants on the Beach**) – a naturalist takes her sketching journal to an elephant seal beach, sketching seals, birds and plants

CAMPSITE CRITTER GUIDES

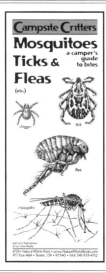    

WILDLIFE AND PLANT CLIP ART

NatureClips, the finest natural history clipart available online. See art throughout this and other books by Irene Brady.

For more information about the books, reviews, guides and natural history clipart, visit **www.natureworksbooks.com** • phone **541-535-3189** • FAX **541-535-4712**

Brady, Irene.
Illustrating nature : right-brain art in a left-brain world / written and illustrated by Irene Brady.
p. cm.
Includes index.
ISBN 0-915965-08-9
1. Natural history illustration. 2. Scientific illustration. 3. Drawing — Technique. 4. Nature (Aesthetics). I. Title.
QH465.B7 2004
508.022—dc22   2004110533

Nature Works Press

PO Box 469
Talent, OR 97540

Printed in the USA
First Edition

ILLUSTRATING NATURE

Right-brain Art in a Left-brain World

written and illustrated by
Irene Brady

with artwork examples
contributed
by students

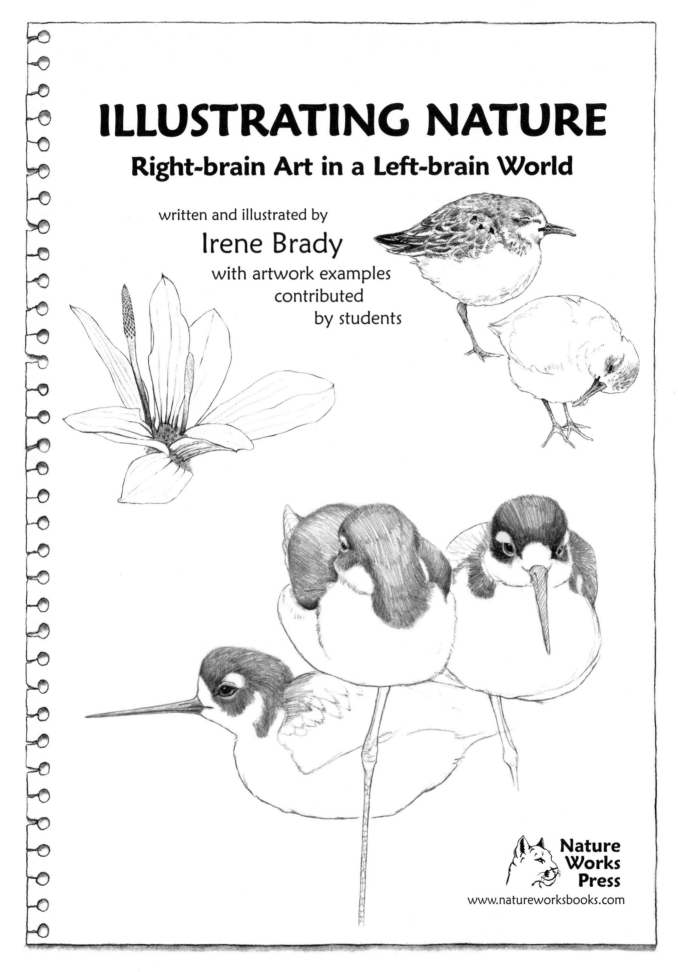

Nature
Works
Press
www.natureworksbooks.com

About the author/illustrator

Irene Brady, is a lifelong naturalist, author, illustrator, and diligent advocate for the environment. She trained as a scientific illustrator at the Museum of Comparative Zoology and the Botanical Museum at Harvard University under Elmer W. Smith, renowned illustrator of *Orchids, A Golden Nature Guide*, and R.E. Schultes, the eminent ethnobotanist and professor. She later studied painting, design and layout at Oregon College of Art and Pacific College of Art and Design to augment her illustration skills.

Her writing and illustrations have appeared in Audubon, Ranger Rick, Your Big Backyard, Cricket, RV Journal, Mushroom, and other natural history magazines.

She has written and illustrated numerous nature books for major U.S. publishers (Scribners, Morrow, Houghton Mifflin, Coward-McCann, etc.), and illustrated numerous books by other writers, traveling widely throughout the United States to sketch, photograph and research them.

helping a student with field sketch

Irene Brady's books have won national awards from the New York Academy of Sciences, The National Science Teachers Association, and the Oregon Library Association for their prose and art, and have also been featured in gift and "suggested reading list" catalogs sent to members of The National Wildlife Federation and the Junior Literary Guild. Her artwork has appeared in national shows celebrating wildlife art and children's book illustration.

While teaching scientific illustration at Southern Oregon University, Irene continues to work on books, wildlife guides and clip art. She also creates wildlife art for museums, nature centers and USFS interpretive site displays.

Visit her website at **www.natureworksbooks.com** for more information.

Nature Works Press
is dedicated to preserving the Earth

Our books and guides focus on our native wildlife and their lives and habitats, as seen through fact and "reality fiction." Our scope also extends into the past to encompass the First Americans and into current areas of field sketching and scientific illustration.

Our readers are lovers of the wild with curious minds, who want to know more about this amazing world. All ages enjoy our publications on wildlife and nature.

Our hope is to expand our readers' love and awe of nature, and foster an enduring empathy for wildlife. This can be accomplished by gaining knowledge and putting it to work in the real world.

Our joy is in making nature come to life in a way so engaging and compelling that the reader will become a partner in making and keeping the natural world safe and secure.

That is a dream and ethic strong enough to clearly light the way as we move forward.

We invite you to join us on the journey.

The Publisher, Nature Works Press

Table of Contents

Extra Credit: Scratchboard (5pts)....47, Alternate Views (3pts)....48, Selecting the Right Font (3pts)....65, Illustrate Your Eye (3pts)....76, Grasshopper Graphic Manipulation (10pts)....112, Missing Items....133, Business Card (5pts)....152.

Acknowledgments

While the techniques and exercises in this book are suitable for all ages, the book originally began life as a textbook. That worked in its favor, since every technique had to survive numerous trials at the hands of students in order to make the final cut. While still used as a textbook, it has been expanded and revised to serve as a useful guide for naturalists, artists and seekers of any age.

I'd like to thank Frank Lang, Professor of Biology (now Emeritus) at Southern Oregon University in Ashland, Oregon, with whom I team-taught biological illustration over the course of several years. Frank graciously gave advice, answered questions and helped me jump-start the course of scientific illustration which led to the formation of this book, **Illustrating Nature, Right-brain Art in a Left-brain World.**

With the enthusiastic participation of students who took the course, I floated new ideas, sent up trial balloons, applied tried-and-true techniques, and sorted through what worked well and what didn't. With their encouragement and help, masses of handouts matured into this book.

Students painstakingly evaluated class materials, gleefully pointed out typos and non-sequiturs, and cheerfully volunteered artwork for publication. They also waded through a few exercises that didn't work as expected and helped me find ways to improve them. To all of my students I extend grateful thanks. To the students listed below, whose illustrations grace the following pages, I offer additional heartfelt gratitude. This book wouldn't exist without the efforts you all have made. Pages where student artwork appears are listed at the end of the index.

The work of the following students appears:

Jerry Aikins, Steve Ballew, Aubrey Bayley, Mudra Bergan, Allison Dew, Kyle Emry, Andrea Fraga, Jamie Heinzelmann, Hillary Hulen, Nicolaj Imhof, Lea Johnson, Noelle Jordan, Vera Kirkpatrick, Andrew Marohl, Allyson McCauley, Zoë Magnolia McLean, Deanna Moore, Lisa Sanchez Navarro, Megan O'Donnell, Michelle Olson, Wendy Olson, Matt Paroulek, Julie Proctor, Lin Roden, Christian Runge, Mary Schnur, Peter Schroeder, Theresa Selvy, Rachel Showalter, Holly Smith, Heidi Soroken, Robert Sweeney, Ilona Sweeten, Bianca Tapia, Sara Trakselis, Shannon Troy, Elizabeth Wasserman, Melinda Whipple-Smith, Eugene Wier, Dylan Zodrow.

All other materials in this book have been attributed to their sources on the pages of their appearances – or were written and illustrated by myself. Any errors or omissions are solely my responsibility.

Special thanks go to my chief critic and editor, Diane Harris. Reading with fresh eyes, and with keen attention to detail, she caught typos, grammatical errors, lapses in connectivity, and leaps of logic. She pointed out repetitions, incomplete sentences, and areas that needed improvement. If there is clarity in this book, she probably had something to do with it.

For assistance in making the manuscript printable, my thanks go to David Brady of Printworks Company, an exemplary print house focusing on high quality production at reasonable prices. David escorted me through the initial printing with calm, professional guidance – a tour-de-force through the state-of-the-art mechanics of print production from PDFs (portable document files) and the intricacies of online uploading, to the delivery of the advance copies – then encouraged its transformation into a book for a wider audience.

Thanks also go to Stewart Janes, Danny and Lydia Kiesecker and their mother, Tree, who field-tested the book, Daniel Bish, Laura O'Brady, and Marcia Way-Brady. Darby Morrell offered insights, approaches, and many other bits of advice and encouragement. Other people have also offered advice in enlarging the scope of this book. You know who you are, and I thank you with a grateful heart.

Irene Brady • November • 2004

Introduction

• Could this be you? •

"**I enjoy drawing** — I think I have potential, but how do I break through?"

"**I can't draw a straight line**, much less anything that looks like the original subject. But I *want to*."

"**I am an artist**, and I'd like to polish my skills, maybe even become a full-time illustrator."

Do you fit one of those descriptions? If so, help is on the way. Because artistic ability isn't a skill given to only a chosen few — we are ALL gifted with the ability to record our observations well enough to delight ourselves daily, and maybe even make a living with our art.

It's all about learning how to SEE. In fact, those artists whom you admire and envy are artists **only** because they stumbled, early on, upon the key of **how to see and then translate the vision into a drawing.** Oddly, they may not even be aware that it happened, which can limit their progress later on.

As a child, you could probably turn out a pretty fair drawing similar to drawings of others in your age group. As you proceeded through the elementary grades, you drew pictures in school or to entertain yourself at home. Then, like most people, you probably stopped. Perhaps somebody ridiculed your masterpiece, or maybe you just got busy elsewhere.

Naturally, your artistic development stopped cold, and since your results haven't improved in years, you may feel you have no artistic talent at all.

But that's not true, even though your lifelong experiences might scream that it IS. You have untapped capabilities, but perhaps they're buried so deeply that you can barely recognize them. And regardless of your youth or age, it's not too late to grab the reins and guide your artistic pony to the destination of your choice.

The job here is to locate and access your right brain hemisphere where your drawing skills dwell. Finding the key, opening the gate, then honing long-abandoned latent skills and abilities is what this book is all about.

• Explore your potential! •

This book wasn't just tossed off in a couple of months as a lark. It began several years ago as a collection of handouts for a scientific illustration class accepting students at all levels of art proficiency — from close to zero to art majors.

As the class grew in popularity, the handouts increased in number until there seemed to be no choice left but to collect them into a textbook. Then nonstudents and homeschoolers started asking for copies.

You'll notice that exercises and projects have points assigned to them. The points are not awarded for the beauty of the final masterpiece but for the very act of ACCOMPLISHING the steps of the exercise. Since point values are assigned according to the importance of the task, you can use them to help you determine the relative usefulness of each task in developing your skills. This is particularly helpful if you have time constraints.

The exercises and projects have been tested, critiqued, enriched and polished by hundreds of eager, sharp-eyed students. Their work is found throughout the book — a distillation of what I have taught them, plus all they have taught me. That partnership has produced a no-frills approach, starting with basics and producing accomplished artists by the end of the book. And it really does. While not everyone can make the total breakthrough — *anyone can achieve measureable improvement and satisfaction.*

Upon completing this course, many students have had artwork published in periodicals. Others have gone into exhibit design and similar positions. The rest engage in journaling, field notes and scrapbooking with far greater skill and enjoyment.

This book is an essential classroom tool, but it is equally valuable for anyone, of any age, who wants to make the most of natural but underdeveloped skills. *It is a highly effective homeschool motivator.*

If you want to explore your artistic potential, learn new ways of seeing, and are willing to take a little time to make it all work, this book is for you.

Chapter 1. Starting Out With The Right Brain

You must become familiar with the differences between the left and right brain in order to understand how to redirect the organizational capabilities of your powerful left brain into a positive force in your art. This chapter is designed to help you come to grips with your left brain.

THE TEMPLATE SYNDROME

Did you ever try to draw pictures of two different people, but end up with the faces looking pretty much the same on both?

If so, you are coming from a standard left-brain position – the place where most of us live and dwell.

Our one-size-fits-all schooling has taught us to subdue the creative viewpoint that characterizes the workings of the right brain in favor of forming efficient, uniform, repetitive templates to represent such things as "a face" or "a flower."

STYLE AND SUBSTANCE

Templates have their place – even the best artists establish templates of a sort. You can recognize a Picasso or Norman Rockwell's art from a mile away. Such templates are the basis of "style," and style is fine, even in scientific illustration, as long as it doesn't get in the way of accuracy.

But most people have developed patterns or templates without the style. And to become the best artist you can be, you may have to alter your established templates, the way you look at things, and how you interpret what you observe.

If you want to draw what you really see, you must learn how to turn down the volume on your well-established left brain and ramp up the decibels on the right. But how?

IN THIS BOOK, YOU'LL LEARN:

• how to really **see** the image coming into your eyes,

  • translate it accurately

    • into impulses that go down your arm,

      • into your hand, and out through the pencil

        • onto the paper in unmistakable form.

Take a look in the next column at what your left brain REALLY wants you to draw. You can turn that preference into a **positive** force with a little bit of help and determination.

A Left Brain Lexicon

It's time to get acquainted with Your Right Brain.

Left Brain vs. Right Brain

(the phrases "right brain," and "left brain" as used in this book, refer to "right brain hemisphere" and "left brain hemisphere")

Left Brain vs. Right Brain

Below are some of the opposing ways our left and right brains operate.

Left Brain

Verbal: Uses words to name, describe, define

Analytical: Figures things out step-by-step, part-by-part

Symbolic: Uses symbols to represent things ($ = "dollar")

Abstract: A snippet represents the whole thing (USA, NBA)

Temporal: Keeps track of time, sequences, etc.

Rational: Draws conclusions based on reason and facts

Digital: Uses numbers, as in counting

Logical: Draws conclusions based on logic

Linear: Links ideas; one thought follows another to a conclusion

left brain
turkey drawing

right brain
turkey
drawing

Right Brain

Nonverbal: Is aware of things, but with minimal ties to words

Synthetic: Puts things together to form a total

Concrete: Relates to things as they are at the present moment

Nontemporal: Ignores time

Spatial: Notices relationships, and how parts fit together to form the whole

Analogical: Sees likenesses between things, understands metaphoric relationships

Nonrational: Doesn't require a basis of reason or facts, can suspend judgement

Holistic: Sees whole things all at once, perceives the overall patterns and structures

Intuitive: Has leaps of insight, based on incomplete patterns, hunches, feelings or visual images

Left Brain – Meet – Right Brain

SYMBOLISM

The **left** brain uses symbols for complicated ideas. The **left** brain is good at math, which deals with difficult concepts, like multiplication and square roots, with simple symbols. Everyday life is full of symbols.

The exercise below will allow your **left** brain to be really "**left**."

In each box below, quickly draw *the most basic symbol you can think of* to illustrate the word.

Don't be artistic, and don't worry about being Politically Correct. Make it so "typical" that even a young child will understand. This will be your **left** brain at work, doing what it's good at.

Take a few seconds to symbolize each word. For instance, here's a symbol for "happy:"

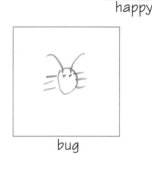

happy

tree

leaf

mouse

bug

frog

bird

flower

butterfly

A biological illustration is a very accurate drawing of an actual object. So shouldn't that be the perfect job for the analytical left brain? No – your left brain only draws symbols.

When illustrating, the problem is not to recognize the subject being drawn, but to see all its areas and parts as the shapes they actually are, then to fit them all together into a drawing that actually looks like the model.

Putting together these pieces is what the **right** brain is really good at.

In our symbol-oriented left-brain culture, most people seldom get to use their artistic right brain hemisphere. So, to illustrate realistically, you must learn to listen to your right brain so that you can draw what you actually see, not a symbol for what you "know" is there.

In fact, your right brain can actually get the jump on – and work with – your left brain if you program it to produce more realistic symbols, which the right brain can then grab and run with.

To be a good artist, you must be able to override your left brain, and let your right brain work, too.

These exercises will show you how to tap into your right brain hemisphere to create more realistic illustrations. After that, improving your aim is up to you. Have fun!

Faces & Vases

This exercise introduces your right brain to your left brain.

Follow instructions exactly. Read 1 - 5 before you begin.

1. In **Box ①** below, draw a face profile (forehead, nose, lips, chin) — see the example →
2. Start at Ax and end at Ao if you are right handed.
3. Start at Bx and end at Bo if you are left handed.
4. Now draw the other profile — but do NOT draw it as a face, just try to make
    an exact mirror image of the first side.
5. When you finish, read the text at the bottom of the page,
    then, if you have time, repeat the exercise in **Box ②**.

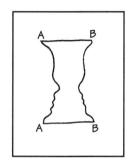

Box ①

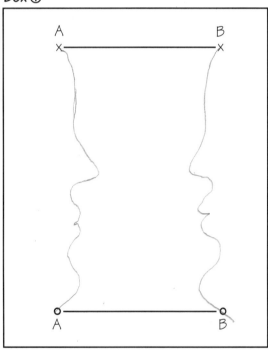

Box ②

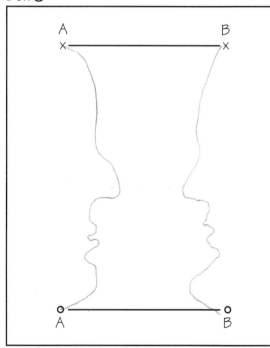

The first half of the exercise was done by your left brain — the second half was done by your right brain.

When you switched sides, did you feel the different ways your two brain halves work?

If you look at your picture one way, it looks like a pair of facing profiles. Looked at another way, it may seem to be a vase. Can you see it both ways?

Was the second side much harder to draw? It is for most people. If it was difficult, you were feeling your right brain struggling with the assignment. That's because it doesn't get much exercise and has to work really hard at what seems like an easy task.

Monsters and Vases

This "monster vase" exercise will more firmly establish the feeling of the right brain in action.

Follow instructions exactly. Read 1 - 5 before you begin.

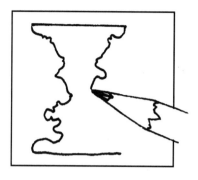

1. In **Box ①** below, draw a monster face profile. Include forehead, long warty, beaky nose, open mouth with teeth, chin with bumps and warts, etc. – see the example →
2. Start at Ax and end at Ao if you are right handed.
3. Start at Bx and end at Bo if you are left handed.
4. Now draw the other side – but do NOT draw it as a monster face, just try to make it an exact mirror image of the first side as shown at right.
5. When you finish, read the text at the bottom of the page, then, if you have time, repeat the exercise in **Box ②**.

Box ①

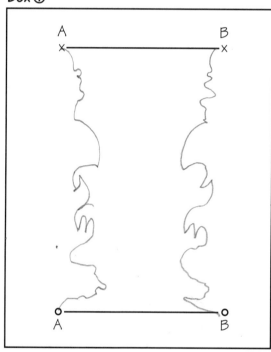

Box ②

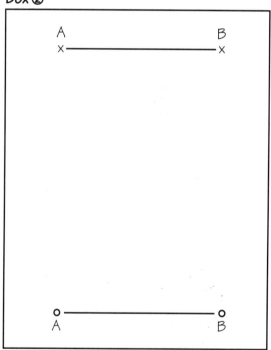

When you switched sides, you may have felt the different ways your two brains work. All the extra curves and jogs really made your out-of-shape right brain work hard.

The more often you do this exercise, the better your right brain will get at drawing – because that is what illustration is – transferring the correct shape of an image to your paper. Doing it backward makes it mutter to itself. Good!

Try doodling "faces and vases" if you have to wait in line for something. It's great drawing exercise.

Drawing Upside Down

Now to give the RIGHT brain the upper hand...

DON'T UP-END THIS PAGE!

(This exercise works better if you haven't seen the picture right side up.)

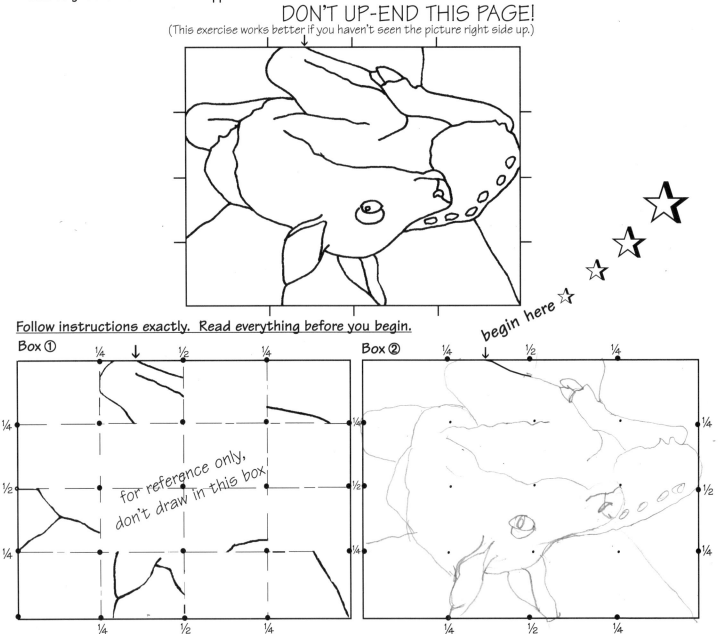

Follow instructions exactly. Read everything before you begin.

Box ①

for reference only, don't draw in this box

begin here ☆

Box ②

The picture at the top would be hard to draw correctly if oriented the usual way because the left brain tries to draw what it "knows" the subject is. But your left brain can't work upside down, so your right brain can take over and draw all of the funny shapes just the way they really are. All together, they will make up the complete picture.

Examine the picture, then in **Box ②** start drawing at the arrow. Don't draw any divisions – just visualize them. Send your pencil off in the correct direction, at the correct angle, and make it go as far as it should go. Notice how it works in **Box ①**. Check your source at the top of the page often as you draw.

As your pencil outlines the shapes, talk to it, i.e. *"loop a shallow arc down to here, then swoop back toward the edge – then jog in, now a 90° corner and straight line (with a blip) to the corner...."*

Notice shapes (triangles, rectangles) and angles (acute, obtuse, etc.), and their relative positions on the paper (halfway down, ¼ of the distance from edge or center, etc.). If you get stuck, begin at a new spot and work your way back toward a finished part.

When you finish, turn it right side up to look at it. How did you do? Don't be too hard on yourself if it isn't perfect – our left brains can be very strong.

Contour Drawing Without Lifting The Pencil From The Paper

This exercise puts your right brain ENTIRELY IN CHARGE.

DURING THIS EXERCISE,
DO NOT LIFT YOUR PENCIL FROM THE PAPER.

Follow instructions exactly.
Read 1 - 5 before you begin.

1. Place the point of your pencil on the head of the correct ant in the box below.

2. Pose your other hand in a comfortable, relaxed position and fasten your eyes on it.

3. Imagine the ant is **slowly** crawling around the outline of your hand, right around the edge. Don't take your eyes off it! Don't look at the paper

Keep your pencil on the ant while it moves around the perimeter of your hand. If your ant follows a crease of your hand inside the border of the outline, retrace your little ant-steps back out to the edge and continue on your way.

This should take 2 or 3 minutes.

If you finish sooner, do this exercise again on a fresh sheet of paper.

---

4. Do not look at your paper at ANY time. It's okay if your line goes outside the box!

5. Take your time. Let your right brain express itself. DO NOT HURRY.

Congratulations! You bypassed your left brain entirely and allowed your right brain to show what it can do.

Although you weren't able to coordinate things with your eyes, the picture is a rough record of what your right brain saw.

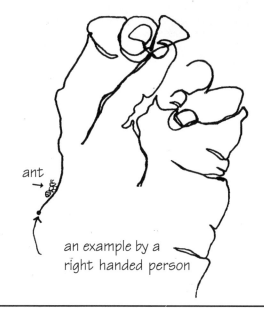

ant →

an example by a right handed person

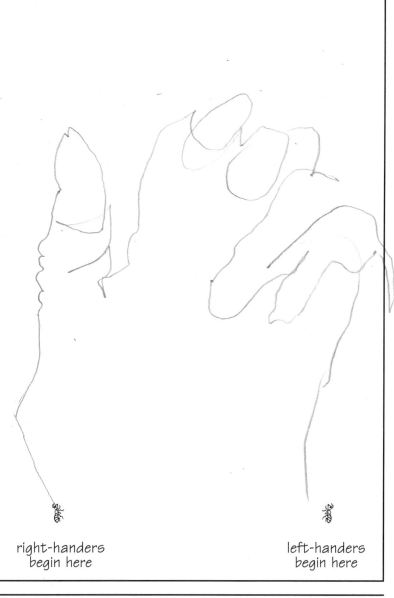

right-handers
begin here

left-handers
begin here

Modified Contour – Don't Lift The Pencil From The Paper

   Now that you've gotten some experience with how using your right brain "feels," this exercise will invite the left brain back into the process (under supervision) in an effort to integrate left brain procedures with your new right brain approach.

Follow instructions exactly.   Read 1 - 5 before you begin.

| Take 2 - 3 MINUTES to draw this. |

1. Place the point of your pencil on the head of the correct ant below.

2. Pose your other hand in exactly the same position as in the previous drawing.

3. Imagine the ant slowly crawling around the outline of your hand, right around the edge. **This time you may watch the ant as you draw.** Be sure to include your nails.

| Look back and forth constantly –
EVERY FEW SECONDS |

4. With your pencil coasting along on the ant's head, again follow the contours **without lifting it.**

   Your pencil speed will still be at an ant's pace, but this time "watching the ant" will help you stay on the paper and connect your right brain to your left brain.

5. Take your time.

Let your right brain express itself.

DO NOT HURRY.

Remember: This should take 2 or 3 minutes. If you finish sooner, do the exercise again on a fresh sheet of paper.

right-handers
begin here

left-handers
begin here

Modified Contour – Don't Lift The Pencil From The Paper

Draw Negative Spaces Using a Frame

You still need some tools to enable you to see correctly when objects are right-side-up and your left brain is part of the process. This exercise will show you how to short-circuit left-brain templates in order to find the true shape of the object.

In this exercise **do not draw the objects.** Draw everything BUT the objects. Arrange objects so that they intersect the edges of the frame to give your right brain some guideposts. Use this technique to help you re-focus on any future sketch that gives you difficulty.

Follow instructions exactly.   Read 1 - 4 before you begin.

1. Arrange (as flat as possible) some odd-shaped things (keys work well) on a background without any pattern or text.

2. Position a 2¼"x 1½" frame or "window" over your objects so that edges of the objects are covered by the frame edge in at least two places. See frame at right and around figure **a** below.

3. Stare at the shapes of the empty spaces around your objects (as in figure **b**).

You will eventually see "negative shapes" (like the black areas in figure **c**).

One side of each negative shape will run along the edge of the frame.

Tape the frame down so it can't move.

a. this is what you see

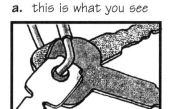

b. this is what you draw

c. "negative shapes."

4. Now draw the outlines of YOUR negative shapes in **Box ①** below. Your drawing should resemble figure **b**, above. Don't draw any details of the items, just **outline the space where they are not.**

DO NOT SHADE!

If you have time, rearrange your objects and repeat the exercise in **Box ②**.

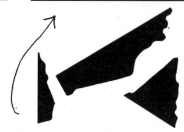

Can you see where each of these "negative shapes" fits above?

Box ①

Box ②

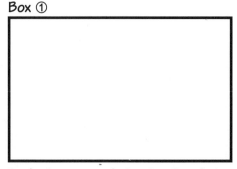

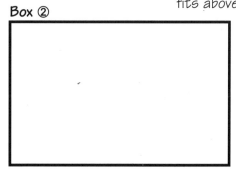

Don't draw any of the details of the objects, and don't draw outside the box borders.

Remember – look for negative shapes AROUND the objects, not the shapes of the objects.

Warming Up

The small frame in the last exercise made the job relatively easy. But how can you apply that concept to get the large picture? Multiply the "frames" into an imaginary grid, and work on a larger scene in sections.

Follow instructions exactly. Read all the way through before beginning.

• In **Box ①**. below, draw a complete outline of the pronghorn antelope, including its chin and the top of its head. After you finish drawing the outline, add eye, nose, and mouth, and the edges of any well-defined markings (white on neck, black on nose), but **don't shade** the markings.

• The horns have been started for you — pick up where those lines leave off. Triangulate (down from the top, in from the side) to see where any given spot on the outline should be. Make light dots where any part of the pronghorn touches the rectangle.

• If such a big blank rectangle seems scary, work within the smaller spaces marked off by the dots on **Box ①** which correspond to dots on **Box ②** (see the smaller area outlined in **Box ①**).

• Now, using your modified contour exercise experience (remember the ant? – but it's okay to look at the paper) draw a little bit of outline, checking back and forth with the dots on the rectangle to make sure you are drawing the right direction, length and angle.

• Stop and look often. Does your outline resemble the outline in the photo of the pronghorn? If not, erase and correct it. Watch for right angles, arcs, circles, blips, curves and so on. Duplicate those shapes. This exercise is similar to the upside-down fawn, but now your left brain is harder to overcome because it "knows" how eyes and ears, etc. "should" be shaped, and will try to insert its symbols for the actual anatomy shown.

• Ignore your left brain as it tells you "an antler looks like THIS" or "an eye is shaped THIS WAY." If your left brain knew how to draw, you'd already be a great artist. So ignore it.

Box ①

Box ②

One way to help your right brain really "see" a shape is to try to describe the shape with words. This combines left-brain verbal skills with your new right-brain way of seeing. This internal dialogue should accompany every drawing you do.

For this exercise, pretend that you must describe the cat skull below to a friend over the telephone so that he/she can sketch a picture of it.

You might narrate it as described below – follow along by stopping to recheck the skull after each •.

cat skull
1½x

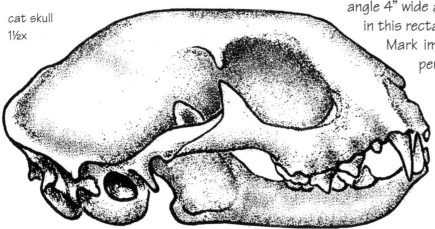

•"Draw a rectangle about twice as wide as it is high.

•At the midpoint of each end of the rectangle, make a dot, then make dots on the top of the rectangle at the 1/3 points.

•Block off the upper corners of the rectangle with diagonal lines running from the side dots to the top dots.

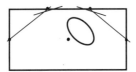

from the description

•Then round off the top corners you just made.

•Make a dot in the center of the rectangle. Draw an ellipse (about twice as high as it is wide) about half the height of the rectangle.

•Tilt it about 45° to the left, so that the top of its curve is about 1/6 of the way down from the top of the rectangle, and its left edge lines up with the central dot."   You get the idea.

This method isn't perfect, but it will get you started, and you can adjust things as you go along.

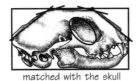

matched with the skull
(pretty close!)

Obviously, you must draw lightly so you can erase and change things that don't work out quite right.

Now for Exercise #1. With your ruler, draw a rectangle around the skull at left. The rectangle should touch the skull at every possible point. You can keep track of steps you do by checking off each ☑ as you do it.

On a clean sheet of paper ☐(1pt) draw a rectangle 4" wide and 2" high. ☐(5pts) Draw the skull in this rectangle, talking to yourself as you draw. Mark important points with dots. Hold your pencil up to the skull to compare and transfer the rough proportions to your paper.

To find the correct angle for a line, line up your pencil along that angle on the skull, move your pencil at that same angle to your drawing, memorize it, then quickly lift it and draw that angle.

☐(2pts) Do not shade – placement of the lines is the most important thing at this point.

☐(1pt) Erase the rectangle on your drawing.

☐(1pt) Apply a cover as shown on page 138.

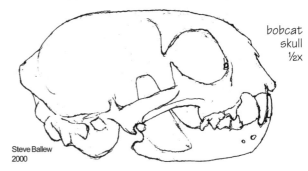

bobcat
skull
½x

Steve Ballew
2000

Give your drawing only about as much detail as you see in this student drawing of a bobcat skull.

Note the captions on the cat and bobcat skulls. The "1½x" means that the cat skull illustration is one and one-half times (x) actual size. An actual cat skull is about 3" long, but this one is drawn about 4½" long (which is 1½ times 3).

A bobcat skull might measure more than 5", so the bobcat skull drawing, at about 2¾", is only about ½x or one half as large as an actual skull.

Learn and use this useful scientific notation.

Right-brain Checkpoints – _Return Frequently To Review This Page_

Find familiar shapes – ellipses, parallel lines and angles (or parts of them) – within the drawing to simplify, improve the accuracy, and speed up your rendering of the outline of your subject. Compare everything – shapes, sizes, positions, etc.

When sketching, use all the right-brain methods you have learned to figure out placement, angles, proportions, etc. The frog at right is a good example of shapes to look for. It contains many angles, parallel lines, ellipses, and other shapes. See **a.** through **c.** below.

Remember, when drawing, to engage your right brain by talking it through the process. For example, as you draw, your mind should be telling your pencil as it moves along:

"...this line goes straight up about half an inch, then shoots off at this angle halfway to the edge, then makes half a circle and goes at a slightly steeper angle until it is opposite that other feature, then it parallels the diagonal line....."

This keeps the left brain from taking over and saying "here's a leg, and legs look like this."

If you have trouble holding onto this concept, try narrating your drawings out loud for awhile (don't do this where you might be overheard!)

While drawing, look up at your subject every five to ten seconds (or oftener) to check your progress. If you don't, your lines may get way off before you notice, then you'll have to erase a lot of work to correct it.

When you make a mistake, don't be afraid to erase and redraw. If you try to fudge lines to make them relate properly, your end result will be skewed.

a. Imagine straight lines going through main features – eyes, edge of outline, etc. What do they intersect or pass nearby?

b. Look for angles and parallel lines. Seek out negative shapes **outside** the outline of the subject.

c. Find recognizable geometrical shapes like circles, ovals and squares to help you draw the subject's parts.

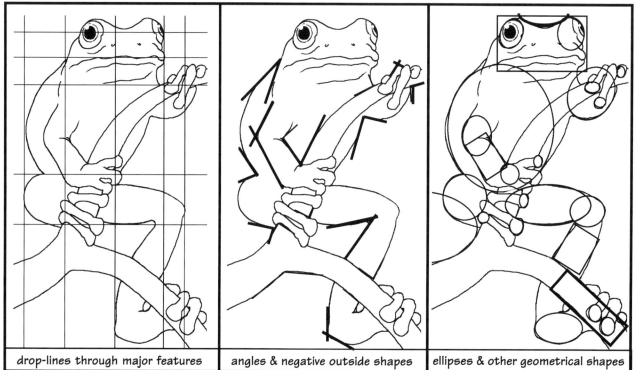

| drop-lines through major features | angles & negative outside shapes | ellipses & other geometrical shapes |

Chapter 2. Sketching Basics

FINDING YOUR RIGHT BRAIN

By now, you have worked on finding your right brain – and perhaps you have felt it begin to stir. It is time to point it in the right direction as you begin to learn the techniques of realistic illustration.

There are two major objectives in drawing a subject accurately. One has to do with preparing your subject and yourself to sketch. The other concerns the actual techniques necessary to draw correctly. Some of them may seem elementary to you – in which case you may have more experience than others. But they're all important. If you ignore any of them, the quality of your drawing will suffer.

PREPARING TO SKETCH

- **Pick an appropriate subject;**
  don't choose an ostrich to show flight feathers.
- **Find a good specimen to illustrate your point;**
  in good condition, with all its parts.
- **Choose the best view;**
  show subject the best way possible.
- **Seat yourself comfortably;**
  in a position you can hold for awhile.

¾ view of an opossum pup

- **Face your model at a right-angle;**
  ¾ views are difficult – draw from front or side unless (or until) you have enough experience to do it confidently.
- **Decide whether the shape is horizontal or vertical;**
  turn the paper to make room for the subject's orientation.
- **Outline a one-inch "dead-zone" border;**
  don't draw within 1" of the border. People hold a picture there, and thumbprints on your drawing are bad news.
- **Place your pad directly between you and the model;**
  if your pad is off to one side or slanted away, your drawing will be skewed (see page 81).
- **Find a reference point in the background;**
  you'll want to maintain exactly the same viewpoint.
- **Study your model before drawing;**
  look for shapes, comparisons, drop-lines (see page 14)
- **Draw the entire outline IN THE AIR, over your paper;**
  this will ensure that your entire drawing will fit.
- **Lightly outline the subject on the paper;**
  draw the entire outline before drawing details. If you start with details, you will draw them too large.
- **Don't shade until drawing passes inspection;**
  check your drawing in a mirror or from the back before you begin shading. If possible, let it sit a day or more before you shade it so that your fresh view will help you see errors and rough spots.

DRAWING TOOLS AND TECHNIQUES

- **Basic tools:**

Sketchbooks, spiral bound – a large one for studio work and a small portable one for field sketching.

.5 mechanical pencil with HB (medium) leads. Spares should be heard rattling in the barrel. 2B (dark) leads may also be useful.

Kneaded eraser removes correct-weight lines without damaging the paper or leaving erasures behind (and perhaps startling your subject when you brush them off). Knead well before using.

White, clickable eraser which advances in its holder erases in tight spots, removes highlights from dark areas, and removes too-dark areas. It will leave no colored streaks on your paper.

.005 mechanical pen is best for most ink exercises and projects.

- **Hold your pencil or pen correctly:**
  Your linework will be too heavy if the entire weight of your hand is on the pencil or pen point. For accurate, clean lines, hold your pencil firmly but lightly, with the weight of your hand and arm resting **on the side of your hand on the paper.**

- **Keep your mechanical pencil sharp:**
  Always have a scrap of paper to rub the lead against to create a sharp point. Turn your pencil as you draw, using the sharpest point available, stopping frequently to wear it down to a point again. When shading, alternate using the wide, broad side thus created for shading, and the sharp point for drawing. Don't shade until the outline is finished.

- **Draw with a single, clear line:**
  Multiple lines create a confusing, ambiguous drawing. Which line is THE line? Train your point to stay on the paper, following the contour, instead of making multiple try-lines.
  If you do make try-lines, erase all but one.

- **Draw with the point resting lightly on the paper:**
  Heavy lines groove the paper, grinding carbon into the fibers. These leftovers will ruin an otherwise good drawing. Avoid dark lines on your drawings. Train yourself to barely rest the lead on the paper as you draw. When you photocopy your work, all lines should show, but none of them should overwhelm.

- **Develop ability to keep drawing as you glance up:**
  Contour drawing will help you gain this skill. It is extremely useful when drawing moving things (like mice, or ducks) and it keeps you from losing your train of thought.

- **Create new LEFT brain templates:**
  As you draw, your LEFT brain is creating new templates of how to draw each subject. Every time you draw a subject, the template will become stronger, and drawing with it will become easier. Remember the bird icon you drew on page 5? After carefully observing and drawing real birds for awhile, your left brain will form new templates of how a bird's wings actually fold over its back, how its legs emerge from its body, typical proportions of feet to the rest of the body, and many other generalizations.
  Using the new left-brain templates, you can get off to a quick and accurate start, while your observant right brain can partially override the templates to supply the characteristics of the particular subject you are drawing.

Student Examples of Contour, Modified Contour, and Timed Drawings

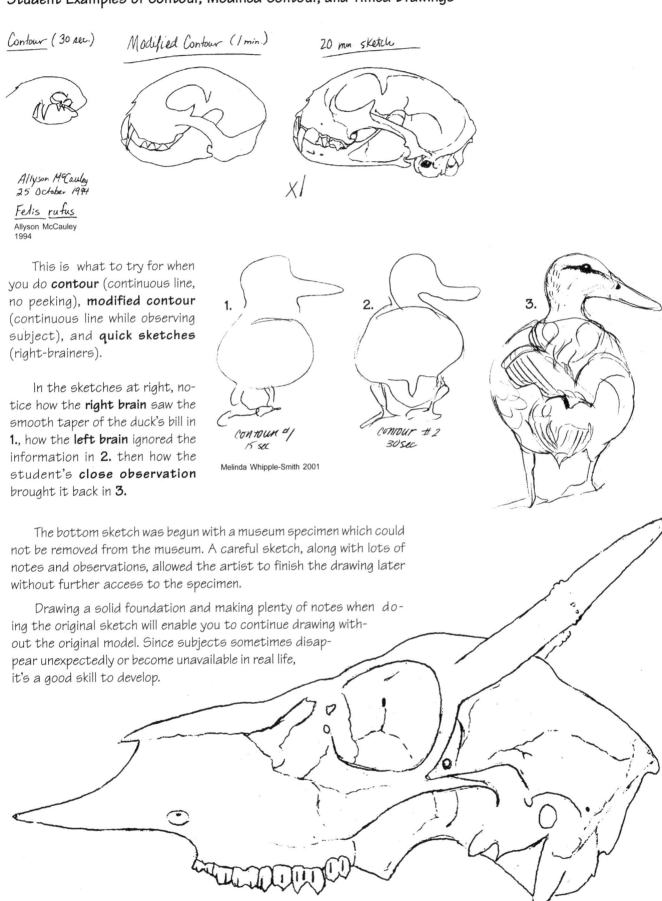

Contour (30 sec.)   Modified Contour (1 min.)   20 mm sketch

Allyson McCauley
25 October 1994
Felis rufus

Allyson McCauley
1994

X1

This is what to try for when you do **contour** (continuous line, no peeking), **modified contour** (continuous line while observing subject), and **quick sketches** (right-brainers).

In the sketches at right, notice how the **right brain** saw the smooth taper of the duck's bill in **1.**, how the **left brain** ignored the information in **2.** then how the student's **close observation** brought it back in **3.**

1.   2.   3.

contour #1
15 sec

contour #2
30 sec

Melinda Whipple-Smith 2001

The bottom sketch was begun with a museum specimen which could not be removed from the museum. A careful sketch, along with lots of notes and observations, allowed the artist to finish the drawing later without further access to the specimen.

Drawing a solid foundation and making plenty of notes when doing the original sketch will enable you to continue drawing without the original model. Since subjects sometimes disappear unexpectedly or become unavailable in real life, it's a good skill to develop.

Mary Schnur, 2000

The object of this exercise is to learn how to use right-brain techniques when sketching a subject. It also requires careful note-taking to develop your labeling skills, a helpful aid if the subject becomes unavailable before the drawing is completed. A skull is a good subject for this, but if a skull is not available, a large seashell could substitute nicely.

For this Exercise you need:

1. .5 mechanical pencil with HB lead (avoid **non**-mechanical pencils as a scientific illustrator)

2. 12" C-thru ruler

3. large 11" x 14" sketchpad

4. kneaded eraser

5. a medium to large skull or seashell

Exercise:

1. Study the figure at right, and position yourself and your subject as shown. Always line up yourself, your sketchpad and your subject in a direct line (see at right and review page 15 for pointers).

2. Find a comfortable sitting position – then maintain or return to this position while drawing. Look past a prominent landmark on your subject with one eye, and find a distant reference point beyond and visible at the chosen point on the model so that you can line up your eye, subject, and viewpoint again later.

3. Study the skull – lean in close to see details. Is your subject vertical or horizontal? Turn your sketchpad accordingly. Draw a light 1" fingerprint margin line. **NOTE:** If your ruler is 1" wide, simply place it along the edge and make a faint line along the inside. This faint line should be erased later.

4. ☐(2pts) Warm-ups, all on the same sketch page off to one side: Do one thirty-second contour sketch (as on p. 9), then a one-minute modified contour sketch (as on p. 10). Warmups should be only 2"-3."

5. ☐(7pts) 20-min. sketch: (This drawing should be at least 6" wide). Quickly estimate and indicate the outermost points of the subject as dots on the sketchpad. Now, use right-brain techniques to draw what you see for 15-20 minutes.

(NOTE: You may want to repeat this exercise later. If so, you may extend the drawing period from 20 minutes to as long as you want. But for this first drawing, try to get the subject onto your paper quickly.)

Make a **full outline drawing**, then include major features found **inside** the outline (e.g. teeth, eyehole and cheekbone on a skull). **Do not shade.**

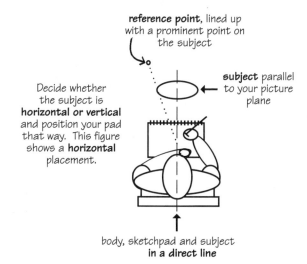

reference point, lined up with a prominent point on the subject

subject parallel to your picture plane

Decide whether the subject is **horizontal or vertical** and position your pad that way. This figure shows a **horizontal** placement.

body, sketchpad and subject **in a direct line**

6. ☐(2pts) Make notes on your sketch page about details you might need for finishing the drawing later. Use materials on pp. 115-116 (or your own research) to finish or improve your drawing later, but DO NOT completely redraw it. Leave your notes on the page.

7. ☐(2pts) Clean up the drawing. Erase the margin line. In the upper right corner put: your name, date, and exercise # for later reference.

Label each drawing with subject ID and drawing type (contour, 20-minute, etc.). Indicate the scale of your 20-minute drawing (2x, 1x, etc. See page 13).

8. ☐(2pt) Trim any torn edges from your paper, then attach a tracing paper coversheet over your original art as instructed on page 138. If your art is larger than your tracing paper, make a large coversheet by "butting" two tracing paper sheets (see at right).

butted coversheet

tracing paper sheet #1

sheets touch but don't overlap.

Transparent tape runs the entire width of the butted sheets on the **underside.**

tracing paper sheet #2

Temporarily hold the butted sheets together with low-tack tape on the front. Then on the backside (not on the front), extend tape the <u>entire width</u> of the coversheet.

TIP: To hone your drawing skills, study an object intensely for two minutes. Turn away and draw from memory for 5 minutes without looking. Repeat.

Student Grid Sketching Example – "Speed Drawing"

Some people can use grids very effectively with excellent results. Other people draw better without them. It has little to do with ability – just different brain settings.

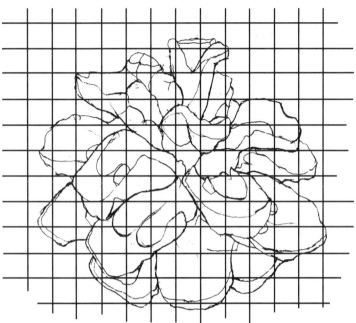

what Sara saw
through the
transparent grid

The very accurate piñon pine cone below was drawn in about fifteen minutes during a student's first attempt at drawing through the grid.

She placed a large grid under (and faintly visible through) the drawing paper, and looked at the actual cone through a transparent grid (photocopied onto a transparency film and securely propped so it couldn't move).

The gridded pine cone at left shows approximately what she saw through the transparent grid while she was sketching. The grid beneath her drawing paper had larger squares. When she drew what was in each square, her drawing turned out larger.

You can create your own transparent grid by photocopying the grid on page 26 onto transparency film intended for making overhead transparencies. Enlarge or reduce it to change the size of the squares. A piece of clear glass or stiff plastic (from a picture frame) makes a good support for the grid.

For more details, read page 19.

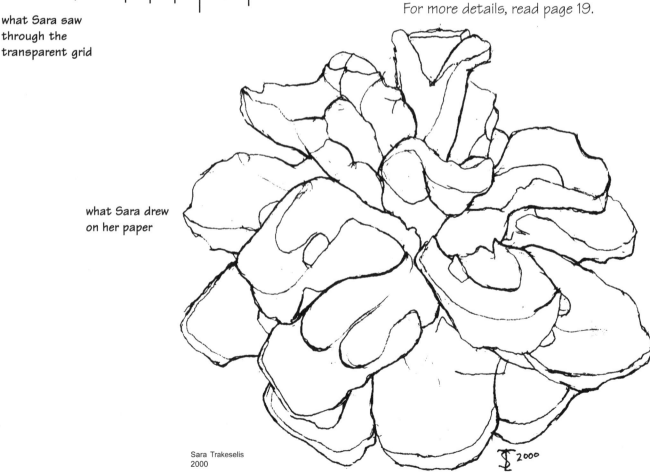

what Sara drew
on her paper

Sara Trakeselis
2000

Try to visualize what this ancient *limner* ("one who makes lines") would have seen (mostly knees? right up her nose?). The rod in front of his face helped him maintain eye position/viewpoint. This art is by Albrecht Durer in the late 1400's.

Alternative approaches:

If a subject is giving you trouble (pinecones, for instance can be difficult to draw) you may want to try a grid. Grid drawing requires two grids – one placed in the picture plane (vertically between you and the subject – see above) and one beneath your drawing paper. It is an ancient and revered method of "limning" (making lines).

Fit your drawing to the page:

Adjust the distance between the grid and the subject to make sure the image fits on your drawing grid. For instance, if you are drawing on a 70-square grid (7 squares by 10 squares), make sure your subject fills no more than 7 squares by 10 squares on the grid between you and the subject. Move the grid closer or farther from your subject to adjust this.

Making the subject larger or smaller:

To enlarge the size of an image, use a large drawing grid and a small vertical transparent grid. To reduce the size of the image, use a small drawing grid and a large vertical transparent grid.

Beginning to draw:

Tape a grid under your sketchpad page (or tracing paper) so it won't shift. The lines must be visible through the paper. Locate a visual viewpoint and lock on it so your head doesn't move while drawing.

Then, **using one eye only**, transfer the image from the viewing grid to the drawing grid.

Working one square at a time is a very right-brain technique similar to the right-brain drawing you did of the pronghorn antelope in Chapter 1. Check your visual anchor every few seconds to make sure your head hasn't moved. If it does, or if you draw with both eyes open, your drawing will get skewed.

If that happens, don't try to fake it or guess where things should be – erase and redo.

Live tracing:

A similar, more direct technique involves viewing the subject through glass or plastic and outlining the image exactly – sort of like "live tracing" onto the glass or plastic. This works if your subject holds still. It's great for rainy-day landscape drawing from inside your car windows.

Draw on a piece of clear plastic (use overhead projector sheets or clear acetate) taped to the window. For your drawing medium, use ink that adheres to acetate. The ink in many mechanical and felt-tip pens works, or you can use crayon-like china markers available at hardware stores. This is also a one-eyed process (see p. 93).

Trace the drawing onto tracing paper and transfer it to a finish surface (see p. 140) to complete.

Exercise #3 — Making Models, Foreshortened Sketching — 15 pts.

Drawing would be easier if every subject could always be drawn in profile or in a symmetrical position, and stylized so that once you learned the pattern you could do it in your sleep. Ancient Egyptian drawings fit this model — artists always drew their people and their gods in profile, identical and in the case of the gods, easily identified through stylized accessories.

Actually, the left brain drawings done on page 5 might be considered examples of the "ideal" illustrative situation. But the real world doesn't work that way. This exercise will show you what to do when you come up against reality — the necessity to show a leaf, for instance, in something other than the face-on outline form favored by the left brain. In this exercise you will practice foreshortening and ways to substitute ingenuity for reality when the need arises.

On occasion, you may need to illustrate something for which you have no specimen — a leaf out of season for example. If you don't have the leaf you need for a sketch, you may be able to find a photo with the leaf at the correct orientation. Or you may be able to find a suitable fake or preserved leaf in a department store or florist shop. But at some point you may need to make a model in a hurry. This exercise will show you how to create a usable leaf. Models for other subjects could be made from clay or other sculptable materials.

1. Tear a page from your small field sketchbook and place it over one of the leaf drawings on the next page. Select one as close as possible to a real leaf you know you can collect for a comparison drawing (below). Trace the leaf onto the sheet, using heavy pressure or a 2B lead to make a dark line.

2. Draw the midrib and veins. Be very careful of the vein placement.

3. Cut it out and float it in a pan of warm water for about five seconds.

4. Remove and pat it nearly dry on a paper towel. Crease the veins with a dull point (a pencil point would work), and shape the damp paper into a leaf shape. Let it dry completely.

For this Exercise you need:

1. .5 mechanical pencils with HB and 2B leads
2. 11" x 14" sketchbook
3. the model leaf you just made
4. one real, fresh leaf, (the same kind as one of the leaves shown on the next page, if possible)

Exercise:

1. Situate yourself, your sketchpad and the real leaf in a direct line. □(3pts) Hold or prop up the leaf in a side view that shows both the underside and upper side of the leaf in a natural-looking position (see drawing below). Make sure this view doesn't change.

2. Measure your **model**, and make the drawing of the real leaf □(2pts) the exact length of your model.

3. Draw with right-brain techniques covered in Chapter 1. Don't let your left brain tell you how to draw this leaf. If your right brain registers an odd shape, pay attention and draw it that way. If you have trouble with foreshortening, draw nearest areas first, then further areas. Also try drawing the negative shapes you see around the leaf (see page 11).

4. □(2pts) Observe carefully, then draw in the midrib and veins. Make sure all veins attach to the midrib.

5. □(1pt) Do not shade.

6. □(3pt) Now, holding your model leaf in the same side view as the real leaf you just drew, draw it as accurately as you can, 1x. Examine the real leaf for any details that are missing from your model, and add to the drawing of your model to reflect this. Use everything you learned from drawing the actual leaf to make this drawing as accurate as possible.

7. □(3pts) When you have finished the second leaf, compare the two closely. What did you learn about leaf construction from this exercise? When comparing the model to a real leaf, what was different? How could you adjust for this when drawing a model?

On the same page as your drawings, write down answers to the above questions and at least one thing about foreshortening that you learned from this exercise.

8. □(1pt) Put your name, date and the exercise number in the upper right corner of the sketch page, and attach the model leaf to the drawing for reference.

Quercus Kellogii
Black Oak Leaf
x1

MUDRA

Mudra Bergan 2000

You can make a single model do multiple duty by using a mirror to sketch a backward version (changing a few details so that it isn't obviously a mirror image). Sketched from various angles, drawings from two or three leaf models could clothe an entire shrub without revealing their origins.

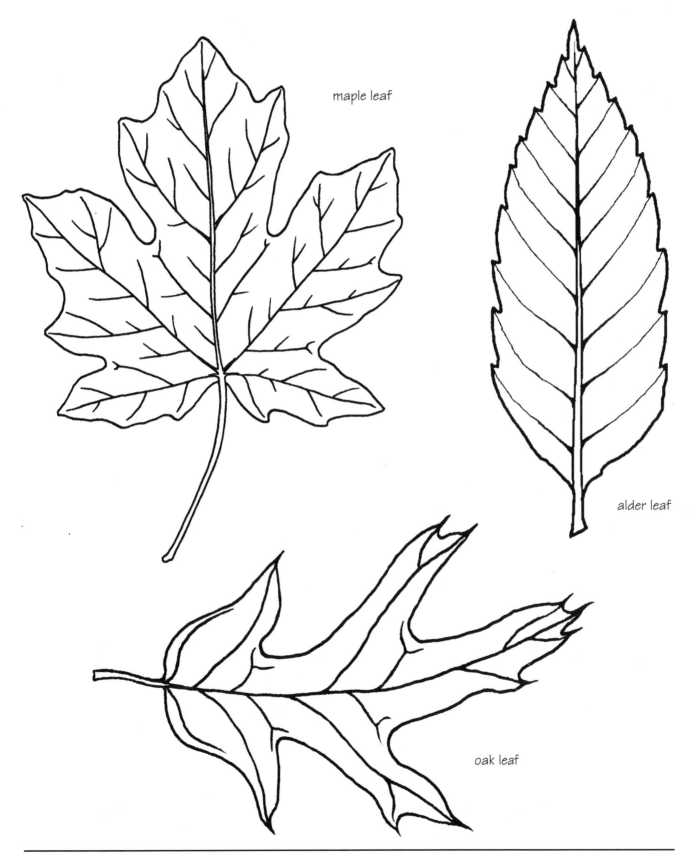

maple leaf

alder leaf

oak leaf

Using a Loupe or Magnifying Glass

A magnifying glass or loupe can open the door to a multitude of tiny wonders. The apparently non-descript rush, for instance, has incredible flowers. If they were larger, they would be grown commercially in greenhouses like orchids, and sold for outrageously high prices.

But that's not all. Those tiny flowers emerge on stalks from a slit in the side of what seems to be a solid stem — but it isn't what it appears.

So what is going on here?

The old identifying rubric goes:

- *Grasses are flat;*
- *Rushes are round;*
- *Sedges have edges.*

In reality, the "round rush" is actually a long, flat leaf, rolled up into a thin, green tube.

You'll never be bored if you have your sketchpad with you. Add a magnifying glass and you can entertain yourself for hours. If you forget your magnifying glass, up-end your binoculars and look at your subject through the "wrong" end — surprise!

Forgot your pencil? Don't be afraid to sketch with a ball-point pen. If you goof, just start over. Make lots of notes — they'll be interesting to read later when you've forgotten the details.

Everything in the world hasn't yet been discovered, and maybe no one has ever looked at whatever you are drawing as closely as you are looking right now. Who knows?

a flowering rush
Lake West 8-1-99

brown & green stripes

spirals coral-red with yellow fuzz

coral red

light yellow

10 X

dark tip

the flowers emerge from a slit in the curled leaf

2x

all emerge from side of tubular leaf

green & brown stripes on petals

Under ten power (10x) magnification, the insignificant flower *petals* are green with brown stripes; the furry, light-yellow *anthers* curl up protectively around a bright coral-red *ovary* out of which rises a thin coral *style* and three corkscrew *stigmas* covered with yellow fuzz. This is probably very familiar to a botanist, but to discover it on your own is quite an adventure.

Refer to the diagram on page 49 to help you identify the parts of the flower above.

And by the way, don't limit yourself to plants — Hey! look over on that sunny section of the path......

tiger beetle 1x

4x

...if you can catch one, look through your magnifying glass at that tiger beetle's MEAN MUG!

P. S. If you don't discover something interesting when you sketch, you aren't looking hard enough!

WHY TAKE NOTES?

A field sketchbook loses a great deal of its use-fulness and beauty if the sketches in it are not annotated. If viewers don't know what the subject is, and have no notes from which to make an intelligent guess, they may as well be looking at a coloring book. A field sketchbook without good notes has little function except to give the sketcher practice.

However, with the addition of thorough notes, a sketch in a naturalist's notebook is given *provenance* – an origin or source, a history and **possibilities**. It becomes a thing of worth to more than just the art-ist. What's more, it becomes more valuable to the artist later, when the details that seemed so obvi-ous while drawing have been forgotten.

It is endlessly absorbing to go through your old field sketchbooks and become immersed again in the scene: the colors and odors, the warmth of the sun or the cool breeze, the challenge of portraying the subject or an electrifying jolt of discovery – an unexpected beauty, a peculiar facet. And a stranger can find it just as interesting to share your trip.

Since you do not know what use your field sketch-book will serve in the future, make it as good and as thorough as you can while you are doing it. That means looking closely at your subject and its sur-roundings; making observations about it; looking closer and closer until you've discovered a secret thing you didn't expect. On a simple walk along the path in the park – or wherever you happen to go or be – you can be as much of an explorer as Lewis and Clark on their Voyage of Discovery.

What constitutes good note-taking seems to stump a lot of people. It may be hard to imagine what you'll want to know later, or how much, or even why. Cultivate the assumption that you'll need to be able to identify a subject in your sketchbook years later and this is the only chance you'll get to look at it closely. It could be true. Even a familiar object may be unavailable when you want it, but you can go look-ing for it in your sketchbooks.

So cover all the bases. Tell more than you think you'll need. Write in complete sentences when possible, legibly enough for a stranger to read.

Include the following items in field sketchbook notes:
- date and name
- location: address, state, Nat. Forest, creek, mileages, etc.
- description of area: rocky slope, forest edge, yard
- name or description: specific/common name, best guess
- labels: leaf, folded petal, confusing areas, details
- scale: 1x, ½x, etc. for EVERY VIEW YOU DRAW
- characteristics: color, texture, other details
- activity or behavior: any you notice, watch carefully
- observations: questions, guesses, speculation
- odor, if any: fruity, like a wet dog, musky
- vocalizations: a low cluck, 1 tap/second, "tee-zit-pee!"
- addenda: insert ID and info or discoveries later

WHAT IS IMPORTANT?

One species of sparrow may look identical to another except that only one's lower beak is pink. If you were sketching it, would you have noticed? Assume everything has importance. As you gain experience, you'll get a better idea of what is unusual, what to draw, and what to make notes about.

Terse labels ("green stem") are neither as interesting nor as useful as in-depth observations such as: *The 6" stem is deep green, tough and springy with a raspy texture, and triangular in cross-sec-tion. Short silver hairs are longer near the base of stem."*

In your field notes, make an effort to produce in-depth observations. How much can you possibly glean from "a stem"? Try it and see.

Most sketches for your field sketchbook should be of native wildlife, plants, insects, etc. There are several reasons for this:

First and foremost, as a responsible person on this planet, it is important to be familiar with the local flora and fauna *wherever you live* even for a short time. You cannot help protect what you do not know. There is no better way to become familiar with some-thing than to draw it. So this will add to your store of local knowledge.

You may want to use your field sketchbook draw-ings as subject material for Project A (page 116), Project B (page 118), or Project C (page 125).

To get a leg up on the projects, make your field notes and sketches with these potential uses in mind.

Exercise #4 – Personal Art Signature Design – 10 pts

Your artwork must always be signed. For this exercise, you must be able to execute your signature in the following manner, using a ☐(2pts) .005 mechanical pen or a flexible pen.

It **should**:

- ☐(1pt) not be your legal signature
- ☐(1pt) include first or last name, not just initials
- ☐(2pts) be readable without a struggle
- ☐(1pt) be artistically interesting, not normal writing
- ☐(1pt) not touch any part of the drawing
- ☐(1pt) look the same each time
- ☐(1pt) be executable also at a small size

Look at the examples below for inspiration.

When signing art, keep your signature compact, modestly sized so that it doesn't overwhelm the work but large enough to see if reduced, and clearly legible.

When you sign your work, place the signature so that if the area surrounding your artwork gets trimmed right down to the art in the final reproduction, your signature won't be sliced off.

Also, don't place it under an animal's tail.

Albrecht Durer, early painter, etcher, and woodcut carver. He did a lot of religious subjects, and he also did botanical and wildlife paintings and drawings with great care and attention to detail. He was one of the earliest illustrators in print, and very well known in his time (see page 19).

Holling Clancy Holling, illustrater of children's books in the 40's and 50's. He is famous for PADDLE-TO-THE-SEA, PAGOO, MINN OF THE MISSISSIPPI and other books. He did both full-color paintings and b/w sidebar drawings. This signature was extremely easy for him to paint on his paintings.

Guy Coheleach (KO-lee-ack), wildlife painter. He is famous for big cats and other assorted subjects, extreme realism and action. This signature is instantly recognizable.

Rien Poortvliet, Dutch painter, famous for his books of GNOMES and FAERIES. He also wrote DOGS, THE LIVING FOREST, and a fascinating book filled with wonderful illustrations, JOURNEY TO THE ICE AGE. The signature is hard to read, but if you're rich and famous, who cares?

Roger Tory Peterson, who created the concept for field identification guides. He did all the illustrations for A FIELD GUIDE TO THE BIRDS and many other field guides. This is a simple, straightforward signature.

Irene Brady, illustrator of nature books for kids and adults. She designed this unassuming and friendly signature for her work (☺).

This is a signature designed by **Leslie Clark** (student). It has good design, is easily recognizable and you can read the name.

This is the signature of **Cindy Harms** (student). It is simple and easy to make, but should contain more name since someone liking her work would not know who to look for to hire her services. She might also be someone with the initials H.C.

This very attractive signature is **Lorna Brindle**'s (student). While quite graceful and pretty, it suffers the same drawback as the signature above, plus the first initial is ambiguous. It could be a Z, an L or a 2.

How well do the student signatures below meet the criteria for good signatures?

Using Left-Brain Templates to Jumpstart Drawings

Drawing a pine or fir cone is not as difficult as it looks if you use your left brain, too. The scales spiral around a central shaft in a regular pattern, so you can begin with a left brain template — then fill in the details with right brain input. Use this technique also with multi-faceted insect eyes, seedpods, etc.

1.

Sketches by student Megan O'Donnell show two ways to draw a Douglas fir cone like the one at left:

For technique **1.**, she drew an ellipse to represent the general cone shape, lightly pencilled in the diagonal grid to contain the scales, then drew a scale in each diamond-shaped opening.

In technique **2.**, she held the cone perfectly still a few inches above the paper and sighted past it to the paper, where she drew the outline (see page 93). Both of these techniques are applicable to many subjects. The #2 method works for things small enough to hold in the hand. The inside lines are easier to position when the outside contour line is in place — it's a bit like connecting the dots.

2.

Megan
O'Donnell
2003

Using contour lines to establish the correct perspective

So, let's say you're drawing a cougar head (**a.**) but there's something not quite right — the nose and that left eye look skewed. It's time to draw a few contour lines — in fact, getting the positioning right before doing all that shading would have saved you some frustration and a whole lot of work.

Treating the head as a mostly symmetrical cylinder, larger in some areas and smaller in others (and slightly flattened and turned away), you draw faint contour lines (as in **b.**) along the lines of the face (**c.**), starting with the big ellipse that divides the face in half. You see that the end of the nose resembles part of a sphere, so you add sphere contour lines to the nose-tip (see sphere inset, **b.**). (This is a nice little outing for your left brain.)

With the contour lines in place, you can now see that the nose is tilted and the left eye, while the correct shape and size, is too high and slopes down on the outside when it should be upturned (compare **c.** and **d.**). You make corrections, erase contour lines, redo shading, and finally "**cougar e.**" seems to purr contentedly from your page. Yes!!!

e.

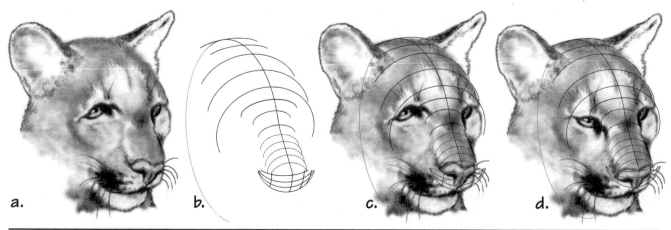

a.   **b.**   **c.**   **d.**

To create a grid with 1" squares, enlarge 260% on a photocopier

1 cm.
squares

Chapter 3. Texture & Tone, Halftone in Perspective

If you think scientific illustration doesn't make much use of perspective techniques since it tends to show objects close-up, think again. Knowledge of perspective is essential, for it is used in every drawing, regardless of its size or proximity.

The rules of perspective apply to close-up items in terms of foreshortening and diminishing size. Closer things, parts, or areas appear larger, while more distant things, parts, or areas appear smaller.

Also, circles and discs encountered in nature may be tipped away or toward the viewer. It is important to know how circles become flattened ellipses when they're tilted back and forth.

Hold a sheet of paper slanted away from the plane of your face, then draw what looks like a perfect circle from that viewpoint. Looked at squarely, you'll notice that you actually drew an ellipse. This underlines why it's important to hold your sketchpad at right angles to the plane of your face. (See page 81).

Most perspective in scientific illustration is "aerial perspective" which is: "the expression of distance by the _loss_ _of_ _definition_ _and_ _value_ _range_ due, in nature, to intervening atmosphere between the observer and the object." You have probably noticed how successive mountain ranges appear fainter with distance — it's the same thing.

In scientific illustration, this effect is shown in close-up perspective by making the nearest areas more detailed — with darker darks and whiter whites. More distant areas are less detailed, lighter or more evenly shaded (even when the "distance" is just fractions of inches).

You can get this effect even without shading by making the nearest **lines** darkest, wider and thicker — and more distant lines lighter, thinner and more delicate (as seen on the kangaroo rat skull at left).

perspective line breaks

light lines are farther away

dark lines are nearer

You can heighten the effect with another common convention, by making **perspective breaks** — break the line where it passes be-

hind a nearer part (see on the skull example below left and the leaf on page 20).

It helps to learn the rules of perspective, but studying a subject carefully and using good sense can often solve perspective problems. If not, you can make a paper model to help figure it out. Also, follow "parallel" lines to their vanishing points with your eye (see page 28).

Squint at **a.** and **b.**, below, notice that they **appear** to be very different from each other. All the lines of the cubes are of identical length, but a heavier line has been used to mark the near end of each box. What is the shape of each box? Could one be a cube? Could both be cubes? What would be the effect of breaking more distant lines?

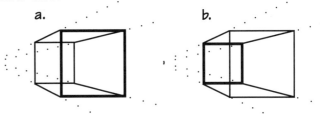

Look at the ellipses below. Could **c.** and **d.** have the same shape? What about **d.** and **e.?** Or **e.** and **f.?**

The ellipses on **d.** and **e.** are exactly the same size and shape. What does this tell us about the shapes of the cylindrical objects of which they are the ends?

We see such ellipses around us every day, and we interpret them correctly in terms of their shape and position, but it is hard to put this intuitive knowledge into words or even a coherent theory. We can tell if something "doesn't look right," so if something in your drawing "doesn't look right," trust your judgement and make or find a model you can move and tilt and compare with your drawing or subject to help you understand what went wrong.

> To help with drawing problems, hold your drawing up to a mirror, or hold it up to a light source (a window works) and view it backward through the paper. This backward point of view will give you amazing new insights into solutions.

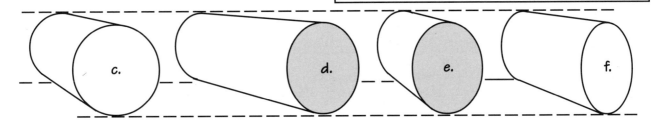

1-, 2-, and 3-Point Perspective in a Nutshell

If you can digest and internalized the information on this page, your future encounters with perspective will be relatively painless. Begin with the legend at right→

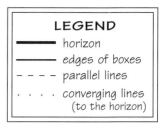

LEGEND
— horizon
— edges of boxes
- - - parallel lines
· · · · converging lines (to the horizon)

1-point perspective

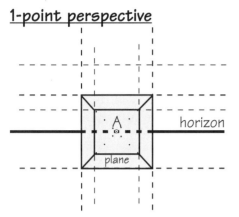

In **1-point perspective**, the **PLANE** is nearest the viewer, and perpendicular to the viewer. Lines drawn from the corners of the plane meet at a single point (A) on the horizon. All other lines/edges appear parallel. This effect is visible on even a small item held close to your eyes, so be aware of perspective when drawing **any** object, small or large.

In **2-point perspective**, one **EDGE** is nearest the viewer, and perpendicular to the viewer. Lines drawn from the ends of the edge converge at two different points (A & B) on the horizon. The length and width of the box are arbitrary (place vertical lines wherever you want *along the front planes* to determine the length of the side) but the far edge will be determined by where the converging lines cross. All vertical line/edges are parallel to each other.

2-point perspective

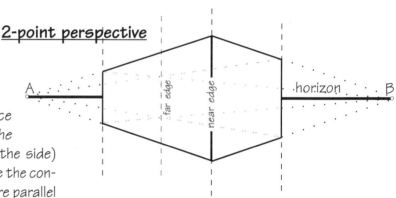

3-point perspective

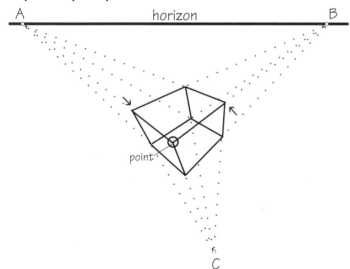

In **3-point perspective**, one **POINT** is nearest the viewer. Lines drawn from the point of this corner (circled at left) converge at two (arbitrary) points (A & B) on the horizon and one point above or below the horizon (C). The length and width of the box are arbitrary (put them where you want by marking each of the top front converging lines — see arrows — **before** establishing C). The far edge and the angle of the planes' edges will be determined by where the converging lines cross. In 3-point perspective **no** lines/edges are parallel to each other

From the information provided on this page, how can you determine that the figure at right is *not* in perspective?

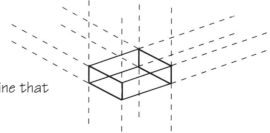

Shadows and Highlights on the Basic Shapes

The lighting conventions of scientific illustration are covered on this page. Learn and use them.

At right are shaded renderings of a sphere, a cylinder and a cube. They are all lit from a source in the upper left corner, and between the subject and the illustrator (not directly to the side of the object or in any way behind it. This is the convention for scientific illustration. Approximate this lighting whenever you create a scientific illustration — always position the subject so that it is lit from this direction. If you can't actually create this lighting situation when drawing, you'll need to fake it — so raise your left arm and "turn on the light!"

Notice that each of the curved objects has:

- a primary highlight
- a main shadowed area
- a secondary highlight (a bounce reflection coming from any surface opposite the light)
- a narrow edge shadow on the far underside of the object (where it doesn't reflect the secondary highlight).

It is the secondary highlight that gives the form much of its three-dimensional aspect. Use this on such things as plant stems and feather shafts.

The shadow at the dark edge often gives important information about the overall shape and texture of the object, and provides a clear edge.

Use shadows sparingly in scientific illustration to help define the outline or details of the object — show them only if they're needed to show a shape.

A shadow has a shape, but never a lined edge, so never outline a shadow or a highlight with a line.

- **Since the subject is the main focus, shadows on the background don't usually improve the illustration. In fact, unnecessary shadows only complicate things.**

- **Don't put a shadow _on the surface under the object_ unless it helps define or clarify the outline of the object. In a scientific illustration it's usually okay for subjects to "float" unless otherwise requested.**

Memorize these shading conventions. They will make any future shading you do vastly simpler — reduced to a left-brain template. USE that left brain!

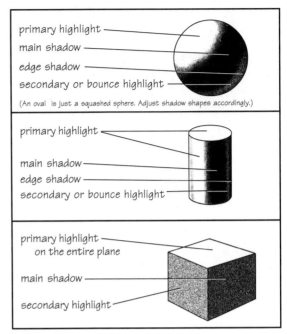

primary highlight ——
main shadow ——
edge shadow ——
secondary or bounce highlight ——

(An oval is just a squashed sphere. Adjust shadow shapes accordingly.)

primary highlight ——
main shadow ——
edge shadow ——
secondary or bounce highlight ——

primary highlight ——
    on the entire plane
main shadow ——
secondary highlight ——

Few natural objects are simple spheres, cylinders or cubes. But portions of these shapes always show up in objects you draw.

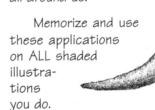

little blue heron
- ellipses
- cylinders
- shadowed underparts

For instance, a flower may have parts of spheres (convex or concave) on each petal, the stem is cylindrical, and flat planes on the leaves may require shading similar to the shading on a cube.

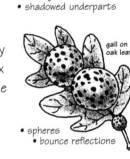

gall on oak leaf
- spheres
- bounce reflections

The undersides of things are in shadow, so they will be darker but will have bounce highlights. We see these concepts every minute, all around us.

morning glory
- ellipse sections
- cylinders

Memorize and use these applications on ALL shaded illustrations you do.

river otter
- ellipses
- cylinders
- shadowed underparts

Line Art Versus Halftone

When creating artwork for print, find out how it will be reproduced. If it will be reproduced as **line art** (black and white with no grays), then the art should be rendered in black and white without any grays, because any grays you put on it will either disappear or show up as solid black. **Strip a., below, is line art** without any shades of gray.

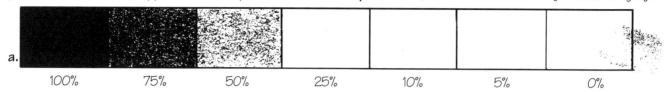

a.
100%   75%   50%   25%   10%   5%   0%

If the artwork is created with shading — degrees of gray between white and black, it is a **halftone**. **Strip b., below, is a halftone.** Halftones **can** be reproduced as line art instead of halftones. When this happens (as when you photocopy a halftone on a non-digital photocopier), the shaded gray halftone areas, as in the pencil shaded boxes below, would appear as the black-and-white line art shown in the boxes above.

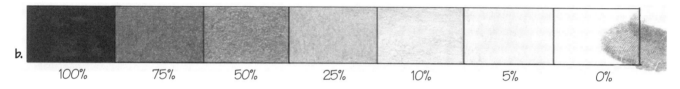

b.
100%   75%   50%   25%   10%   5%   0%

Preliminary checks:

Most illustrators photocopy their art as they work, to test tones and estimate final printing results.

Non-digital photocopiers produce line-art results (strip **a.**) from both half tone and black-and-white (like pen & ink) art. For half tone art, use a digital copier to project results. For line art, use a non-digital photocopy setting.

Digital photocopiers produce halftone images (strip **b.**).

Reproduction:

Printed gray tones are an optical illusion since they are actually printed with black ink, not gray. The illusion is achieved by "screening," breaking the image into dots with the scanner, which causes varying dot sizes and/or distances between the dots to create lighter or darker tones.

The original boxes above (**b.**) were shaded with pencil. The digital scanner broke the illustration into a dot pattern to produce a halftone illustration with shades of gray.

If art will be printed as a halftone, every mark on the paper will reproduce, including poorly erased pencil lines and dirty fingerprints, as shown on strip **b.** So keep it clean if it will be reproduced as a halftone.

If a halftone is reproduced as line art, grays will become either white or black. Use the strip below and strip **a.** above to estimate whether a gray will turn black or white.

Preparing art for reproduction/publication:

• Find out whether your art will be reproduced as line art or halftone before you begin working.

• Prepare your art in the best way possible to ensure that it can be successfully reproduced.

• Don't send off artwork that needs to be cleaned up by a technician in order to reproduce well.

In halftone reproduction, pure whites may not be possible (see 0% below) unless the dot pattern is manually removed after the artwork is made into a graphic (if on disk) or removed later from the photographic plate.

If an illustration MUST have pure whites, you should scan it, erase the dots in a graphics program and send it to the printer as a .PDF (Portable Document File) via email, or on a CD disk via land mail.

Every printer's specifications and preferences are different. If you will be sending files, contact the printer first for specific instructions before beginning. If the file must be sent in pieces via email, make sure someone at the other end has the expertise to reassemble it.

Sometimes it is possible to manipulate these rules to produce useful results. Read pages 44 and 45 for a different way to deal with halftone versus line art.

<u>PERCENTAGE STRIP:</u> Below is a computer-generated strip of percentages for reference (do you see an optical illusion where the blocks meet?). Punch one hole in the center of each box below with a paper punch. Slide your original artwork beneath the holes to find the closest percentage of a tone.

100%   75%   50%   25%   10%   5%   0%   Make holes about this size:

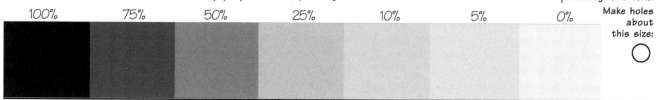

Exercise #5 – Cylinders and Spheres In Nature – 10 pts

Many natural objects consist of partial cylinders, partial spheres, cones, and combinations of these – in various placements and blends. Another shape which appears often in nature is the squashed cylinder. If you can shade a cylinder, you should be able to shade a squashed cylinder.

For this Exercise you need:

1. .5 mechanical pencil with HB lead
2. shading stump (to blend pencil marks)
3. tracing paper at least 4" x 8"
4. kneaded eraser
5. facial tissue and a rubber band

☐(1pt) **Before beginning the exercise,** practice shading on the little robot bear made of cylinders and spheres below. Copy the shading from the bear at left.

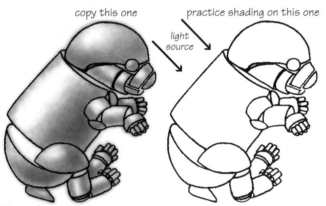

copy this one   practice shading on this one

light source

Exercise:

To shade a complex shape like a newborn bear, extend shading from a partial sphere or cylinder to the next by blending and erasing until they form one seamless shape. Think of the bear as a series of cones, cylinders and spheres blended together.

1. ☐(1pt) Trace the bear cub at bottom left onto one half of the tracing paper (see next page). Repeat the techniques you just practiced on the robot bear.

2. ☐(1pt) Shade, using the correct light source (page 29).

3. Prepare to shade by rubbing the HB lead of your .5 pencil in the box at right to shape the tip. You can take total control. By holding the pencil in one position, you can make a broad, soft line; by rotating it half a turn you can make a thin line.

4. ☐(1pt) Darken gradually to avoid making visible strokes. Move the broad lead surface in light circular movements to create solid dark masses (not tiny circles). Don't blacken too quickly by applying hard pressure – it will indent the paper and make lines in/on it.

5. ☐(1pt) Don't create abrupt edges as you shade from dark to light. Use a gentle touch as you near the end of a cylinder or edge of a spherical area.

6. ☐(1pt) Apply tones from 100% white to about 50% black. Check your shading against the percentage strip on page 30 by sliding your art under the holes you punched in each box. Leave plenty of white because you will be blending the pencil shading into the white areas gradually, and you need lots of room (see below).

scribble here to shape pencil lead

thick line   thin line

broad for shading   narrow for outlines

curlicue here shows direction. It won't actually appear in your stroke.

continued on next page...

light source

newborn black bear

apply pencil shading but leave plenty of white area

blend with stump, kneaded eraser and more pencil shading

A newborn bear is plump and velvety smooth, so try to show no individual pencil strokes within the shaded areas.

Exercise #5 – Cylinders and Spheres In Nature (continued from previous page)

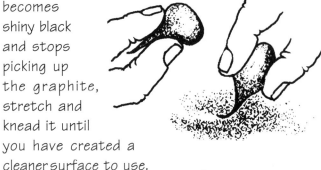

7. When you have pencil-shaded all of the cylinders and hemispheres on the bear with your pencil, use a stump (read #8, below) to rub the graphite out of the dark areas into the white areas and to join the shaded areas together.

stump

8. To blend large areas, you need a big stump to avoid making streaks. You can make a large stump quickly and inexpensively with tissue and a rubber band as illustrated at right. ☐(1pt) Make a big stump and use it to blend the shadows on your baby bear.

9. ☐(1pt) Leave highlights white. If they get accidentally smudged, use the kneaded eraser to remove the graphite from them. It's easier to leave them white than to try to erase them clean again.

10. Re-shade with your pencil to darken or fill in too-light areas, then blend again with the stump. You may need to do this several times.

If any area becomes too dark, squeeze your kneaded eraser into a thin flap and lightly stroke or dab the dark area a few times (see below). When the eraser becomes shiny black and stops picking up the graphite, stretch and knead it until you have created a cleaner surface to use.

11. Check to make sure your very darkest areas are 50% black. It is important to leave some white highlights (look again at the example on the previous page) to make the baby bear look really 3-dimensional.

Make a BIG Stump for Shading Large Areas.

One or two facial tissues or three to five squares of toilet paper make a good smudger or stump (the softest tissues work best).

If you don't have a rubber band to fasten the tissue, wrap the stump with tape, leaving ½" of the tissue's folded end free.

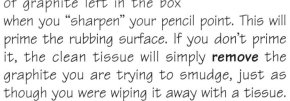

To prepare your big stump for its first use, rub it around in the blackened area of graphite left in the box when you "sharpen" your pencil point. This will prime the rubbing surface. If you don't prime it, the clean tissue will simply **remove** the graphite you are trying to smudge, just as though you were wiping it away with a tissue.

Be sure to test it on a scrap before use to make sure there isn't too much or too little graphite on it for the particular blending job you're doing.

When this home-made smudger wears through or gets tatty, make another. Always keep at least one of these on hand. Make a larger one with several tissues if you need to lightly blend a very large area.

---

12. ☐(1pt) Your last step is to erase any shading that went outside the lines, and clean up any other smudges on the paper. Put your name, date and exercise number on the upper right corner.

14. ☐(1pt) To make sure your drawing won't smear or smudge anything else, fold the unused half of the tracing paper down over the bear. To protect pencil work, you might want to buy a spray can of "workable fixatif." **Use very sparingly** – it's not good to breathe and it's not good for the environment.

a. METHOD OF FINISHING RIM OF DIAGONALLY PLAITED BASKET
Drawn by Irene Brady from page 131 of CEDAR by Hilary Steward, University of Washington Press, Seattle, 1984. Inset shows final stage, the forming of the rim.

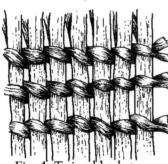

The Role of Texture in Scientific Illustration

There is room in the many scientific fields to accommodate the interests of almost any illustrator. And there is plenty of work to be had, although you may have to actively search it out.

Some illustrators illustrate only archaeological fragments — potsherds and stone, flint and obsidian points and tools. Some illustrators concentrate on mammals, others on birds or insects or only microscopic subjects. Some specialize, others take any job that comes along. Some work directly with individual scientists, others are hired by textbook companies to create spot illustrations. And some people illustrate their own work: books, articles, brochures or displays needed in their jobs.

But no matter what the artist illustrates, one of the most important skills needed is the ability to correctly show texture.

Textures include such aspects as smooth, rough, shiny, dull, fuzzy, pitted, furry, wet, hairy, etc. Texture also includes patterns such as wood grain, bone — both lengthwise and across the grain, woven fragments, tree barks, various stone types (think sandstone vs. obsidian), worked patterns on textiles or pottery, etc. If a basket is made with cattail leaves as opposed to yucca fibers or cedar bark, the differences between them should show in the illustration (**b.**).

The illustrator achieves this skill through observation and practice.

It is always challenging to find the

b. Drawn by Irene Brady from PRIMITIVE ART by Franz Boas, Harvard University Press, 1928.

Fig. 4. Twined basketry
(cattail or tule and grasses)

best way to show a texture, particularly when a "colored" pattern is combined with texture and structural shadows in a piece of art produced in black and white or shades of gray (**c.**). The "color" must be shown without compromising the shadows and textures. This sounds difficult, but with the application of right-brain techniques, it is possible.

c. (photo above) A fragment of handwoven Peruvian textile, for which reference photos of similar paintings are available. The design can be reconstructed (above left) using the fragment and other resource photos for reference, restoring and clarifying the pattern.

Many people assume that a photograph tells more "truth" than an illustration. But an illustration may do a much better job. With some subjects, it would take several photographs from different angles, perhaps even with manipulation in a graphics program, to show all the important aspects required. But an illustrator can often pull all the pertinent views together into one picture. It is here that the scientific illustrator's skills come fully into play

The design on the cloth fragment in **c.** is more clear as an illustration than as a photo. But if the fragment itself is the subject, it should be illustrated exactly as it is, shredded edges and all. If the pattern or the weave is more important, frayed parts may be "illustratively mended" to clarify them, as shown.

Sometimes part of the texture is not important, and might even distract the viewer. In that case, less important areas may be shown with little or no texture, while the texture of the more important area is illustrated in detail as shown in **d.** at right.

d. Drawn by Irene Brady from "Fig. 35. Pot of coiled pottery, Prehistoric Pueblo Indians," from PRIMITIVE ART by Franz Boas, Harvard University Press, 1928.

The Role of Convention in Scientific Illustration (more on page 61)

Conventions are the "rules" of a discipline or field. For example, the convention of breaking a line to show that a more distant part of an object is behind a nearer part is a scientific illustration convention. Making nearer lines darker, and more distant lines lighter to show perspective, is another convention.

There are "field specific" conventions as well.

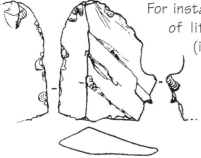

For instance, conventions of lithic illustration (illustrating stone tools and other stone items — flint, granite, obsidian, etc.), dictate which end is "up" when portraying a point or a hand tool such as an axe, a scraper,

a. Obsidian scraper, drawn by Irene Brady at Mt. Hebron, CA, PaleoIndian Site, Summer 1996. Several views may be needed, and their format and position are strictly defined, as shown in this instance, above.

etc. A cross section shown with the wrong orientation would convey the wrong information to an archaeologist. In lithic illustration, stipple dots represent very specific surface types and ages.

Conventions may not be intuitive. A dotted or dashed line may have a specific meaning in an illustration for one discipline, but an entirely different meaning in an illustration for another discipline. Ask about conventions before starting an illustration.

Insets (**a.** on previous page) may show close-ups, exploded components to clarify positioning or parts, or details of a larger illustration in which a construction is not clear. The style of showing various aspects could differ between disciplines, with results different from what the artist intended.

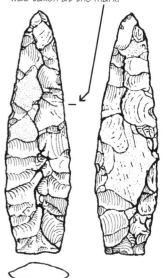

When an artifact (such as a broken pot or sculpture) is reassembled (**b.**), missing parts may be shown in various ways — sometimes left out,

b. Obsidian tool, drawn by Irene Brady at Mt. Hebron, CA, PaleoIndian Site, Summer 1996. A dashed line has been used to approximate a missing portion.

sometimes inferred or reconstructed, sometimes rendered differently. But the style must be consistent within the illustration and it must be obvious that the missing parts were not available to be illustrated.

c. Obsidian projectile points, drawn by Irene Brady at Mt. Hebron, CA, Paleoindian Site, Summer 1996. The cross-section was taken at the mark.

Scientific illustrations may show comparisons. (**a.** and **c.**).

This requires close attention to exactly what is being compared and how to show the differences with clarity.

When comparing, items should be shown with similar sizes, and identical parts should be rendered with the same technique in order to simplify the comparison and make the differences stand out.

d. Drawn by Irene Brady from PRIMITIVE ART by Franz Boas, Harvard University Press, 1928.

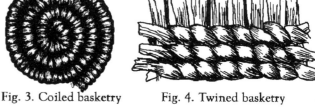

Fig. 3. Coiled basketry   Fig. 4. Twined basketry

Conventions aren't always unyielding, and there may be a number of different ways to show a given characteristic — so find out before beginning to draw. One very important rule of thumb is to remain consistent within the illustration or series of illustrations.

If you illustrate for a book or magazine, find out the in-house conventions of that book or magazine so that illustrations done by you and the other artists don't have wildly differing styles. While some magazines either don't care or have no established conventions, others are very particular.

Texture Shortcuts

At times, seasoned illustrators revert to time-saving devices to either speed things up or produce effects that would be difficult or impossible (or very time-consuming) to do by hand. Below are some examples of texture that can save time if used judiciously, and might improve the drawing dramatically.

It is not "cheating" to use your imagination to get the illustrative effect you want unless you have used someone else's photographs or artwork to get your results. Such use is an infringement of someone else's copyright, and can ruin your reputation, as well as get you fired and/or expose you to lawsuits. So don't copy or lift other people's work.

The textures below were made by "rubbing." Tracing paper was laid over the subject and a broad piece of graphite was rubbed over the surface. You've surely done this with a coin. The effect is extremely real. Rubbings of natural textures, like those below, are not copyright infringements of anything or any-body. However, a rubbing of someone else's 3-D artwork might be, if they got fussy about it.

Rather than using the actual texture you create by rubbing, you may decide to study, then render, a similar effect by hand on your illustration. Sometimes this is easier than visually interpreting three-dimensional shapes and shadows from the actual subject to the paper. You might think of it as a sort of jump-start on rendering the texture.

A texture doesn't have to represent the original object — for instance, the steering wheel cover texture below looks like skin, the plaster wall texture would illustrate rock or soil well, and the flat board resembles a weathered tree trunk, etc.

The rubbings here have been reproduced as a halftone (at left) and photocopied non-digitally as line art (below). The photocopy looks similar to a pen and ink drawing. See pages 44-45.

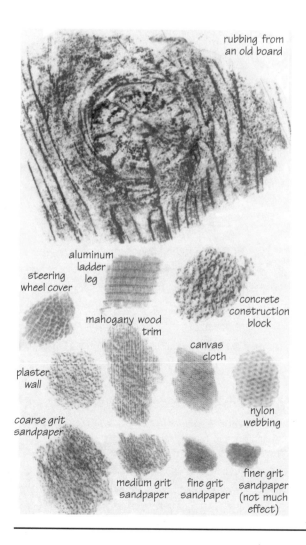

rubbing from an old board

steering wheel cover — aluminum ladder leg — mahogany wood trim — concrete construction block — canvas cloth — plaster wall — coarse grit sandpaper — nylon webbing — medium grit sandpaper — fine grit sandpaper — finer grit sandpaper (not much effect)

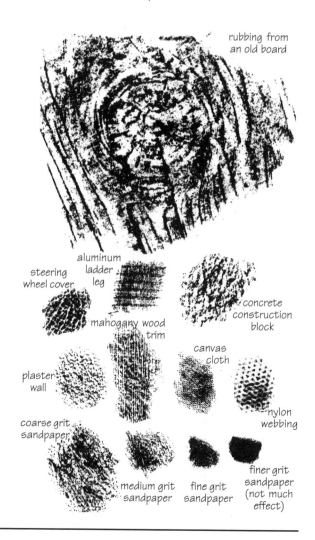

rubbing from an old board

steering wheel cover — aluminum ladder leg — mahogany wood trim — concrete construction block — canvas cloth — plaster wall — coarse grit sandpaper — nylon webbing — medium grit sandpaper — fine grit sandpaper — finer grit sandpaper (not much effect)

Exercise #6 – Surface Textures – 20 pts

In this exercise you will learn how to see and draw textures, and how to handle and illustrate artifacts. To draw an artifact well, you may need to learn something about the item and how it was created. This exercise uses a textured Anasazi potsherd (see below) and a heavy, woven fabric fragment (see halftone and line art examples in left column).

photo
**Anasazi
potsherd**

**DO NOT COPY THE
TEXTURES BELOW.
THEY ARE
EXAMPLES ONLY.**

DRAW FROM ACTUAL OBJECTS.

PINE NEEDLE BASKET
PEN + INK X1
Mudra Bergen, 2000

Textile Weave
Mechanical Pen 1x
Theresa Selvey, 2001

Do not copy these.

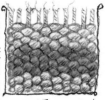

Braided Fragment x1
Pencil, HB + 2B lead
Jerry Aikins, 2004

These are examples only.

Pumice Stone 3x
mechanical pencil
Michelle Olson, 2004

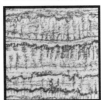

BANANA PEEL (inside)
PENCIL 1x
Deanne Moore, 2000

For this Exercise you need:

1. .005 mechanical pen
2. flexible pen points and nibs.
3. .5 mechanical pencils, HB and 2B leads
4. kneaded and clickable erasers
5. small and large stumps (see p. 32)
6. 12" ruler
7. 11" x 14" sketchbook
8. field sketchbook for "sketching notes"
9. magnifying glass
10. artifacts to draw

Exercise: NOTE: in general, always ask a curator for instructions before handling an artifact (or even touching it). Special gloves may be required, and sometimes an item may not be touched at all.

1. Freehand, very lightly and quickly, a 1" fingerprint border on a page in your 11" x 14" sketchbook. This will be erased later, so do it faintly. Do not write or do any artwork outside this line.

2. With your sketchbook vertical, on the far left edge mark off six 1" squares, like those at left. Leave at least half an inch between squares. Make your guidelines very light. Later you will ink outlines for all but one of the boxes with a ruled line or with a freeform line that follows the guideline closely but with some freedom of expression (see box around pine-needle texture). Pencilling in the boxes should take five to ten minutes.

3. **TEXTILE FRAGMENT:** Observing any artifact-handling requirements, examine a woven textile scrap carefully with your magnifying glass. Notice that the horizontal yarn passes over and under the vertical strands, and notice that the yarn is visibly twisted. This looks complex, but step-by-step, it is not as difficult to draw as it seems.

4. To begin, sketch a <u>very</u> <u>light</u> diagonal grid, then draw ellipses in each opening as shown in the diagrams below. Shade each ellipse with diagonal strokes going the direction the yarn twists. Stroke the ellipses darker on the underside (remember the conventional shading) but don't extend the strokes all the way to the top of the ellipse (the light hits there).

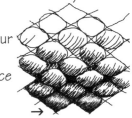

In the example at right, to show how your choice of tools can change the appearance of the texture, the bottom two ellipses were shaded with a narrower pen point.

Darken the sunken area between the ellipses to gain a 3-dimensional effect.

Vertical strands don't show except at the fringe (see below), so draw them only there, if you draw the edge.

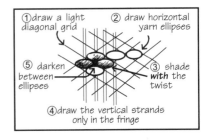

① draw a light diagonal grid
② draw horizontal yarn ellipses
⑤ darken between ellipses
③ shade **with** the twist
④ draw the vertical strands only in the fringe

5. **POTSHERD:** Now examine an Anasazi potsherd with a magnifying glass (or work from the photo at top left). The sherd is part of a "coiled" pot formed by rolling out a pencil-sized cylinder of clay then coiling and pressing it in a spiral to form the pot. There may be fingerprints on the sherd where the potter pressed the clay roll to adhere it to the coil below (see next page). Knowing this, can you tell which edge of the

cont...

IMPORTANT: Handle artifacts carefully. If you damage or break an artifact, DO NOT try to mend it or hide the evidence. Mending of any kind can destroy or invalidate the integrity of the piece and make it worthless as an artifact. 'Fess up,' and take your medicine.

sherd would be "up"? Imagine pressing one roll of clay upon another and deduce what clay pattern that would make. Be sure that you illustrate your sherd "right side up" on the page.

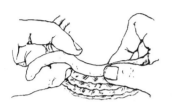

The sides of the pot are built up as a roll of clay is pinched and pressed against the coil below it.

Potsherds at an archaeological site must often be drawn *in situ* (on site). If you cannot remove the specimen or draw at your leisure, sketch the entire form quickly, then finish one representative part fully. Make enough notes to allow you to finish the rest later.

If you want to experiment with textures, try them first in your field sketchbook so that your tested options will be available for later reference and use.

☐(1pt) Make sure your conventional light source comes from upper left (review page 29).

☐(1pt) Ink only five of the squares (put no box around the potsherd). In each square except that of the close-up, draw a different texture **actual size**.

Include the following:

> ☐(2pts) a 1" portion of the <u>textile</u> showing the weave clearly; use lighter or darker tones to indicate at least one colored area
>
> ☐(2pts) the entire <u>potsherd at 1x</u> (no box)
>
> ☐(1pt) the bowl of a <u>shiny</u> spoon, front or back
>
> ☐(1pt) something with a <u>rough</u> texture (not wood)
>
> ☐(1pt) <u>wood</u> (a finished surface) with contrasting grain
>
> ☐(1pt) your choice of <u>close-up</u> texture, done with a magnifying glass at <u>3x</u>. (**no rocks or wood**).
>
> **Select the medium and technique you think best illustrates each subject. Show textures, not shapes or colors. Push your skills envelope. Get up close and personal with the magnifying glass.**

6. ☐(1pt) After studying Chapter 4, **draw three textures in pen and ink**. Use a flexible penpoint for one, and the mechanical pen for the other two (or vice versa). In the drawing done with the flexible penpoint ☐(1pt) show lines that are variable from wide to narrow, adjusting pressure against the paper to widen or narrow the line. Pen textures are covered in the next chapter. <u>**Stipple**</u> **the subject done with mechanical pen** (see page 39).

7. ☐(1pt) **Draw three textures in pencil**, using both .5 HB and 2B leads. Blend the subjects in two or more of these squares with the stump to make the shading span the tonal spectrum ☐(1pt) from 100% black to 100% white.

Make pencil textures dark enough to reproduce well, but don't gouge the paper. Build up dark areas gradually and evenly with repeated strokes so that ☐(1pt) individual pencil strokes don't show (unless they form an element of the texture). See page 31.

> **Texture Tips:**
>
> <u>Lighting:</u> Use a lamp or other sharp, bright light source to light your subject. If you are working outdoors, position yourself or your subject so that from your view the light is shining onto the upper left and front of your subject.
>
> <u>Contours:</u> Remember that the texture should show very strongly along (and roughen) any edges shown.
>
> <u>Wood:</u> When illustrating wood, remember that the grain isn't just decorative – it consists of tubes that carry the water and tree nutrients up and down the stem. So examine your wood specimen carefully to make sure you don't disconnect the tubes. Look at it with your magnifying glass before you begin so that you will know what you are drawing.
>
> <u>Textile Color:</u> Don't work on the "color" of the textile until you have completely drawn all the texture. Then slightly darken the darker-colored areas. Don't lose highlights through overzealous shading.

8. ☐(1pt) Label each drawing beneath its box with the subject, medium used, tool type and scale, e.g.

orange peel,
flexible point, 2x

9. ☐(1pt) Clean up and remove all extra lines, dirt and smudges, and the 1" fingerprint border line.

10. ☐(2pts) To the right of each box, write a short, legible note (at least 25 words) detailing the observations, problems, or successes you had while making that texture. This will confirm the experience in your conscious mind, and make you aware of processes you used to get results.

11. ☐(1pt) Apply coversheet, as shown on page 138.

Lines and Shadows – The Way We See

"Shading" is the artistic use of shadows, one of an artist's more useful tools. Our left brain sees shadows differently from our right brain – without shadows, we don't understand shapes nearly as well. The exercise below <u>may</u> show you how the right brain can freely interpret seemingly meaningless shapes.

Below is a map. All of the land masses are marked with letters, **a** through **f**. The water bodies are not marked. Read the following instructions **all the way through** before you begin the exercise.

1. Quickly blacken the land masses –in order – from **b.** through **f.** Mass **a.** has been darkened already. Shade the masses smoothly because scribbly marks will make identification harder (but don't spend a lot of time at it).

2. After shading each area, turn the page clockwise three or four times, squinting at the image after each turn. Watch for a form, design or shape to emerge. If you are doing this within a group, do not comment or help anyone else search.

3. Stop when you see the form.
   (End of instructions. Begin the exercise).

The answer to this puzzle is on page 119. Don't peek until you have given the puzzle a good, solid attempt.

4. Some people see the form after very few masses are darkened, others only after all masses are black and it is pointed out to them. If you are one of the latter, don't worry – you have lots of company.

Did references to "land" and "water" guide your perceptions? If so, why do you suppose?

The image at right is the answer to a puzzler found further along in the book. If you have only just gotten to this page, you don't need it yet. You'll find out what it's about later. ☺

As you discovered in the exercise at left, contrast is important and you can convey a great deal of information with solid blacks and whites. But gradual shading is important, also. If you are illustrating a white object, the only way to keep it "white" is by using the least shading possible to give it form.

This is true for both halftone and line art.

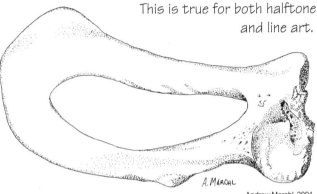

Andrew Marohl, 2001

When illustrating a white object, make the shadows no more than about 50% black in the darkest areas and leave plenty of pure white. The illustration of the white bone, above, is a good example of this. Dense black shadows on a white object will appear to be stains or dark markings, rather than shadows. So make a solid outline, but shade lightly.

To shade something that is black or very dark, make the darkest shadows deep black. The 3-dimensional form and the shape of the contours can be created with highlights as shown on the black and yellow wasp below. The ability to draw strong contrasts is one sign of artistic confidence (except when illustrating white or light objects). Just be careful that you understand and use the correct shading and lighting conventions.

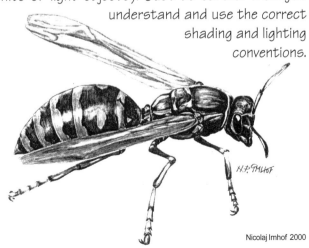

Nicolaj Imhof 2000

Chapter 4. Texture & Tone, Line Art Techniques

Texture and shading are vitally important to show details about an object. In pen and ink, the artist has the use of only a limited number of stroke types, applications and combinations to create textures and the illusion of shades of gray.

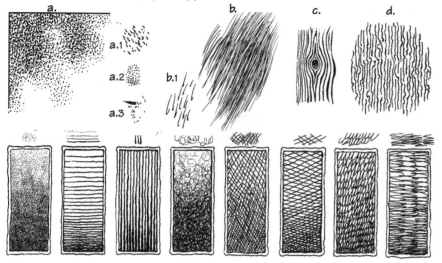

The textures at left were all rendered with a flexible pen nib. Try all of these strokes, particularly stipple (**a.**), fur (**b.**), and wood (**c.**).

Sit down with this when you have some time. Don't hurry or stab at the paper with your point, which creates uneven stipples (**a.1**) and "hooking" at the end of strokes (**b.1**). If you don't try to hurry, you can create convincing textures and shading (**a.2**).

A great deal of scientific illustration is stippled, so stippling is an important skill to acquire. Dots can convey a lot of information. Examine **a.3** above. Do you see an image formed by the dots? It was made with only 60 dots.

To learn how to show fur and hair (**b.**) like on the skunk (at right), practice those strokes.

In the boxes above are various textures rendered in ink. Each texture is graded, that is, it shades gradually from light to dark. Study them, and try to get the same effect with your flexible pen point.

The textures above are outlined with casual frames. Such frames are easier to draw than ruled ones, but will look sloppy unless you lightly rule the lines first with pencil and ruler for a general guide (erase pencil lines away gently when the ink is dry — too-vigorous erasing will remove ink).

When ruling an ink line, use a ruler with a beveled under-edge and a "riser" beneath, so the ink can't crawl under the ruler and blotch your drawing as shown at right.

You can create a riser with 2-3 layers of masking tape, applied the length of the ruler, about 1/16" back from the edge (see cross-section below).

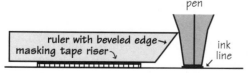

A wooden ruler with a metal-strip edge also works)

Ink rendering is versatile. It allows the artist to show textures and shapes in many different ways.

rough bark

downy chick, smooth egg

nest of lichens & spiderweb

smooth cricket grainy sand

glassy obsidian arrow point

wooden kachina, feathers, fur, coarse hair, rattlesnake rattle, leather pouches

long, coarse fur and short, smooth fur

warty canyon treefrog

muskrat skull, smooth, stipple

bobcat skull, smooth, line/crosshatch

The Flexible Nib

This is a flexible point

or "nib." It makes variable lines and dots.

Flexible nibs are meant to be dipped in ink especially formulated for drawing — often called India ink.

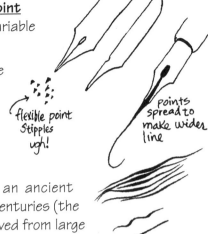

flexible point stipples ugh!

points spread to make wider line

Pen dipping is an ancient art, practiced for centuries (the first pens were carved from large bird feathers or bamboo).

There are all sizes and shapes of nibs designed for various jobs. Calligraphy nibs have wide points that give calligraphy its characteristic look. For scientific illustration, a Gilotte point makes a fine line with normal use, or a broad line when pressure is applied. There are other good brands as well.

For scientific illustration, do not use a flexible point to make stipples (see above) – stipples should be circular dots, and a flexible point makes jagged dots unless you use the utmost care and work slowly and deliberately. The tendency is to jab at the paper, and with a flexible point this gives jaggy, messy results. Sometimes, though, you need a few stipples while using a flexible point. With care, you can make a neat stipple. Place the point onto the paper and lift it. The mark will probably be V-shaped, ➤ but if you make it carefully it may not be obvious. If you can **hear** the point hit the paper, you're jabbing.

A flexible point is excellent for drawing fur and feathers, and it can liven up an illustration. But it must be dipped, cleaned, and otherwise tended carefully since the parts of the point can spread, bend, or get encrusted with ink or fuzz. Keep it clean.

this is a goner. get a new one

Professional inkers treat their favorite points like treasures, and let nobody else use them. Each point has its own holder, and is never removed, since removing the point from the holder puts pressure on the curve and can spread the points. The points eventually wear away and must be replaced, but with good care they can last for years.

Using The Flexible Nib

To insert the flexible nib into the holder, grasp it carefully like this: →
and slide it into the holder so that the curved stem rests inside the curve of the holder barrel. Be careful to not flatten the nib as you push it in, as this could separate the prongs and ruin your point.

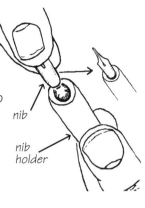

nib

nib holder

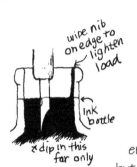

wipe nib on edge to lighten load

ink bottle

& dip in this far only

The nib is curved like half a cylinder in order to carry a supply of ink. The slot in the half-cylinder "holds" the ink from sliding off onto your paper. To make it all work, just dip the point into the ink far enough to submerge the slot — but not much further, as this would overload the point and make it drippy. (If you get the nib holder inky, you will end up with black fingers.) Then pull the tip out, wiping the underside of it on the rim as you do. Expect to get inky occasionally anyway — nobody's perfect.

The point is applied to the paper with the hollow side of the nib down. You'd think the ink would drip out, but the notch and groove in the point hold the ink tightly and it won't drip.

apply ink at this angle

Never try to ink on your artwork without first trying out a few strokes on a sheet of paper kept beside your artwork for this purpose. Stroke the same direction and type of stroke you plan to use next on your drawing.

If you will be making fine lines, practice some fine lines before putting the point to your paper. If you will be making a long curve, practice a long curve.

This sounds like a nuisance, but it prepares your brain for the task it will do (so that you don't make a poor line) and it makes sure you don't have any glops on your point that will drip out onto your drawing. A couple of nasty blotches will make you a believer. **ALWAYS** test it first. ***Don't forget!***

The Care and Feeding of Flexible Pen Points

Using a flexible point isn't difficult, but it takes some getting used to. If you *push* it or use it on rough paper, the sharp point can catch and fling ink all over. To avoid splatters, *pull it toward you* or move it sideways on the paper. Spend some time experimenting to see what the point will and won't do. Below are some pointers.

OOPS...

To begin, hold the pen as you would a pencil. You need to exert firm control, but almost no pressure, since you'll be "laying a strip" of ink on the paper's surface with each stroke — not **in**laying it.

Before you touch it to the paper, arc the pen back and forth above the paper to see what the natural curve of your hand is. Right-handers will make a stroke like **a.**, left-handers will make a stroke like **b.**

MAKE THESE STROKES!

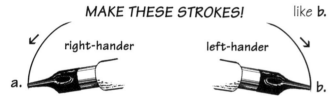

right-hander   left-hander

a.   b.

Pay attention to this natural curve. If you use it for most of your strokes, your lines will be smooth and easy. If you don't, they will be wobbly and uncertain. But since it's obvious that all the lines don't happen to go in that direction, what can you do?

When you are inking, don't fasten your paper down. Turn it often to take advantage of this natural stroke. Any major line that you draw should be drawn with this downward stroke. Smaller strokes can be made curving in toward the hand, but the strokes shown below, pushing the point out into the paper, will cause the prongs to catch in the fibers of the paper and spatter ink or give you a rough line, as shown at the top of this page.

DON'T MAKE THESE STROKES!

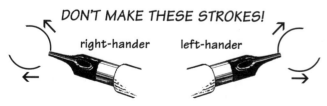

right-hander   left-hander

This may sound complicated, but after a short while your hand will recognize the evil stroke and avoid it carefully without conscious thought.

As the nib crosses the paper, the point sometimes picks up a hair or fiber. The ink won't flow past it and you'll have to clean it and remove the fiber.

Dried ink must be cleaned from the point every five minutes or so during use with a small piece of chamois (goat skin, pronounced SHAM-ee). Use the side of the chamois with the least fuzzy nap, because chamois fibers can get caught in the hole and plug

fibers sometimes lodge here from cleaning with chamois

up the flow. Don't use tissue or other cloth — they have far nastier fibers. Keep a sharp instrument handy (the point of your dissecting tool, a compass or a pin will work) to slide up the groove toward the hole on the nib. This will dislodge the fiber and clean out the channel.

To clean the point, drape the chamois cloth over your index finger and press the nib down lengthwise against the finger beneath. Fold the chamois over it and press lightly with your thumb as you pull (but don't pull the nib out!). This will remove most of the loose ink.

chamois "cloth"
cleaning a dirty nib
finger under chamois

Next, press the *wiped* point against your tongue to moisten both sides, then once more pull it through a fold of the chamois. Repeat until it is clean. Now you are ready to work again (see below).

Some people object to licking the point, but India ink is relatively harmless (carbon and water) and artists have been doing it for centuries without ill effect. Saliva is a great solvent, better even than water since it has enzymes in it. If you don't do the tongue bit, the ink gradually accumulates until the pen no longer works. You can substitute water if you still feel squeamish, but clean it more frequently.

As you can see, using the flexible point has a learning curve. But with practice, the dipping and cleaning become a short and barely noticeable pause in your drawing, and the lively results are worth it. Give it a fair try — several hours — before making a decision.

NOTE: Widening a flexible point line by applying pressure is much easier and faster than widening a mechanical pen line by adding parallel lines.

The Mechanical Pen

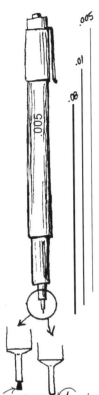

The mechanical pen makes very even lines and dots. You can use a mechanical pen and ruler to make straight lines if you are careful and slightly raise the edge of the ruler by slipping a piece of paper under it, a bit back from the edge (also see page 39).

Three ruled lines and the sizes of points that made ← them are shown at left.

Mechanical pens are easy to use; but if you press really hard, the little carbon tip can bend or flatten, or it will wear down and make a wider line. So use your mechanical pen with a light touch to make it last longer in its original condition. It requires no particular care except to be kept capped between uses.

The mechanical pen is ideal for stipple (dots) since the dots are uniform and circular (flexible points make jaggy triangular dots which don't suggest a smooth surface.)

The linework of three sizes, .005, .01 and .08 are illustrated below. Use a .005 for general work. If an illustration will be greatly reduced, use a larger point.

Use a .01 for making heavy lines and filling in black areas.

A .08 (or any large point) illustrates something very black or which must be reduced a great deal. When reduced, the wide lines become narrow and finer. It looks coarse when you are drawing, but reduces beautifully.

Mechanical pens don't need dipping, and they last a long time, but all lines are the same width throughout the drawing. While that *can* be a positive aspect, some illustrations, ones which need a livelier aspect, may look better with a varying line. In that case, you should switch to the flexible point (see at right).

Look at these two ink renderings carefully.

Examine them very closely — what differences do you see?

What is the overall effect?

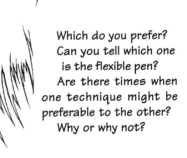

Which do you prefer? Can you tell which one is the flexible pen? Are there times when one technique might be preferable to the other? Why or why not?

The object of this exercise is to encourage experimentation with the mechanical and flexible pen points to create textures and to practice meeting specifications (specs). Your subject is a "Ticklebooty."

☐(4pts, ½ pt each) **What's a ticklebooty?** Ticklebooties look like ①scaly lizards, but have ② wings and ③segmented antennae. ④Brushy crests on their elbows erect when they're angry. ⑤There are four toes on each foot; the outside toe being the longest. ⑥Huge, shiny eyes poke out on ⑦short stalks. Ticklebooties are ⑧boldly striped.

#2 -flexible point

This is not a Ticklebooty

This isn't a complete description of a Ticklebooty, so there are many textures and features you could add. . . . but follow the description that **is** provided faithfully. The illustrations on this page were created by students to showcase various textures. *Below is ONE version of a Ticklebooty. Yours could look <u>very</u> different.*

"Texture" implies 3-dimensionality, e.g. fuzzy, nubbly, smooth, wrinkled, rough, scaly, hairy, feathery, bumpy, grooved, etc.

A textured outline won't be smooth. A texture always protrudes out past the contour — so you will see the texture along the edge. The scales at right would be even more interesting if the outline reflected the individual scales. ——→

Dylan Zodrow 2002

#1 - mechanical point

For this Exercise you need:

1. tracing paper upon which to draw original Ticklebooty
2. .5 mechanical pencil for original drawing, HB lead
3. .005 mechanical pen (.01 pen is good for large black areas)
4. heavy, smooth 2-ply paper, at least 6" x 8"
5. flexible nib and holder
6. India ink and chamois
7. kneaded eraser to remove pencil lines
8. correction fluid or tape

Exercise:

1. ☐(½pt) When you have created a Ticklebooty design you like, transfer it to smooth, heavy, 2-ply paper (see page 140 for transfer advice).

2. ☐(½pt) Ticklebooty must measure exactly 4" x 6" 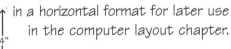 in a horizontal format for later use in the computer layout chapter.

4"

6"

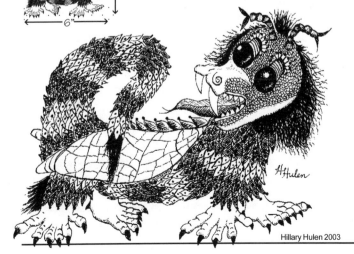

Hillary Hulen 2003

3. ☐(½pt) Leave 1" fingerprint borders.

4. ☐(1pt) Show textures along the outline, as well as on surfaces. Use textures from p. 39, or your own.

5. ☐(1½pt) On your Ticklebooty, show at least three .005 mechanical pen textures. One must be stipple.

6. ☐(1½pt) Render at least 3 textures in flexible nib pen. Show characteristic flexible nib thick/thin lines.

7. ☐(½pt) Make sure all marks are 100% black, no brown or gray strokes.

8. ☐(½pt) Apply your new signature (from p. 24).

9. ☐(1pt) Erase all pencil lines when ink is dry.

10. ☐(1pt) All blots, smudges, smears, etc. must be removed, covered, or incorporated into the design so that they are not obvious cover-ups. Use correction tape or fluid.

11. ☐(1pt) Apply a coversheet as shown on page 138.

12. ☐(1pt) **<u>On</u> <u>the</u> <u>cover</u> <u>sheet</u>,** label textures with numbers 1 through 6 (or more, for later reference).

e.g. #1 - mechanical point, #2 - flexible point (see above).

Don't label directly ON your drawing.

13. ☐(½pt) Put name, date and exercise # on back.

Faux Pen & Ink Using a NON-DIGITAL Photocopier Setting

A versatile tool has been added to the illustrator's traditional kit. It is pencil photocopy as line-art – non-digital, no-gray-tone photocopies. Grays drop out when pencilled notes or halftone photos or drawings are copied on a non-digital photocopier. The examples below demonstrate a creative approach – the use of pencil/photocopy as an illustration medium when you have (or want to do) an illustration in pencil but line art is required.

CREATIVITY:

The big advantage of using a copier to create a pen & ink effect is that people are more creative and at ease with a pencil knowing they can erase at any time. Artists tend to freeze up when they grip the pen. So, try this quick and easy process that takes advantage of the freedom of pencil drawing.

HOW IT WORKS (see also next page):
(Remember, all copies must be NON-DIGITAL)

The original drawing (a.) is done rather darkly in pencil so that on the first photocopy most lines and shadows will remain. There may still be grayish or messy-looking areas.

Photocopy the photocopy. This second pass will make the illustration look more like an ink drawing as grays drop out.

Photocopy the second photocopy to get rid of more junk. Images **b.** and **c.** at right are photocopied pencil drawings at two different stages:

b. is a 3rd generation photocopy – photocopy the photocopy of the photocopy. Much of the fine detail in the original halftone pencil rendering disappeared in the process, but the basic form and details remain. It looks like a pen and ink drawing.

In **c.**, ink stippling was added to the water, and fine lines tidied up the feathers making the rendering very similar to a pen and ink drawing.

Why bother? The original pencil drawing had many erasures and changes that disappeared during photocopying and are not visible in this final "ink" rendering. The photocopies were made in minutes, and a few more minutes with a mechanical pen finished the drawing.

The longer and more daunting process of original inking was skipped. With practice, your results can equal or even exceed the quality of an ink drawing.

REVERSING THE IMAGE:

If you need art reversed, some photocopiers will reverse the image for you. If not, place a pencil drawing made on tracing paper **image-side-up** on the glass and photocopy the image **through** the tracing paper. The result is lighter than a direct copy and will need more retouching, but if you need to reverse an image, this is a possible solution.

EXPERIMENT WITH YOUR TECHNIQUE:

Experiment to adapt this technique to your own personal style. If your pencil work is faint, you will have to darken it to make it copyable.

USE A GOOD QUALITY PHOTOCOPIER:

Experiment with different photocopiers to find one that doesn't remove too much of the grays on the first run-through. Some copiers remove a lot more than 50% black, thus requiring more retouching.

> Repeated photocopy generations quickly lose quality, and applying whiteout may not solve problems.

If you discover your illustration needs major changes (not just additions) after the photocopy has already been inked, all of your inking will have to be redone after you correct and recopy the pencil drawing. Three copy generations is about the limit.

So try to be sure your drawing is 100% finished and ready to go before you start to ink.

If you plan to photocopy a halftone pencil drawing with the intent of making it into a faux ink drawing, there are ways to optimize the quality of your product and minimize the time you spend on it. Once you learn the technique, it will become a favorite tool for many applications.

EXPERIMENT

You must experiment to get good results. Begin with your very best pencil drawing, and seek out and use the best non-digital photocopy machine you can locate. Become familiar with its idiosyncracies, good and bad points, then use the same copier every time. Test with one of your **typical** drawings. Make sure the lines of the pencil drawing are dark enough to reproduce as **black** when you make a copy. Annotate the copies so you can repeat the results later.

If you redraw or darken lines, remember – sloppy or multiple pencil lines will look like sloppy or multiple ink lines on your copy – and they aren't easily removable. Wide, coarse pencil lines will look like wide, coarse, and very **ugly** ink lines on your photocopy.

Erase smudges and blemishes first, or you will have to remove them from your photocopy – a more difficult job after copying, than before. Check your drawing in a mirror to detect any last minute changes needed.

Make a trial copy. If some lines drop out, 1) darken the original pencil drawing 2) copy at a darker setting or 3) plan to ink back in whatever lines drop out.

The 1st-Generation Photocopy:

(photocopy of your original art)

- **has enough details from the original drawing to look good and be easy to see,**
- **may have a light gray background** – but that will drop out (or nearly so) on the 2nd-generation photocopy,
- **doesn't have many "artifacts"** – specks and spots that were on the original pencil drawing or the glass plate.
- **probably has fuzzy or grayish areas that don't look like pen strokes.**

The first photocopy is your foundation. Make it as clean and clear as possible. If there are a few light gray areas. erase them **as soon as the copy comes out of the machine.** Don't wait; the carbon will set permanently. If there is a lot of gray, re-copy at a lighter setting.

Experiment to see what is possible. Cover black artifacts with paper, or correction tape or fluid. Then make your 2nd-generation copy.

> NOTE: **Make sure corrections are dry before copying. Correction fluid on the copier glass will make black specks on future copies (and will mess up other people's copies, too). Specks on the glass may be gently scraped off with a fingernail. (Careful – scratches on the glass leave black marks on photocopies.)**

The 2nd-Generation Photocopy:

(photocopy of the 1st-generation photocopy)

- **looks more like a pen drawing than the first photocopy ,**
- **has lost some or all of the grayish or fuzzy areas that were in the first copy,**
- **dark background is gone, it now has a white background.**

If not, lighten the setting and try again, or use correction tape or fluid to correct small blemishes. If it is good enough, copy it onto high quality paper and use this as your final photocopy to ink on. If it needs more work...

The 3rd-generation or final photocopy:

(photocopy of the 2nd-generation photocopy on 24# ultra-bright smooth laser paper for best results)

- **needs some touch-up to look like pen and ink, but none of the remaining lines look like pencil anymore,**
- **doesn't catch on your pen point, and the ink doesn't sink in or blur because paper is heavy and smooth,**
- **allows you to create a quality "ink drawing" in far less time than an ink drawing started from scratch.**

NOTE: **Photocopying causes lines to deteriorate. Carefully compare the photocopy with the original before moving on. If there are problems, catch them NOW.**

The Final Touch-up:

When re-inking your photocopied drawing, don't redraw every line. Most of your lines should already be there, and you should merely improve the drawing's looks. You may decide to add stipple shading at this point.

Mistakes can be removed with correction tape or fluid, or an X-acto blade – scrape sideways with the edge; don't dig or cut with the sharp point, which will groove or scratch the surface (see page 82). An electric eraser can remove ink that hasn't sunk through the paper (see page 85).

Make sure any correction tape or fluid dries before you ink over it. Work very lightly. Inking over correction materials may produce wider or narrower ink lines, so watch for problems. If your mechanical pen point clogs with correction material, you can lick or suck it clean. If the correction looks bad, let it dry, remove or cover it, and try again. Do whatever works.

It's Not Done Yet:

IMPORTANT! When you've finished the touch-up, make a final photocopy to see how it might appear in print. Examine the copy carefully and correct where needed to produce a clean, clear, drawing without visible corrections.

Scratchboard As An Illustration Medium

Scratchboard is the artist's "mystery medium" – you may have seen it many times, but never heard of it. A mostly-black illustration with clean white lines is either scratchboard or a computer version of it. The computer effect may be gotten by starting with a black fill and drawing on it in white with a brush tool, or reversing a black/white graphic (with adjustments).

The fox at right was illustrated on genuine scratchboard (see descriptions below). But the white egret was drawn first on paper, then scanned into a computer graphics program where a filled black ellipse was added. Stipple dots outlined it and the white feather vanes were drawn in white on the black using a computer pen/tablet combination. The results are not visibly different from scratchboard unless it is enlarged enough to make the pixels visible. Keep in mind that very thin lines might become dotted if the pixel size is relatively large. With fine lines, it's a good idea to scan at 600dpi so that lines won't break up into dots – the egret shows some dotted lines.

Irene Brady

TYPES OF SCRATCHBOARD

Scratchboard is a useful medium, and was once a standard offering in biological illustration courses. However, it may go the way of the dodo bird as computer pen/tablets become more common. Scratchboard is a wonderfully tactile and satisfying medium.

If you need to make a mostly black scene and you don't have access to computer graphics or a pen/tablet setup (don't bother trying to use a mouse, you have far too little control), scratchboard might be the perfect answer. So, just in case, here is what you need to know to use scratchboard. More detailed how-to instructions are on the following page.

Commercial scratchboard comes coated or uncoated, and listed as "black" or "white" respectively. Scratchboard is great for night scenes, or something dark that needs white lines – or both black and white lines.

COATED SCRATCHBOARD. The fox illustration was done on black scratchboard – heavy paper coated with white clay then a topcoat of black. Use this if your picture will be mostly black and you can leave the black background intact. But it's hard to remove large areas with scrapers because the coating is firmly bonded. No surface preparation is needed – just start scratching.

UNCOATED SCRATCHBOARD. This is a clay-coated paper without the black overcoat. It is suitable for most scratchboard projects. Black ink is applied to dark areas out of which you scratch white lines or areas. Parts of the picture which will remain mostly light remain uncoated. Add black lines in white areas with pen and ink (see the egret below, and the student's scratchboard sea lion pup on page 47).

Irene Brady © 2001

FROSTED ACETATE. Available in art supply stores, this also makes good scratchboard. Ink the frosted side, cool air-dry (heat makes the ink crack), then scratch the illustration out, as with ordinary scratchboard.

Extra Credit – Scratchboard – 5 pts.

Scratchboard is available in some large art stores or may be ordered. This project features white scratchboard, but if you want to use black scratchboard you may skip to Step 3 after transferring your design

For this extra credit exercise you need:

1. original 3"- 4" drawing of something dark
2. uncoated white scratchboard
3. large white eraser
4. scratching tools (including *regular scrapers, X-acto blade, needle,* etc.)
5. India ink
6. paintbrush ("dedicated" for use only with India ink)
7. flexible pen and nibs (not mechanical pen!)
8. small empty bottle with lid
9. chamois to clean pen points.

EXERCISE:

1. Before you begin, vigorously erase the entire surface of the scratchboard to remove fingerprint oils which repel ink. Brush off eraser crumbs. Transfer design to surface, outlining shadow areas.

2. Mix 2 parts water to 1 part India ink in the lidded bottle. Paint a light layer over shadow areas (don't worry about precision – just ink it, but don't let it pool). Allow to dry, then apply a second layer to make a smooth, dense, black coat. If it is not solid black, apply a third coat. If you try to cover it in one coat, it will crack off when you try to scratch through it.

While waiting for the last layer to dry, wash the ink brush with soapy water and rinse well. "Point" the clean brush by wetting the hairs in your mouth then pulling it straight out while forming a small "o" with your lips. Always do this before storing brushes.

3. Practice stroking to see what each tool does, then begin scratching your drawing. Blow off the ink dust frequently to see how you're doing. You may recoat and rescratch repeatedly if you don't cut too deeply into the surface.

4. Try various tools to get different results. Create large white areas with broad blades, make thin lines with sharp points. Experiment with X-acto blades and needles – insert a needle into a clickable eraser for a fine-line scratch tool.

5. Add some black lines with the pen point, using full-strength India ink. **_Mechanical pens will clog instantly. Do not use!_**

Ink over any accidental scrapes and scratches, and add texture. Ink with medium pressure: too light and your line will be gray or brown, which doesn't reproduce well. Work with a light touch or your point will clog with clay.

Use a flexible point and clean it frequently with chamois and saliva.

Sara Trakselis
2000

TECHNIQUE: Make scratch lines firm enough to reproduce well. Use a shallow angle for strokes (see below). Gouging deep lines will score the scratchboard, making it difficult to change or correct. With care, if you make a mistake you can re-ink and re-scratch several times before it gets too grooved to continue inking over.

angle
blade like
this

not
this

IN A NUTSHELL: Paint ink on the scratchboard until the area is 100% black, then scratch image area 100% white. Gray areas (less than 50% black) don't reproduce consistently. They may go black OR white during reproduction.

NOTE: On furry or rough EDGES, ink the black lines out into white areas & scratch the white lines *back into black areas.* This gets rid of sharp, unrealistic edges. See examples below.

Apply a coversheet to avoid further scratches.

If you feel adventuresome, and have access to a computer with pen-tablet, try your hand at creating a computer scratchboard illustration.

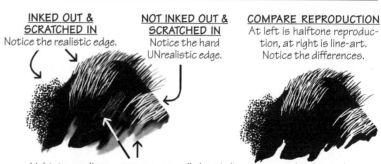

INKED OUT & SCRATCHED IN
Notice the realistic edge.

NOT INKED OUT & SCRATCHED IN
Notice the hard UNrealistic edge.

COMPARE REPRODUCTION
At left is halftone reproduction, at right is line-art. Notice the differences.

Light-to-medium grays are generally lost in line-art reproduction and non-digital photocopies, while medium to dark grays fill in to become black (right).

Extra Credit – Alternate Views and Critical Thinking – 3 pts.

This page is designed to make you think about possible problems encountered in making a scientific illustration. Make no assumptions without good reasons. Parts of the fish at bottom right are incorrect. Can you find them?

Scientific illustrators must sometimes draw several views of the same subject to show markings, shapes, or other aspects. This requires reasoning, skills, close observation, logic, and a lot of attention to detail.

With a ruler, extend more parallel lines from the edges of "landmarks" on the original subject (**b.**) across **c.** to about (**d.**). Now, carefully observing **a.** and **b.**, decide what you could see from an overhead view (**c.**).

1. ☐(½pt) From your observations of **a.** and **c.**, what would <u>not</u> show from directly overhead._____
_____

2. ☐(½pt) What additional view of the fish would be most useful? _____
_____

3. ☐ (½pt)Bluegills are relatively tall, flat fish compared to their girth. From looking at **a.** or **b.**, is it possible to determine the correct width for **c.**? How certain would you feel about the silhouette shown ?
☐ quite certain ☐ maybe ☐ think it's wrong
Give reasons:_____
_____
_____

4. ☐(½pt) There are several errors on **c.** at right (but maybe not 6). Whiteout all the errors you find and correct the drawing with pencil. What are the errors?
1_____
2_____
3_____
4_____
5_____
6_____

5. ☐(½pt) Using your ruler to find the correct information, draw and shade the stripes on the correct side of the fish.

6. ☐(½pt) Would stripes be identical on both sides of the fish? ☐ yes ☐ no
Give reasons:_____

THIS IS A DIAGRAM OF THE...

BLUEGILL, BREAM, BALDFACE, BRIM, GILL, REDBREASTED SUNFISH, SUNNY, YELLOWBELLY, PLUM GRANNY, SUNFISH, COPPERHEAD, BLUEMOUTH, SUN PERCH, KIVVER, ROACH....

or *Lepomis macrochirus*
(fifteen good reasons to use specific names!)

1st dorsal fin — 2nd dorsal fin — caudal fin — anal fin — pelvic fin — pectoral fin — **a.** **b.** **c.** **d.**

p.s. You're on your own with this one – no answers have been provided. Do it with a friend ☺.

Chapter 5. Illustrating Plants

Whether you plan to illustrate for a living or simply want to be able to put your artistic ideas on paper, one of your most logical subjects will be a plant. If you plan to identify the plant from your sketch later, you should be able to recognize and draw at least those parts shown below.

Botany is a good starting place for the budding illustrator (or recreational artist). Unlike beetles or jackrabbits, a plant is going nowhere, at least during the time-frame in which you sit to draw it. You'll have time to study it, absorb its varied and interesting shapes, and get it down on paper before it gets up and walks away.

Whether you plan to illustrate for a living or simply want to be able to put your artistic ideas or scientific observations on paper, one of your most logical subjects will be a plant.

The problem with drawing an unfamiliar object is that you don't know:
- the significance of what you are seeing,
- whether what you do see is typical, or
- whether you are drawing everything that is important.

This can cause trouble when you are in the field sketching. One solution is to learn the basic details you need to record so that you can make an identification later from a guide.

VERY BASIC PLANT ANATOMY:

Having a basic knowledge of plant anatomy will help you draw plants since it will give you confidence in the accuracy and usefulness of your drawings.

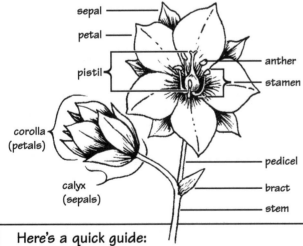

- sepal
- petal
- pistil
- anther
- stamen
- corolla (petals)
- calyx (sepals)
- pedicel
- bract
- stem

Here's a quick guide:
petals.....single or grown together in a tube
sepals.....just below the petals – they may *look* like petals
stamen.....anthers/filaments (male section)
pistil.....stigma/style/ovary/ovules (female section)
pedicel.....the flower stem (think "pedestal")

BASIC FLOWER ANATOMY:

The color, number and shape of petals are sometimes all you need to make an identification. But there may be other essential parts that escape a casual inspection: parts that mimic petals or stems (but aren't), parts which escape your notice due to your unfamiliarity with the plant, and parts inside the flower which could easily clinch an identification.

As with all flowers, the cross-section below shows mainly a collection of sexual organs, male and female.

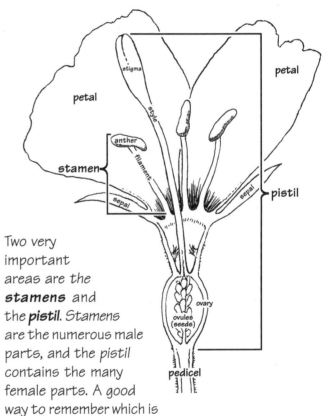

- stigma
- petal
- style
- petal
- anther
- filament
- stamen
- sepal
- sepal
- pistil
- ovary
- ovules (seeds)
- pedicel

Two very important areas are *the* **stamens** and the **pistil**. Stamens are the numerous male parts, and the *pistil* contains the many female parts. A good way to remember which is which, is that **stamens** tend to have "stems," and the **pistil** has a barrel which "shoots" out fertile fruits (seeds) when they ripen. The bulgy ripening ovary may be above or below where petals and sepals attach — compare the diagrams.

NOTE:

There are variations on this pattern, such as the asters and sunflowers with petal-like ray flowers, and orchids with highly modified parts. But the general construction remains the same. Look for more information in field guides or botany books.

Student Plant Drawings

On this page are excerpts from student plant sketches. The top drawing below is accurate, with good scale notation, and very thorough notes and labels.

At bottom left, notice how the artist indicated color on the houseplant leaves without any actual shading. The leaf outlines show close attention to right brain input — no left-brain leaves here.

Below, clean lines and a sharp eye produced a drawing that clearly shows the important details of what happens where a leaf meets the stem, an area most viewers would consider featureless.

On the cactus at bottom right, notice the good warm-up contour and quick sketches. The ¾-view is angled correctly and the detail sketch is excellent.

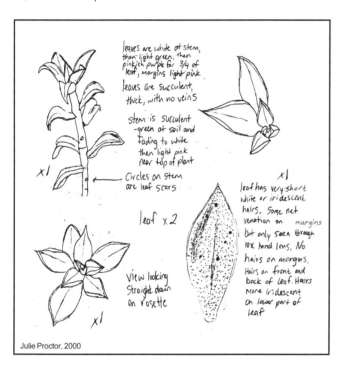

Julie Proctor, 2000

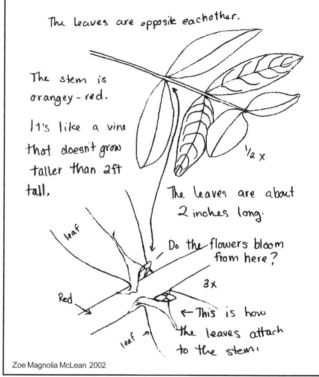

Zoe Magnolia McLean 2002

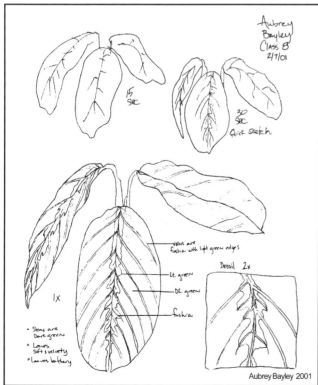

Aubrey Bayley 2001

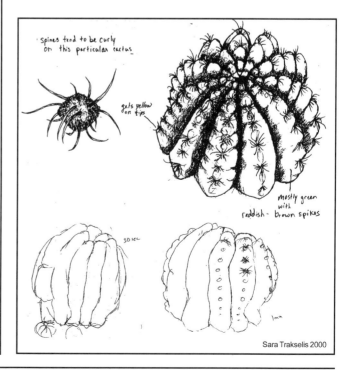

Sara Trakselis 2000

Chapter 5. Illustrating Plants

The object of this exercise is to observe, become familiar with and sketch a living plant. Read all the instructions before beginning. Sketch only one plant, on one 11" x 14" sketchbook page. Keep track of what you do by checking off everything marked with a ☐ below. Do not shade – the emphasis is on plant form and construction. Read page 52 before beginning.

For this Exercise you need:

1. 11" x 14" sketchbook
2. .5 mechanical pencil with HB leads
3. kneaded and clickable erasers
4. magnifying glass (required)
5. tracing paper for cover sheet
6. **a plant less than 12" high x 9" wide**

Exercise: Study the entire chapter before you begin.

Examine the student examples on the previous page, but follow directions on this page in case the contributing student didn't cover all the bases.

1. Choose a plant with some aspect that will make an interesting enlarged detail. Choose a plant smaller than your sketch page. Rule a light margin.

Turn the plant so all important parts are visible. Draw the stem down to the soil line (NO POT). Indicate soil line with a squiggly line as shown here →

2. Before you start to sketch, do a small 15-second warm-up contour drawing and a 30-second quick-sketch at the top of your sketch page (or on another page if you prefer). Do the warmups first, not afterward. *Even if they're good, leave them and start over again to begin your main drawing.*

3. ☐(1pt) Draw the plant 1x – actual size or larger. Use right-brain tactics to check for drop lines (see page 14) and mark some reference dots on your sheet, i.e. the widest part of the plant, the highest, the place where the stems split and go different directions, etc. Do it lightly. For now, only make four or five dots, you can add reference dots as you need them.

4. Very lightly sketch the general shape (skeleton) of the plant to make sure you can get it all on the sheet. You'll erase this later, so make it barely visible. Now it's time to draw your main plant sketch.

5. ☐(1pt)Use medium weight, clean, clear lines. ☐(2pts)Draw right-brain leaves. ☐(1pt)Make stem lines parallel. ☐(1pt)Break lines that pass behind other lines (page 27). ☐(1pt)Add scale.

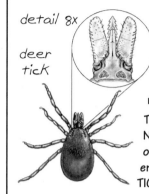

detail 8x

deer tick

Regardless of the scientific illustration subject, this is the preferred way to show a close-up enlargement. Use a compass (or a bottle lid) to make a <u>round</u> circle.

The detail size here (½" wide) is NOT the magnification of the original drawing (a common error) but of the ACTUAL LIVE TICK'S HEAD, which is about ¹/₁₆."

6. Make ☐(2pts)copious notes, 10 to 50 words in complete sentences and ☐(1pt) labels describing the plant's leaves, stems, buds, etc., e.g.

- **color (dark green, yellowish veins, red spots, etc.)**
- **quality/aspect (stiff, leathery, fragile, papery, etc.)**
- **texture (soft, velvety, prickly, fuzzy, smooth, etc.)**
- **anything else of interest that you notice**

7. ☐(1pt) Do a 3x (or larger) detail (use your magnifying glass) of some portion of the plant that is more interesting than the rest, or that is unclear in your main drawing (not just a section of a blah area).

☐(1pt) Show clearly where the detail originated (see the circle and connecting lines on the detail above).

☐(1pt) Label it with magnification.

☐(1pt) Write notes about what makes it interesting.

8. Connect labels with leaders if needed (see page 63).

9. When your drawing is complete, with 3x detail, labels and notes(see #6 above), go back and improve your drawing, or draw another detail if you have time. ☐(1pt) Don't shade.

10. Make sure you have erased all try-lines, that the sides of stems are parallel (not bulgy, wider toward the tip than the base, or with discontinuous outlines). The lines of your drawing should be clearly visible, but not coarse or dark (see next page).

Check off boxes on this sheet as you do the steps. Add your name, date and exercise # in the upper right corner, and apply the coversheet.

Concepts in Botanical Illustration

DRAWING A PLANT USING YOUR RIGHT BRAIN

• get comfortable, sitting in a direct line with your subject

• next, examine the plant carefully

• before you start to draw, do warm-up contour sketches

• choose a view that shows important elements of plant

• count veins, leaflets, branches—anything may be important

• draw a phantom plant in the air over paper before beginning

• use dots (5-6 max.) to get the initial placement right

• use right-brain techniques to lightly sketch the plant

• erase/replace to remove try-lines and improve drawing

• use crisp medium line weight, no fuzzy or ultra-black lines

• break outlines only to show perspective

• avoid shading if possible—use sparsely and only to clarify

• apply scale accurately, note details with clear labels

• clarify every aspect with copious notes, 10-50 words each

MORE FORMAL BOTANICAL DRAWINGS

• idealize while maintaining accuracy

• choose view which shows parts clearly, shift parts to clarify

• count veins, leaflets, serrations, lobes, everything

• first draw a simple outline, erase/replace to add detail

• skeletonize leaves to get edges, midrib and veins correct

• outlines and midribs are primary lines

• veins are secondary lines, about 2/3 as dark as primary lines

• don't show markings unless they are prominent or defining

• don't show insect damage unless it has significant meaning

• to add variety and clarify a view, twist a leaf to show sides

• break lines where they pass behind others

ABOUT LEAF VEINS

• on upperside, veins sink in; on underside, veins bulge out

• veins always connect firmly to the midrib

• veins don't extend off leaf edge, they curve toward the tip

• veins may connect with other veins but don't return to midrib

• the number, placement and arrangement of veins is crucial for identifying the plant, and must be drawn accurately

THIS IS NOT A HOPELESS DRAWING!

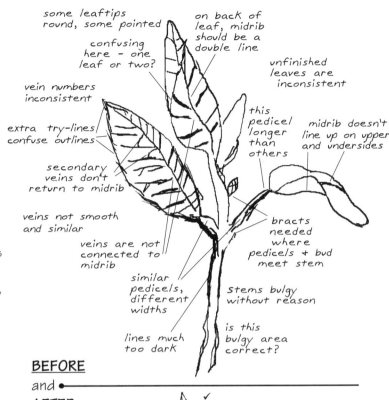

some leaftips round, some pointed

confusing here - one leaf or two?

on back of leaf, midrib should be a double line

unfinished leaves are inconsistent

vein numbers inconsistent

this pedicel longer than others

midrib doesn't line up on upper and undersides

extra try-lines confuse outlines

secondary veins don't return to midrib

veins not smooth and similar

veins are not connected to midrib

bracts needed where pedicels + bud meet stem

similar pedicels, different widths

stems bulgy without reason

lines much too dark

is this bulgy area correct?

BEFORE
and •
AFTER

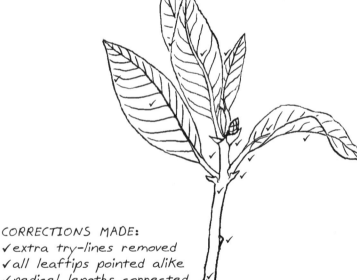

CORRECTIONS MADE:

✓extra try-lines removed

✓all leaftips pointed alike

✓pedicel lengths corrected

✓veins smoothed, made similar

✓all veins connected to midribs

✓veins counted and with consistent number per leaf

✓similar pedicels now have similar widths/lengths

✓main stem bulges smoothed out

✓midrib doubled on leaf underside (convention)

✓midribs line up on upper and underside of leaf

✓confusing leaf area redrawn to clarify

✓lines now medium weight, not too dark or light

✓perspective line-breaks added

✓bracts added where pedicels + bud meet stem

✓lower stem re-examined and corrected

THE PROBLEM: You are trying to illustrate a simple serrated (toothed) leaf. How do you know where to put the teeth? (**a.** at right is the original leaf)

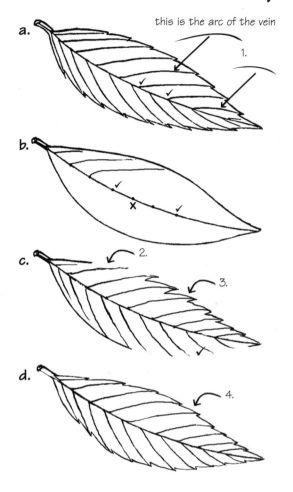

this is the arc of the vein

STEPS TO TAKE:

1. Draw the right-brain outline of the leaf. Draw lightly, because the entire edge will have to be erased as you adjust it for the teeth. (**b.**)

2. Draw the midrib, from stem to tip. (**b.**)

3. On the real leaf, count the number of veins leading from the midrib to the edges. (9 or 10)

4. You must subdivide the edge of the leaf into as many sections as there are veins — indicate the end of each vein with a dot. Put a dot at the half-way point of the midrib (**b. x**)(or divide in thirds — see **b.** — if the math works better). Then you know you must add half (or one third) of the dots on each side. Continue subdividing until you can estimate the placement of the dots in the remaining space. Put that many dots into each section.

5. Notice whether the veins start out opposite each other on left and right sides of the leaf (**a.✓**). If they are independent, vary the placement slightly on each side.

6. Notice and memorize the angle/arc at which the veins emerge from the midrib (**a.** 1.). Turn your paper to accommodate the arc of your pencil movement.

7. Place your pencil on a dot at the midrib and copy that angle/arc as you move your pencil out toward the edge. If you have trouble with the angle, make a dot where the line should end to give you something to aim for. Make all the veins on each side. The veins should be smooth and slightly curved. Compare your sketch to the leaf. Does it look the same? If it doesn't, erase and try again. Do the other side of the leaf.

8. When you have drawn the veins to your satisfaction, look again at the leaf and you will see that each tooth of the serration has its own vein (or, if it is multiply-toothed, subveins coming from the vein). Erase part of the edge (**c.** 2), and copy the tooth/vein alignment in the empty space, Continue down the edge, replacing the line as you go. As you gain confidence, you can erase the entire outline (**c.** ✓) and replace it with serrations very quickly.

9. In fact, after doing a few leaves, you will be able to draw a toothed leaf much faster than you can read these instructions. Clean it up, tidy the lines, and you're ready to move on to the next leaf.

THE FINAL STEP:

When you finish a part, compare it with the subject. Is it similar? If there are differences, are they significant? Does it matter? This may require some background knowledge to know for sure. Ask someone who knows.

If you see significant differences (notice the size of the tooth notches between **c.** 3 and **d.** 4 above) make corrections.

On **c.** above, it wasn't noticed that the veins on the lower edge were too few and at the wrong angle until after it was nearly finished.

The veins were erased and replaced, adding an extra vein in the process and slanting them more toward the tip.

This was a nuisance (taking several minutes to fix) but making the changes was not as bad as drawing the leaf incorrectly and misrepresenting the form of the plant.

Make a habit of regularly comparing your drawing to the subject during sketching to avoid such errors.

Botanical Techniques #2

THE PROBLEM: You are trying to draw a complex foreshortened leaf (one that points toward you), and you are having trouble figuring out how the surfaces of the leaf lobes look as they curl up, toward you, then down.

STEPS TO TAKE:

1. Examine the leaf to decide what its UNCURLED shape is. For this problem, a difficult *palmate* shape will demonstrate how the process works (**a.**).

2. Looking at the midrib only, draw it as it begins at the base of the stem and curves upward and probably to one side, then curves back down toward the leaf tip. This should be a smooth curve unless the leaf is broken (**b.**).

3. The longest, central vein is the midrib, and the other leaflets are supported by veins (perhaps even as large as the midrib). Notice where the veins originate — in this case they begin at the base, but in other cases, they might begin along the midrib (see maple leaf, **d.**) — and draw those lines as they rise, curve over the top and back down to the leaf tip.

4. On this drawing, which will look somewhat like a garden rake, put **light** dots where the divisions between the leaves begin (**b.**).

5. One leaflet has been drawn on **b.** 1. Next (**b.** 2) the top surface of the leaflet was added to connect the edges of the leaf to the mid vein. Then the lines from the under side of the leaflet (which wouldn't be visible from the top side of the leaf) were erased (**b.** 3). Finally, perspective breaks were erased out beneath to clarify that the far edge of the leaf is more distant than the tip (**b.** 4).

6. Try to draw this leaf, using the skeleton ribs in **c.** Starting at the base of the leaf and using the shape in **a.** as a guide, draw the outline of the leaf as it must be if it is to stay in the same plane as the curve.   Check **a.** regularly for correct form.

HINT: If a part of the leaf stumps you, begin at another place and work from there. Sometimes this resolves a problem without any further difficulty. Sometimes you may have to erase repeatedly. However, if your line weight is not too heavy, you can erase many times before the carbon from the pencil reaches a point where it can't be totally removed.

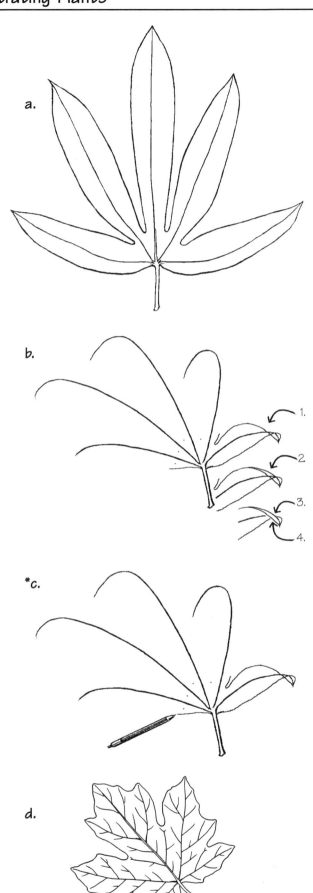

a.

b.

1.
2.
3.
4.

*c.

d.

---

*Your results on **c.** should resemble the finished drawing on page 38 but don't look until you have finished your attempt.

Chapter 6. Advanced Field Sketching Techniques

The following fictional account outlines the details of a perfect illustration project

THE SCENE: An artist is hired to do an illustration of a young green-backed heron chick. It is spring and she knows of a nest near a road on private property with young green-backed heron chicks in it, so the next day, with pleasant weather, she approaches the nest tree in her car, being careful not to disturb them. Using her car as a blind, she sketches and takes notes of their activities for several hours. Between sketches, she photographs the young and adult herons using the zoom lens on her digital camera.

On the way home she spots a fresh roadkill specimen of that species. Parking well off the road, she pushes it onto the grassy verge with a stick and makes detailed sketches and photos of feet, bill and facial features which were hard to see through binoculars. Now she won't need to visit the wildlife rehab center to sketch orphaned young green herons.

At the library and from her own bookshelves, plus her scrapbooks of animal photos, she finds other references and photos to check details.

She also examines a museum specimen at the nearby college to see undertail markings, which she failed to notice at the nest and roadkill.

At home, she uploads her digital photos to the computer and selects poses which meet the requirements of the illustration.

A web search for "green-backed heron chicks" produces several printout pages of info and photos.

Using her sketches as a basis, she roughs out her illustration. After checking over the rough with her client and reviewing her references frequently, she finishes the illustration well under the deadline.

Both she and her client are delighted with the illustration, and the client pays her on delivery.

Now, THAT is the perfect illustration job.

(Read Appendix II for more fascinating details and examples of student field sketch pages.)

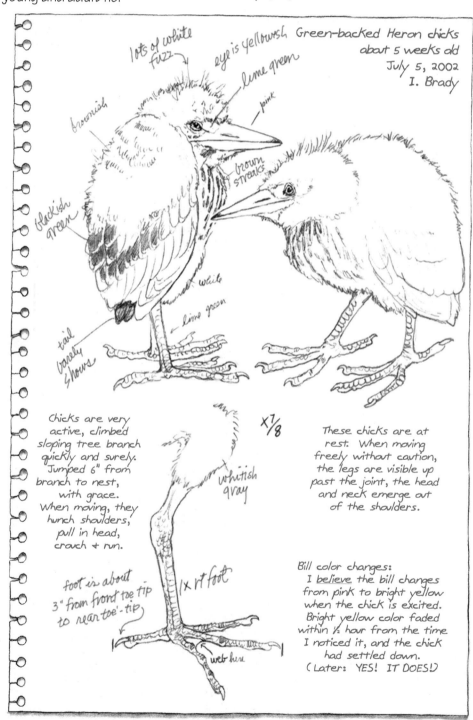

Sketch for Tomorrow

If life were more predictable, it would save us all a lot of trouble and many false starts.

But since we don't know what we'll end up doing with our lives (or next year, or even tomorrow, for that matter) it makes sense to draw field sketches as though we might be called upon to use them later in an illustration.

Being able to use these live sketches (at left) for the coyote in The REDROCK CANYON EXPLORER (below) greatly simplified the task of designing and executing this page — much of the work was done years before. Both the large side view and the "poopy" one (a favorite of kids, by the way) came from this page in one of my old field sketchbooks.

Sandy the Coyote
May 17, 1976, 13 mo. old
Irene Brady

about the coyote. By looking at scat and where it is placed, you
o, what

look quite a bit
Shepherd pup, by the time
year old you probably
wouldn't mistake this
slim "songdog" for a
domestic dog.

Eastern coyotes look a bit more "doggy" than western coyotes.

a good idea,
on the ground. Use a magnifying
for small scats. Pry larger scats apart
with a stick. In a coyote scat you'll
find things like fur, bones, seeds,
mouse skulls, rabbit teeth,
feathers, and insect
parts -- things it ate
that were too tough for
its digestive juices to dissolve.

coyote track & scat

left hind foot   2½"   left front foot   · about 16" ·

walking along →

coyote scat about ⅓ natural size

Exercise #9 – Field Sketching For A Purpose – 15 pts

This exercise replicates a real-life illustration assignment for which an actual field trip or subject materials are not available. It requires a previously collected assortment of items, photos, and sketches and notes (gathered "on site") to provide materials for a facsimile "Sketchbook Page." Your results should resemble the diagram below, but placement of items will call on your design capabilities – to be covered in the next chapter. <u>Convince the viewer that you sketched it on site.</u>

For this Exercise you need:

1. 11" x 14" sketchbook in vertical position
2. .5 mechanical pencil with HB lead
3. kneaded and clickable erasers
4. magnifying glass
5. ruler
6. a representative collection of items, photos and notes from a genuine habitat
7. compass for detail circle

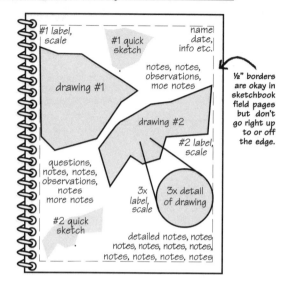

Exercise: **Do this exercise on a single page. Work to inject yourself into the scene – imagine scents, sounds, feelings. As in real life, you may run out of time – imagine a storm is coming, and do vital things first. If you spend too much time on this facsimile sketchpage , you'll overwork it, so allow no more than an hour or two. Read entire exercise before starting.**

In a genuine outing, you would would be limited by time and/or weather in drawing these items. Examine them and the photos and notes about the collection and site. Select two items to feature on your sketch page.

Lightly draw a ½" border around your page, then decide roughly where you will put each drawing – plan ahead. Copy the diagram's format (above right) if you don't have a better idea. Note that the 3x drawing must end up near it's source, connected by lines.

1. ☐(1pt) At top right, write your name, then add the collector's notes and data.

2. Do the ☐(1pt) #1 quick sketch – a 15-second warm-up contour drawing of your first object.

3.☐(2pt)Draw the first object for 10-15 minutes, using right-brain techniques. Stop and make notes.

☐(1pt) Note the scale (1x, ½x , etc.) (see page 51).

☐(1pt) Legibly label item's name or your best guess.

☐ (1pt)Notes: 10-50 words, with at least one observation or question **(maintain the ambience!).**

4. Select a good view of your second subject and repeat steps 2 and 3, beginning with the 15-second quick sketch, then the 10-15 minute drawing with scale, label, and observations and/or questions.

5. On the same page, <u>near its source</u>, use your magnifying glass to draw a ☐(2pts) magnified detail (at least 3x) of one interesting or unclear area in your main drawing. Apply the circle AFTER you finish the enlargement. The area you choose to enlarge should reveal, magnify and clarify an element that was intricate, complex, or confusing in the original view – the whole point of a magnification. You may make the enlargement more than 3x if you wish. Draw a formal circle around the magnification with a compass or template (not freehand). Make the view exactly the same as the original, but larger.

☐(1pt) connect it to the area being magnified

☐(1pt) label and ID (or "best guess" the enlargement)

☐(1pt) estimate or measure to determine scale

☐(1pt) make notes about it (10 - 50 words)

6. When you have finished the field-sketching page, look it over to make sure you have included all the notes, labels, etc., and that you:

☐(1pt) put name, date, and "Ex. #9" **on the back.**

☐(1pt) erase the border.

7. If you finish within the allotted time, add details and sketches or improve the drawings. You may also improve, shade, or add more sketches later. DON'T REDRAW. **Does it look like a real field sketch page?**

8. Apply a coversheet. Take your sketch page to a photocopier and copy all the art and notes at various sizes: 150%, 125%, 100%, and 85%. It's okay to tile the photocopies if the original is too large.

You'll need these copies to complete Exercise 10.

Actual Student Field Sketching Examples

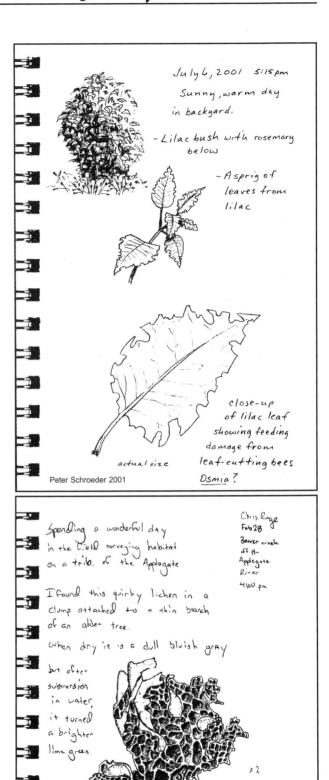

The student fieldsketch pages here are excellent examples of sitting and drawing what comes to hand. Perching quietly by a creek is generally rewarding, as Heidi discovered (above).

Peter (top right) spent the time in his back yard, drawing the lilac bush habit, then closer in, a branch, then closest of all, the work of leaf-cutting bees on the leaves. As you can see, the observations need not be earth-shaking to be good.

Chris (right) did a rough sketch of the lichen in the field, then took it home for a more detailed treatment with shading. This is always an option, as long as removing a specimen won't impoverish the environment.

Many people with some training in biological illustration find themselves keeping a personal journal as a natural offshoot. Being able to illustrate your own journal is a very rewarding experience, even if you don't continue on as an illustrator or use your drawing capabilities in any other way.

So, what if you aren't quite in tune with social activities going on around you? Grab your sketchbook and pencil, and disappear. It may just make your day.

It's Labor Day Weekend and all the best campsites have been taken, but there's plenty to see and do around the edge of the lake. The area is boggy enough to produce swamp huckleberries, which are covered with blue berries (eaten by the birds; some have ended up splatted on the tent) and some big mushrooms that don't get identified. Not even a guess.

Notes about one huckleberry's bright red fruit clinch the identification later, because the plant's size could allow it to be either V. caespitosum (the dwarf blueberry) or V. scoparium (grouse whortleberry). But the dwarf blueberry has blue berries while whortleberries are red.

The "molarized" berry adds a humorous touch, making it a fun read.

You don't have to know a lot to create a good field sketchbook. Just draw what is in front of you with as much curiosity and skill as you have. Enjoy!

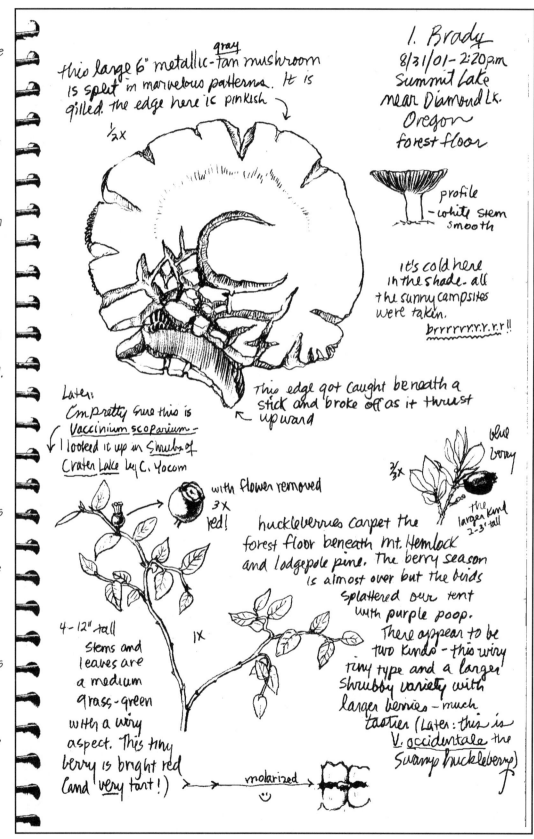

this large 6" metallic-tan mushroom is split in marvelous patterns. It is gilled. the edge here is pinkish

½x

1. Brady
8/31/01 - 2:20 p.m.
Summit Lake
near Diamond Lk.
Oregon
forest floor

profile
- white stem
smooth

It's cold here in the shade. all the sunny campsites were takin.
brrrrrr.r.r.r.r !!

This edge got caught beneath a stick and broke off as it thrust upward

Later:
I'm pretty sure this is Vaccinium scoparium - I looked it up in Shrubs of Crater Lake by C. Yocom

with flower removed
3x
red!

blue berry
⅔x
the larger kind 2-3' tall

huckleberries carpet the forest floor beneath Mt. Hemlock and lodgepole pine. The berry season is almost over but the birds splattered our tent with purple poop. There appear to be two kinds - this wiry tiny type and a larger shrubby variety with larger berries - much tastier (Later: this is V. occidentale the swamp huckleberry)

4-12" tall
Stems and leaves are a medium grass-green with a wiry aspect. This tiny berry is bright red (and very tart!)

1X

molarized

The "CODA" of Field Sketching

If you go about it with a sense of adventure, you will realize that field sketching is:
- **great entertainment** – a quick fix for the blahs.
- **challenging** – especially in bad weather.
- **demanding** – accuracy can be difficult in the field.

You can characterize field sketching with the acronym "**CODA**":

Curiosity, **O**bservation, **D**iscovery, **A**ccuracy

Webster's dictionary says a **coda** is "*something that serves to round out, conclude or summarize, yet has its own interest.*"

Well, hey, that sounds like a good field sketch page. Here's a thought:

The purpose of a <u>good</u> <u>education</u> is to encourage:

- **acute observations**
- **making discoveries,**
- **asking questions,**
- **making connections between ideas,**
- **and forming educated deductions.**

A field sketch page is a combination of all those things made visual.

So where do you start? What follows is a narrative of what led up to my sketch below:

"I was walking down a trail next to a swamp in central South Carolina with only a small unlined journal and a ballpoint pen. I spotted this ichneumonid wasp and crept up as quickly and quietly as I could. It didn't seem to notice me, so I opened to an empty page in my little journal and started to draw.

I had to sketch fast, in ink, so I didn't worry about getting it right or wrong, I just observed and drew as fast as I could for about three minutes, then it flew away.

After it left, I kept drawing for nearly ten minutes: notes, labels, a correction to the drawing – that the abdomen should have been longer and higher. I made a tiny sketch with just a few lines to show what it should have looked like. If I'd been using pencil, THEN would have been the time to erase and correct, not during sketching (it might have flown and I'd have nothing sketched.)

This isn't a terrific drawing, but it illustrates an experience I personally had, and it nudged me to look up these fascinating wasps and learn more about them. Having sketched it, I'll always remember this amazing sight."

That narrative points up a number of important things. The situation could have proceeded VERY differently in MANY ways. For instance, I might have ✓left my sketchpad at home. I might have ✓failed to notice the wasp. I might have ✓been scared to get close enough to watch. I might have ✓been afraid to draw in ink. If using a pencil, I might have ✓stopped to erase and correct. I might have ✓tried to do a detailed drawing of just one part and got a single partial drawing that wouldn't show what transpired. I might have ✓quit when it flew and ✓failed to make notes while the visual memories were fresh. If I had made notes later, I might have ✓remembered inaccurately. I might have ✓been too proud to admit my drawing was inaccurate and make a correction, thus perpetuating a false impression of the wasp. Whew!

(The illustration below is a "computer-improved" field sketch.)

<u>DOING IT RIGHT</u>

- be observant, questioning, and open to wonder.
- write down thoughts, observations and questions.
  - get close enough to see lots of detail
  - sketch, then get closer and sketch again – then again.
- make a habit sketch (quick sketch of a more distant view)
- take enough notes to fill in the empty spaces.
- ponder what you are seeing (in addition to drawing)
- describe what you see (even if you're unsure what it is).
- assume you will never see this phenomenon again.
  It might fly away, hatch, get eaten, go to seed,
    be stepped on, or carried off by a woodrat.
  Or you may just never go there again.
- carpe diem! Seize the day! Draw the day!
  The world is yours to illustrate!

Although clarified, the text remains much the same to retain the sense of excitement. Compare with the raw sketch on page 129.)

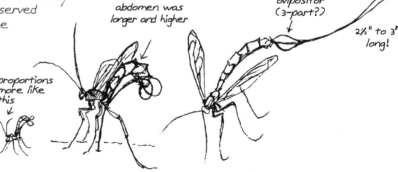

abdomen was longer and higher

ovipositor (3-part?)

2½" to 3" long!

proportions more like this

Wow! I just saw this huge wasp, a yellow, red + brown ichneumon, inserting its eggs into a rotten log! When it was done, it stood on its head with abdomen straight up and pulled until it freed its ovipositor (3-part), then pulsed until it had slicked down to a single 3-inch "tail", and flew away. I sketched it from 12 inches away for about three minutes total, but I don't know how long it had been laying eggs before I came along.

Chapter 7. Design & Layout in Scientific Illustration

DESIGN is the process of planning, organizing, fitting elements together effectively, then rendering them. It includes arranging the subject, selecting the viewpoint, choosing the medium, and aligning things within the design area. To be the best artist you can be, you should study and internalize these concepts.

Design includes all the parts — illustrations, title, text, labels, captions, and scale notation arranged into a suitable format for publication, poster or display. Later you can use design principles learned in this chapter to put together your portfolio (p. 135).

The design process begins when you examine a subject with the idea of making it into an illustration.

A scientific illustration must be designed to give the viewer factual information about a subject. It is just a piece of art unless it has been correctly titled, captioned, labeled, and given a text that defines it.

People are used to professionally prepared information, and give less credibility to amateurish work, even when it presents a significant idea. If you dump the elements all together on the page, the careless organization will make viewers suspicious of the information and cause them to doubt its accuracy. See also pages 145-50.

THESE ARE THE BASIC ELEMENTS OF DESIGN
- Conventions
- Orientation
- Element size
- Balance
- Flow
- Progress
- Text

<u>CONVENTIONS:</u> *Every discipline has its own conventions and requirements. These overrule other design considerations. Find out conventions before you begin, and observe them scrupulously.*

For instance, in archaeology, projectiles (spears and arrowheads) are illustrated point up, and tools with striking or cutting edges are illustrated point down. If numerous views are shown, side views, profiles and the reverse side are placed to the right of the front view, while top views are placed above, and cross sections and end views are placed below.

These conventions apply even if the tools fit into the design better when arranged differently or pointing another direction. This is only one of numerous archaeological illustrative conventions.

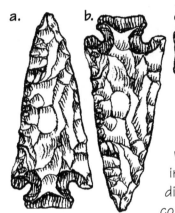

a. **b.** **c.**

In this grouping, **a.** is correct but **b.** and **c.** would not be acceptable in a formal paper. Other disciplines have their own conventions.

<u>ORIENTATION:</u> *Specific requirements or design constrictions may influence the design layout*

- a page layout may be horizontal or vertical, each requiring a different approach to layout

- the page design may include a specific column size, required illustration proportions, etc.

- wall space designated for a conference poster may require a particular shape and size of display

- a brochure may have a specified number of panels which will open and orient in a particular way

<u>ELEMENT SIZE:</u> *The most important items should be largest. Things with a lot of detail must be big enough to see the detail clearly.*

An important detailed part should be larger than something equally important but less detailed.

For instance, a close-up showing the facial markings of a chipmunk might be accompanied by only a small silhouette of the animal if the markings are most important and the silhouette works for simple identification. In comparing acorn shapes, the acorns would be all the same scale unless you chose one to show some particular

cont...

Elements of Design, cont...

detail, then it would be shown larger. Text for more important items would be larger than text for less important items.

BALANCE: *How things fit together on a page is called "balance."* A title or headline is usually placed at or near the top. Size and tone cause elements to appear larger or smaller – so place large or dark items near the bottom to keep the layout from looking top-heavy. Bright or dark colors draw the eye, and are more compelling than white, pastel or light colors. These general rules can be sidestepped to fit the needs of convention, relationships to other parts of the format and other requirements, but they are a good place to start.

There are several formats for balance:

• *formal* or symmetrical – shapes, order and orientation of items are symmetrical.

• gridded – similar sized/shaped items in a grid in a symmetrical arrangement.

• *informal* or asymmetrical – elements arranged in a creative, free-form style, but still balanced.

• any combination of the others – for instance, a gridded part of the design may be combined with a more informal arrangement of elements.

Margins are a major element of balance. The margin is the white space left between a text and the edge of the page or display . A large display requires wider margins than a smaller one. While part of the design may be made to purposely breach the edge of the outline, the rest of the display still needs to have a distinct margin to hold the eye inside until it has finished absorbing the message. It is better to leave too much margin than too little. Many good layouts have been compromised or marred by skimpy margins.

On an 8½" by 11" page, a ¾" margin is considered about right. On a large display, a 2" margin would be more appropriate.

FLOW: *The balance of elements in a pattern that first catches your eye, then leads in a natural sequence from one point to the next, is called "flow."* Ideally, you should first attract the viewer's eye to the upper or center left and lead it right and down or around. The eye's trip should end near the

bottom right corner or the lower half of the right side. Don't use any strong thrusting elements that would lead the viewer's eyes off the page or display before they see everything.

Text is a classical example of flow, from top left, to the right, then down through the text block. Other 述賓結構 連謂結構 偏正結構 疑問句 cultures may have different text flow patterns. In cultures where printed text starts at the lower right corner then goes up and to the left, design may follow different rules.

The laws of flow become complex when you combine illustrations and titles, blocks of text, captions and diagrams, but the designer still must compel the eye to start at the beginning then progress in an orderly way through the rest of the design.

PROGRESS: *Say what you mean to say with your design.* Probably because of our reading patterns, most people in Western cultures think of "PROGRESS" as going from left to right. Also, something headed left is "returning." Hard to believe? Look at the following symbols found on every VCR, CD or DVD player

Which of these buttons on a CD player would you push to go backward? [>] [<] Forward? You didn't even have to think about it, right?

Now, think of the concept of "speed." Which is "speedier," going left or going right? It's subtle, but we sense it – something running to the right looks "faster" than something running to the left.

This may be an artifact of horse-racing. Dredge up a memory of watching the starting and final moments of a horse race. From your memory, which direction were the horses running? Left to right, almost certainly. Race stadiums are set up so that at their closest points the races proceed from left to right. So are most track events, and skating rinks. Olympics events? And which direction are most basketball shots filmed from. Left to right? It isn't just chance.

So to show action happening, or to imply "speed," lead the eye from left to right.

cont...

TEXT: *Design text to be readable at the distance and under the conditions at which it will be read. Labels and captions should be next to their subjects and give a unified look to the arrangement.*

Learn first how much distance will be between the text and the viewer. If the viewer is kept at a distance, the text must be readable from that distance. If the viewer will only have a quick glance or if visibility may not be the best, keep it large and simple. TV graphics will only be viewed for seconds.

Make the text easily readable – don't use all caps, except in small amounts to emphasize a point.

• Text must be big enough to read easily. Middle-aged and older people may have trouble with fine print.

• Text must be consistent, with all the same font – or one splashy title font and the rest a smaller related or logical font. For instance Tinkertoy could make an interesting title font while its relative **Tekton** (Tinkertoy without with blobs on the tips) would be a good accompanying text.

• Choose text that doesn't call attention to itself – don't use more than one or two different fonts in a single display.

• Choose san serif fonts like **Helvetica** and **Arial** (they're basically the same font) for most scientific illustration. *San serif* means "without serifs." Serifs are the little feet on **Times Roman**, `Courier` and other fonts. Helvetica has a businesslike look. San serif fonts are usually used for "serious" materials.

Don't use informal fonts like Curlz or Tinkertoy for serious subjects – although you have some leeway with a **title font**. An interesting title font which relates to the subject (like **Playbill** for a Western treatment or **Broadway** for a play) might catch people's attention without being distracting.

• Size text in order of importance: **TITLES** must be the biggest, **SUBTITLES** are smaller, **Text** is next, and labels and captions are smallest. Unless they conflict with other conventions such as specific names, *italics* can be used for minor emphasis. Initial Caps on Important Words or Subtitles can also be effective if not overused.

• Leading (say "ledding"), the space between the lines, should be at least equal to the height of a lowercase letter. Notice the leading between lines of this paragraph. This is the default spacing.

(Leading between the lines of *this* paragraph has been narrowed to less than the height of a lowercase letter. Its cramped look discourages reading.)

• Placement: keep text blocks compact and together – don't break a paragraph unnecessarily.
  - read phrases out loud to determine line breaks
  - put text directly next to its illustration
  - use consistent margin width around text
  - don't crowd the edge of the display.

• Use colors, if any, conservatively – choose a color theme and stick to it.

• Follow conventions for labels and leaders. Captions and measurements should accompany the correct elements as closely as possible without crowding. Don't use leaders (lines) unless you have to. If you do, make them straight and horizontal, not crossed. If a horizontal straight line won't lead to the object, angle a short portion of the leader (see below). Make leaders parallel if possible. Don't touch the diagram with a leader unless it points to something specific **inside** the subject's perimeter.

Don't assign letters or numbers to parts of a technical illustration if you can label its parts with names. It is annoying to try to match letters on an illustration with their counterparts in a distant caption.   See diagram below.

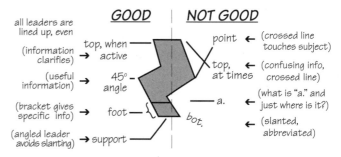

In short:

• avoid abbreviations
• don't cross leaders (lines)
• don't allow leaders to touch diagram
• use consistent placement – line things up
• make labels and leaders parallel, or angle a part
• make sure labels are meaningful and clear

Selecting The Right Font

The relationship of font type to printed material is similar to the relationship of color to a painting. Both set the scene, determine the proper attitude of the viewer, and with varying degrees of subtlety, tell you how you are supposed to feel about it.

Want proof? Look at the fonts on pp. 65 and 109.

If you have access to a computer and will be using decorative fonts regularly, print out examples of each font offered in the font list so that you can quickly choose an appropriate one. If you have special font needs or just want to play, you can purchase an incredible variety of fonts on CD. The "sketchbook" font used on some of these pages is a font called Kramer's Hand. It was purchased separately on a disc devoted to handwritten fonts: KarinsHand, BrooksHand and CoreysHand are some others from that disk. Such fonts must be used with care as they may be difficult to read in large blocks (KarinsHand). But they do look convincing as facsimile hand-written notes (BrooksHand).

Choosing a font can seem intimidating. Font names may be useful – or not. Names for fonts #10. Tinker Toy and #15. Comic Sans (next page) are descriptive, but #11. Westminster? Obviously, it makes sense to print them out for reference. It also helps to print out the entire set of alphabet and numbers if you're going to make a font catalog. (Hint: save time by typing out everything on the keyboard ONCE, then copy the entire set and paste it in multiples down the page. Then select each set and change it to a new font, then retitle each set with the correct name (not the one you copied/pasted).

There are various categories of fonts – such as those for kids, like Tinker Toy, Kristen, Snap and Bees Knees. You can group them any way you want:

- <u>Humorous</u>: Curlz, Critter, Comic Sans.
- <u>Creepy</u>: Chiller, Matisse, Ransom and Quake.
- <u>Regional</u>: Moravian, Harrington, and Papyrus.
- <u>Antique</u>: Papyrus, Old English.
- <u>Cultural</u>: Old English, Playbill, Broadway.
- <u>Scripts</u>: Vivaldi, Brush Script, Viner Hand.
- <u>Handwriting</u>: KramersHand, KristensHand, etc.
- <u>Specialty</u>: Gradl (Art Deco), Courier (newspaper), and Westminster (computer).

The choice of a font can make or break the printed material it clothes. Using more than two fonts in a layout will make it look amateurish. Find a font that says most of what you want, and stick with it.

Imagine a scientific paper being presented in ANY of the fonts on the list except **Arial** or Times New Roman, the two most accepted "serious" fonts.

Wouldn't you find it hard to take a treatise on DNA seriously if the display text were set in Old English? What about Chili Pepper? (#6 on page 65.) The material would be passed over with a suspicious look, or ignored completely. Or it might be taken as a joke. And rightly so.

You might get away with a catchy title to attract attention (Flexure, #24, for instance) for a serious subject, but not much more than that.

But what about text in a Nature Center display dealing with salamanders? That could be Arial or Comic Sans, which *would* make it simple for the youngest viewers to read (you should consider that point), but chances are they might be more attracted to a "salamanderish" font like Curlz or ChiliPepper or Tinkertoy. And how about Papyrus for a historical article on papermaking from Egyptian times? If it's easy to read, it might work for text. However, if it's hard to read, just use it for titles.

Make allowances for differences in fonts. Sizes vary. Amazing though it seems, the following are all 12pt: Tekton, French Script, **Arial**, MATISSE and Onyx.

Another important point in selecting fonts is that some only come in CAPITALS with no lowercase options – Goudy Stout and Stencil, for example. They are designed as titling fonts, because titles are typically confined to one line (three at most). Large blocks of capitalized text can be nearly unreadable – but in a short title, all-caps can be very attention-getting and still be readable.

If your handwriting isn't good and you want to give a casual look to a note, use a *handwriting* computer font. There are some nearly unreadable handwriting fonts, though, so be sure to choose one that is legible and doesn't stop the text flow.

Extra Credit – 3 pts | Selecting The Right FONT

On the lines following the fonts below, write down in 10 words or less the mood you feel each font evokes, and what subjects, ambience, atmosphere, environment or setting you might choose to characterize with that font. Evaluate the fonts seriously, spending a little time and thought on each. You will have similar REAL choices like this to make in the future.

Font Name	Text Sample	Your Evaluation

1. Bees Knees -- when I was young _____

2. Jokerman -- my skin was tight. _____

3. Viner Hand -- My hair was brown _____

4. Vivaldi - my teeth were white. _____

5. French Script -- But now I'm old and quite a sight _elegant, correct, use for classical music flyer_

6. Chili Pepper -- my teeth are brown, _____

7. GOUDY STOUT -- MY HAIR _____

8. Ransom -- is white! Bummer! _____

9. ROMULUS OUTLINE -- KATIE, KATIE, CAN'T _____

10. Tinker Toy -- catch me, Climbing in the _____

11. Westminster -- willow tree! Time _____

12. KramersHand -- to eat, then you'll find me, _____

13. MATISSE -- OLLIE-OLLIE OX-IN FREE! _____

14. Curlz -- My kitty isn't very _____

15. Comic Sans -- big. His tail is _____

16. Arial -- kinky like a pig. _____

17. CRITTER -- FOR TREATS, _____

18. Times New Roman -- he will sit up and beg, _____

19. STENCIL -- BUT THEN HE BITES ME _____

20. Broadway -- on the leg. _____

21. Courier New -- Don't you love it _____

22. Brush Script -- when the fog _____

23. Chiller -- makes things fuzzy, _____

24. Flexure -- makes things sog? _____

25. Gradl -- Blinds us with a furry shroud, _____

26. Kristen -- quiet footsteps crunch _____

27. Harrington -- quite loud. Everything _____

28. Lucida Blackletter -- seems strange and _____

29. Moravian -- weird, usual things _____

30. Old English -- have disappeared. _____

31. Papyrus -- Don't you love the _____

32. Playbill -- transformation? Life _____

33. Snap -- becomes a new sensation. _____

34. Quake -- Don't you love it when the fog _____

35. Tempus Sans -- makes things fuzzy, makes things sog? _____

Student Design & Layout, Improved Field Sketchbook Page, shown ¾x

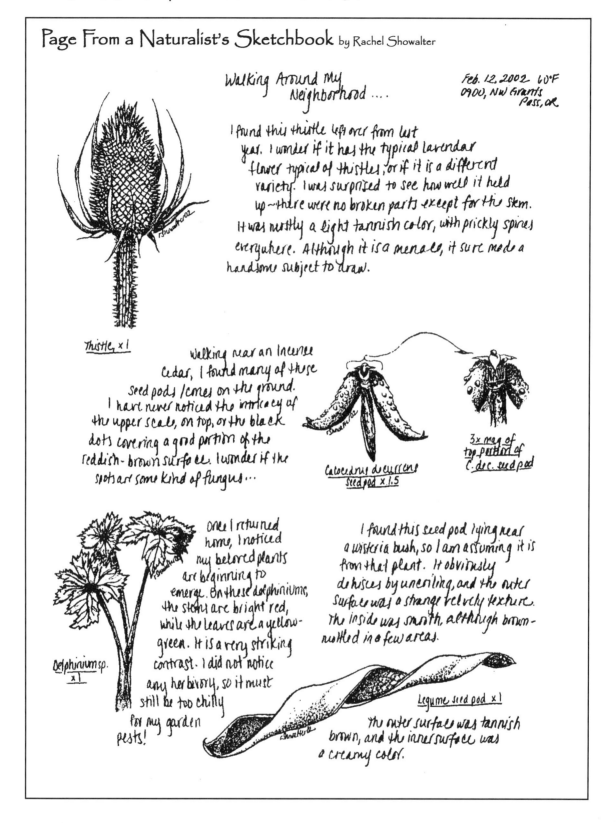

Page From a Naturalist's Sketchbook by Rachel Showalter

(photocopy the title below at 120% to cut out and use on your Exercise #10 – Design & Layout page)

Page From a Naturalist's Sketchbook

Exercise #10 – Design & Layout "Page From a Naturalist's Sketchbook" – 20 pts.

For this exercise, concentrate on the elements of design and the mechanics of shifting text and illustrations around on the page (and fastening them in place), using a photocopied assortment of your own text and drawings from the previous chapter. This exercise will help you learn elements of page design and layout, but the more immediate goal is to produce a well-arranged sketchbook page suitable for publication in an environmental magazine. Study page 68 for details.

For this Exercise you need:

1. .5 mechanical pencil with HB lead
2. tracing paper
3. kneaded and clickable erasers
4. 12" C-thru ruler
5. 11" x 14" sketchbook
6. regular tape and low-tack tape
7. photocopied layout pieces in several sizes
8. scissors
9. whiteout tape or correction fluid
10. a sheet of 8½" x 11" copier paper

> **SPECIFICATIONS FOR "PAGE FROM A NATURALIST'S SKETCHBOOK"** :
>
> Design a layout for an environmental journal's **"Page From a Naturalist's Sketchbook"** with an outside page measurement of 8½" x 11," and ½" margins all around (see ¾x example on page 66). Your original artwork must be larger than the to-be-published piece, but there are no specs for enlargement.
>
> **Your goal is to create a pleasing left-hand page format with the fresh appearance of having been spontaneously sketched in the field.**

Exercise: Read the client's needs in the box above. Now find the proportions of the area you are to illustrate (don't include the margins): On an 8½" x 11" sheet of paper (the size of the journal's page), trim off the specified ½" margins all around. **What remains is the size the published work will be.** Now you need to enlarge it to an 11" x 14" sheet.

1. ☐(2pts) On a sheet from your 11" x 14" pad, lightly rule off 1" fingerprint margins on **top, left** and **bottom only** (gray areas at left), ruling the line all the way to the edges. Lay the sheet of paper you trimmed in the bottom left corner inside the margins (see at left). Rule a diagonal line as shown. Where that line crosses the top margin, drop a vertical line to the bottom margin. This will be your right margin (see also page 137). Design your sketch page within this area. Discard the trimmed sheet.

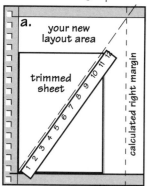

2. Tape your enlarged title (photocopied from page 66) in the top left corner. Cut out all of the sizes of layout pieces and try out various arrangements. *Don't tape anything down yet.* Make sure everything is in your layout. If something seems missing or you have a great idea of something you could add, make a rough sketch (two minutes, max) on a piece of paper and add it to your collection of possibilities.

3. Review the design and layout guidelines (pages 61–66) for ideas and conventions. You may use any layout you wish, as long as it is ☐(3pts) logical within the framework of an actual field sketch page and the subjects you sketched. ☐(1pt) Arrange enlargements close to their sources, with nothing else between.

4. When you have a design you like, attach to sheet with low-tack tape on only one edge so you can easily reposition it (**b.**).

tape only 1 edge **b.**

5. ☐(1pt) Place a T-square ruler against the edge of the paper and line up all text. Squint at it to make sure the layout looks balanced. Replace any dirty tape. Look for more details on page 142.

6. ☐(1pt) Erase border and corners, leaving only crop marks (**c.**), (also see page 152). Erase or whiteout any smudges.

c.

7. Set it aside for a couple of days if possible. You may be able to see errors after a pause.

crop marks

8. **Make an article facsimile:** Experiment to reduce the paste-up on a photocopier ☐(2pts) to make the layout with cropmarks and a ½" margin all around fill an 8½"x11" page. Use a setting light enough that ☐(1pt) tape and paper edges don't show **but** ☐(1pt) no text or art is lost. Clean up if needed. Create a ☐(1pt) clean 1st-generation copy (see pp. 44–45) to check for speckles and other "artifacts." If it is too grubby, use whiteout to create a good 2nd generation.

NOTE: See pages 81–82 for clean-up hints. If any part of the art "drops out" on the photocopy, carefully re-ink the lines. Don't re-ink the entire drawing. Don't cut it out — maintain the ½" fingerprint margin. ☐(2pts) Coversheet both original and final photocopy.

FINAL CHECK — *would a viewer of the journal believe this is an actual page from your journal?*

Student Layout Page – In Process

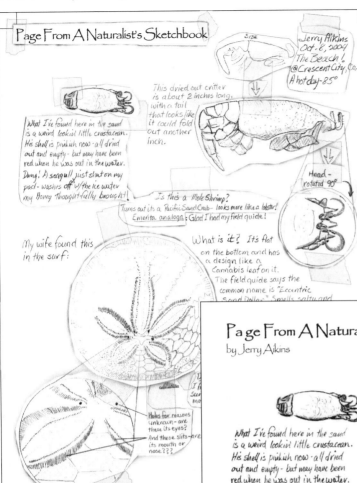

The student work at at left shows what your layout should look like as you arrange it, before pasting things down. (Tape has been emphasized to show better.) The final result, at bottom, looks very similar to how it would appear in print (the editors would insert the actual title and credit).

As you cut and tape, arrange and rearrange, you may decide to rewrite some of the text to make it work better, add an illustration, or improve or add some text, correct some spelling, etc. After the final photocopy, be sure to add any lost "ink" lines, and whiteout any leftover lines and speckles.

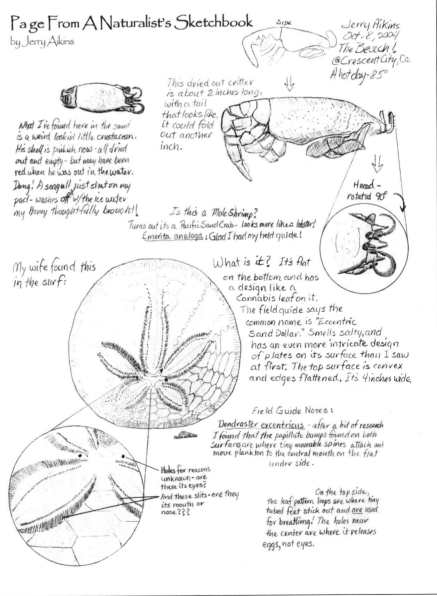

Don't lose sight of the fact that the object of this exercise is to create a facsimile of a sketch page done out in the field. Don't make it too neat, or it will lose its authentic feel. And try to inject some personality into it.

Whatever you do, make it easy to read — have someone check the legibility for you. For this sketch page, the notes were rewritten more neatly.

Re-penning the text only takes a few minutes, and it can improve the looks of the page immensely. Aim for a controlled but spontaneous and interesting appearance.

Chapter 8. Illustrating Animals

Caged mice and rats are rodents, and they make good sketching subjects because they are calm around movement and noise (when sketching a wild animal you may not be able to move much or speak). You can learn what you need to know about live sketching by drawing a mouse or rat. Sketching pets like hamsters, iguanas, cats, or dogs works well, too, and is great practice.

Every mammal has a characteristic shape, stance, size, number of teeth and toes, and other distinguishing traits. Rodents have the following:

BODY: tends to be oval in outline, with short legs. Sometimes only the feet show.

EYES: are relatively large and black, and may bulge up to one half of their diameter from the head.

TAIL: long and narrow — hairs may be short and inconspicuous, but are generally present. When drawing a near-naked tail, determine its correct length in relation to the body and draw it as a cylinder with slightly-tapered smooth, parallel sides. Indicate hairs only lightly. Avoid drawing each scale, segment, and hair on a sparsely-haired tail. The "parallelness" of a tail is its main characteristic.

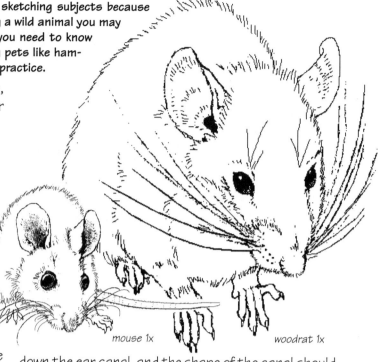

mouse 1x   woodrat 1x

mouse carrying nesting materials

FEET AND TOES: Most rodents have only very short hairs on their feet, which look most realistic when drawn as though nearly hairless (body fur generally ends at the wrist and ankle). Sketch a few tiny hairs at a bend or curve on the foot, or at the edge of markings. Toes (four or five, check it out) are usually slim and flexed and the thumb may be only a nub, useful for grasping (see woodrat thumb, above right).

Rodents sit up on their haunches to free their front feet for holding food. When walking, the body may be held low to the ground, with feet barely showing. The head is relatively large compared to the body.

EARS: Many rodents have large, tissue-thin, mobile ears. They may be lightly-haired inside and out with tiny, fine hairs. Hairs may be sparsely sketched to help show curvature of the ear (see woodrat, above right). A single thin line can be used on a near edge to show the thickness of the ear. Looking directly into an ear, you may be able to see a considerable distance down the ear canal, and the shape of the canal should be shown if visible. Make it black.

VISUAL INTEREST: Choose poses that include the parts of the body that have the most character, e.g. feet, ears, eyes, face and tail, whenever possible. Body language conveys the animal's attitude: crouching, ears back or forward, head up or down, tail and whisker position; all can show the animal's status, what it is sensing, feeling, thinking, and what it may do next. The best drawings show body language.

CHARACTERISTIC POSES: Be careful that you show a subject in a pose it would naturally assume. Also notice the sizes of ears, eyes, feet, etc., relative to body size. While both rats and mice have the same parts, a viewer should be able to tell the difference — even if they're shown at the same size — because a rat's eyes and ears will be relatively smaller in proportion to its size than those of a mouse (see below). Other related animals have similar comparative characteristics (compare a lion with a cat), so pay close attention to shape and form as you draw your subject.

from the information given above, decide which one is the rat

Student Examples of Mouse Sketches

Drawing from living, moving, breathing animals is a challenge. They usually move before you are finished.

Your attitude is all-important. If you *expect* the animal to change position (and you must), you will be able to move on to another sketch with less fuss (see below). Always sketch the head first – it's the most important part. A bodiless head can always be called "a portrait," while a headless body, well........a corpse?

When your subject moves again, be ready to start another sketch – or, if you're lucky, you might be able to add more form or details to the first drawing. It's important to have several sketches going on the same page so you can add more lines to each one without much paper movement. Flipping sketch pages may startle your subject. Keep movement like erasing to a minimum if it might disturb your model. Conversely, don't harrass your model to make it move.

Completely finish only small items or a small portion of something that extends over a larger area (a pattern, fur length, texture).

Make notes about it as you go along, as you notice things. Imagine you will never get a chance to sketch this subject again, and that you are planning to do a completed illustration using only your sketches (it could be true!). This will encourage you to take lots of notes, which improve your field sketches greatly.

Generally speaking, don't try to produce a "finished" drawing in the field. Your time will be better spent picking up details, markings, and changes in pose, observing movements, activities and stances, and making good notes. Record only enough to make recognition or improvement possible later.

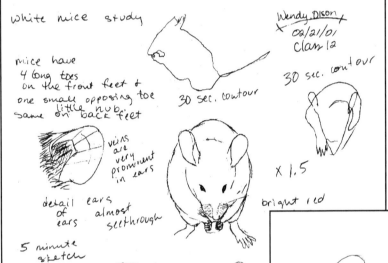

Wendy Olson 2001

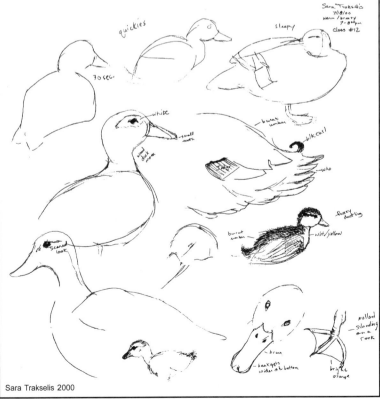

Sara Trakselis 2000

Above are good examples of copious sketches and notes: there are details about color, structures, sizes, comparisons, behavior, observations, etc.

At right, notice the notations on color and the nearly completed duckling – finished in just a few moments. While good, the page at right would be even better with more notes about activities and other details.

These sketch pages are reduced. Your sketches should be larger.

It helps to have a solid foundation of knowledge of your subject. Learn a few basics before you start to draw, and be aware of things to watch for.

Mouse parts are fairly standard, but they vary somewhat from species to species, so if you are doing technical work it doesn't pay to be sloppy. The mouse parts below and the mice on this page are those of a lab mouse or house mouse, *Mus musculus*. Compare them with the *Peromyscus truei* on page 77. What differences do you see (besides markings)?

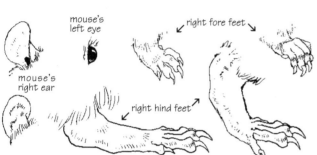

mouse's left eye

mouse's right ear

right fore feet →

right hind feet→

Think of a mouse's ear as a cylinder with a flared edge. A semicircle of tiny hairs inside or outside gives 3-dimensionality to a drawing of an ear (see above).

Notice the shape of a mouse's head from above. It is essentially a triangle or cone with cheeks.

Many rodents are "bug-eyed." How far out would you estimate the eyes of these mice bulge? A quarter of their diameter? Half?

Carefully count a mouse's toes as you draw. Different species seem to have varying numbers of toes, although there is usually a nub where a "missing" toe should be. Most mice have barely a nub for a thumb.

A mouse's apparent size changes radically with its posture. The two mice at right are the same size, but the one at far right is stretched out like this →.

A common left-brain error is to draw the head as a separate shape from the body when it actually merges fully and smoothly into the body's form.

the two mice at right, in side view.

In the case of the mouse, the typical left-brain model is not far off. Just for fun, try beginning one of your mouse drawings like this and see whether it makes a good starting point.

Duck Template Construction & Techniques

Duck, goose and swan parts are somewhat interchangeable — once you learn how to draw bills, heads and feet, you can apply them to your model with slight modifications. Pay close attention, to make sure you catch all the differences.

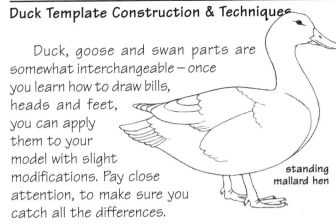

standing mallard hen

The ducks and duck parts on this page are mallards, Anas platyrhynchos. What differences can you see between a duck and a Canada goose (far right) besides markings?

basic body shape changes very little

A bird's body shape may tilt, fluff up, or flatten, but it retains the same basic rigid shape to give the wings a solid base from which to flap.

Duck's are made of ovals (ellipses). In the drawings above, the exact same head and body shapes are used for three different poses, the main variation being the curve of the neck and the slight flattening when lying.

The wings follow the contour of the duck's body when folded. They unfurl as shown on page 73.

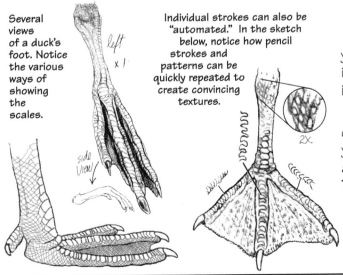

Several views of a duck's foot. Notice the various ways of showing the scales.

left x 1

side view

Individual strokes can also be "automated." In the sketch below, notice how pencil strokes and patterns can be quickly repeated to create convincing textures.

2x

One basic difference between species is the length, shape, and color of the feathers. Learn the wing template with your left brain, then adjust the variables by drawing them with your right brain.

Duck, geese and swan feet are similar from one species to the next, with variation in the amount of webbing and the length of the toes. You can also memorize other animal genres, plants (or anything else) to make left-brain templates for future use.

Canada goose

A duck's bill is a complex tool designed for sifting goodies out of water and mud. It is flexible, and warm to the touch. Your left brain can learn the template for its outline and how it fits onto the head, then your right brain can change and fill in the details to show its actual shape and position.

Once you have committed patterns like these to your left brain, you can zip out lifelike drawings very quickly.

A duck's eye lies in a horizontal crease, visible below and at right. The eye's location is in the top third of the head's ellipse.

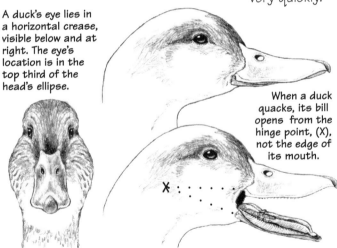

When a duck quacks, its bill opens from the hinge point, (X), not the edge of its mouth.

X . . . . . .

Amazingly, you can "learn" a template just as you learn a poem or how to form letters or numbers in kindergarten — by repeating a shape until you have it memorized.

Memorize a template by tracing it from a picture onto tracing paper — then practice the shape. As your hand traces the outline, it learns the shape and imprints that information on your left brain. **Trace the shapes on this page several times.** Now draw the shapes freehand. Later, when you are drawing an actual duck, start with this left-brain template and make changes as you note real-life variations from your left-brain duck pattern.

When drawing birds, it is easier to draw quickly and accurately if you know something about their anatomy.

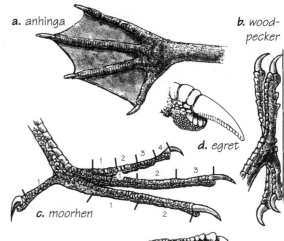

a. anhinga

b. wood-pecker

d. egret

c. moorhen

e. osprey

BIRD FEET: There are usually four toes, one of which points backward, but may point forward in swimming birds to give more webbed area (**a.**), which helps in paddling. Climbing birds like woodpeckers (**b.**) may have two toes pointing backward to help them brace on vertical surfaces. Wading birds (**c.**) often have long toes to support them in mud. Raptors (**e.**) kill and carry with their sharp, curved claws, and the toe scales are rough for holding prey firmly.

There are two main types of scales on bird feet. Small circular scales (rough or smooth) cover the bottoms and sides of the toes, and large, flat scales may cover the tops of the toes and the fronts of the shins. There are variations on this, but it is a fair assumption with which to begin a drawing — then check to make sure. There also may be structures on one or more nails for grooming (**d.**), especially on water birds.

On most birds, each toe has a different number of bones (**c.**). The outer front toe has 4, the middle has 3, the inner has 2 and the rear toe has only one bone. Start with this premise any time you draw close-up bird feet.

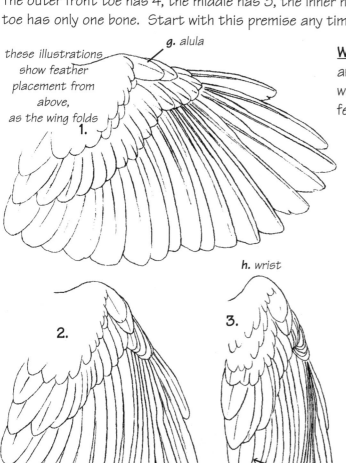

these illustrations show feather placement from above, as the wing folds

1.

g. alula

h. wrist

2.

3.

WINGS: A bird's wing is the equivalent of a human hand and arm (**f.**). However, it has fewer bones to reduce weight, and is modified to provide a surface for feather attachment.

The "thumb" provides an attachment point for the alula feather (**g. at left**).

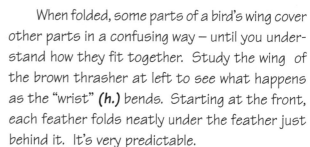

f. wing construction

When folded, some parts of a bird's wing cover other parts in a confusing way — until you understand how they fit together. Study the wing of the brown thrasher at left to see what happens as the "wrist" (**h.**) bends. Starting at the front, each feather folds neatly under the feather just behind it. It's very predictable.

IMPORTANT: Always check that you have the correct *edge* of a feather visible. On the top side of the wing, a feather shows its leading edge. So if the front edge of a feather shows from above, the rear edge of that feather will show from beneath. If not, your bird "won't fly."

Animal Fur Direction Guide

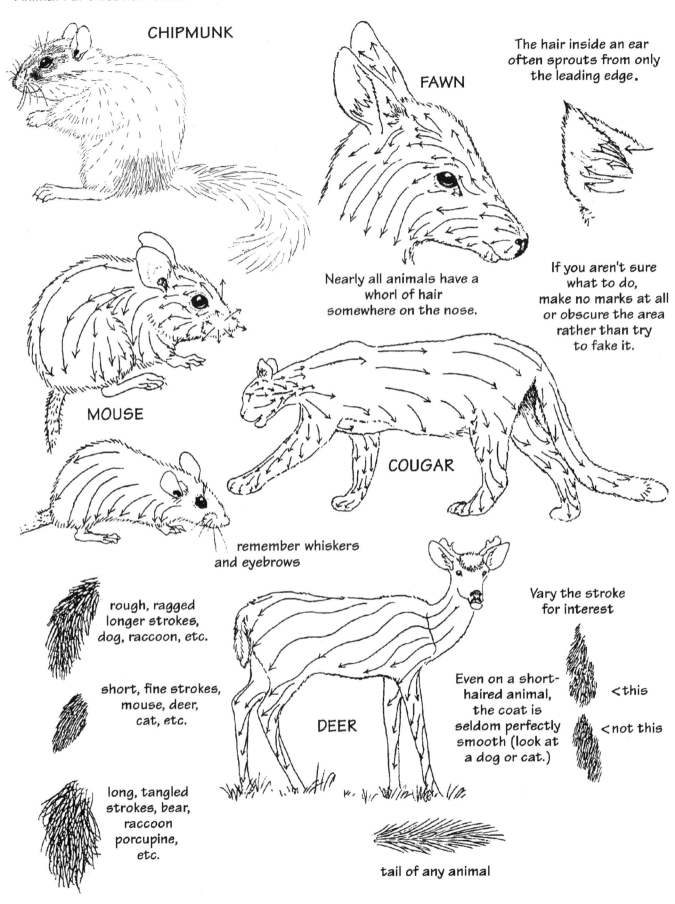

CHIPMUNK

FAWN

The hair inside an ear often sprouts from only the leading edge.

Nearly all animals have a whorl of hair somewhere on the nose.

If you aren't sure what to do, make no marks at all or obscure the area rather than try to fake it.

MOUSE

COUGAR

remember whiskers and eyebrows

rough, ragged longer strokes, dog, raccoon, etc.

short, fine strokes, mouse, deer, cat, etc.

long, tangled strokes, bear, raccoon porcupine, etc.

DEER

Vary the stroke for interest

Even on a short-haired animal, the coat is seldom perfectly smooth (look at a dog or cat.)

<this

<not this

tail of any animal

In this exercise you will learn how to draw and shade fur, paying close attention to how your pencil strokes affect the texture of the hairs. You will also practice making a believable eye, with jet black pupil and sparkling white highlight.

For this Exercise you need:

1. .5 mechanical pencils with HB and 2B leads
2. kneaded and clickable erasers
3. one piece tracing paper 6" x 8"
4. small and large stumps (see page 32)

Exercise: Trace the **LARGE** chipmunk and the outline of the box below onto one side of the 6" x 8" tracing paper piece (follow instructions on page 32).

1. As shown on page 74, sketch 6 to 8 very light lines the entire length of the chipmunk's body about ¼" apart, following the hair direction. Also put guide lines on the tail. Referring to page 74, shade your chipmunk with the HB lead □(1pt)using short, varied strokes about ¼" long on the body. □(2pt) Stay between the guides.

Practice hair strokes in the box here. Also sharpen your pencil here.

2. Sharpen your pencil often in the box at left by scribbling until the point is sharp. Start each hair stroke at its base and end at its tip, reducing pressure as you go to make the hair thicker at the base than the tip. This gives the fur a very realistic look. It's also fast. Practice in the box.

□(1pt) Don't stroke too firmly, or your chipmunk will look like a porcupine. ☺

3. □(2pt) Stroke from the root to the tip of each long tail hair in one movement, keeping within the guides. Blend your strokes seamlessly into the hair strokes shown on the chipmunk's **outline.** Turn the paper often to follow the arc of your stroke.

4. □(1pt) Don't stroke entirely dark the areas that will need highlights. Think "cylinder" and "sphere."

5. □(2pt) Add more hairs to make the chipmunk darker or to create shadows, and fewer hairs to create highlights. This chipmunk is tan. Too many hairs will make it appear to be black, so keep the tonal values in mind as you stroke. Remove too-dark areas with your kneaded eraser.

6. Punch holes on the **PERCENTAGE STRIP** on page 30 now if you didn't before. Give your drawing a 100% black

to 100% white tonal range. Black markings and eyes will be 100% black. Tonal values for a medium tan are about 25%. Check your percentages with the strip.

7. □(1pt) With your small smudger, shade the paws, chin, and inside the ear, using the lighting conventions (see lower chipmunk). □(1pt)With 2B lead, give your chipmunk's eye a conventional highlight and reflection.

8. In the box you traced on your tracing paper, **draw a close-up of this chipmunk's eye (below).** Make the eye the identical shape of this chipmunk's eye, and □(1pt) make it about 2/3 the width of the box.

Use the rodent eye on page 76 as a guide. But note that the eye on page 76 is that rodent's <u>right</u> eye. **So don't just copy it** – use its information to draw the **left** eye of your chipmunk. Include a □(1pt) conventional highlight and reflected light.

9. After completing the fur strokes, □(1pt) blend the shadows on the chipmunk with your small smudger.

When blending, move your smudger in the direction of the strokes.

Trace this chipmunk and the box at left onto tracing paper. Draw an enlarged eye in the box on the tracing paper (but first read #8. above).

□(1pt) Stroke hairs back in with a sharp HB point to replace fur details lost when you smudge to get the tonal values.

Use the drawing at right as a shading guide. When you finish, fold the tracing paper over your drawing to protect it from smearing. Add your name, date and Exercise #.

Believable Eyes

The eye is the first thing a viewer notices, so learn to draw it well. Practice until you can do it automatically, because you'll often have to fake it. We see eyes every day, but we seldom notice how they are shaped, colored or highlighted. Look at another person's eyes. Look in a mirror at your own eyes. Very few animals have visible eye-whites (sclera) as humans do.

The eye is spherical (see at right) with a hole (the pupil) in the center of a disk (the iris) which lies a short distance behind the front of the sphere. The pupil alters in shape and size to control the amount of light that enters the eye. The lens, just behind the iris is filled with a clear jelly, which appears black. If it is not 100% BLACK the animal is either dead or blind.

The pupil's shape varies with the species of animal. Don't make any assumptions – make sure (see at right). If you can't find out, shade the eye so that the pupil shape is ambiguous.

When shading a sphere (eyeball), remember that the light comes from the upper left.

There is a pure white reflection on the upper left curve of the sphere. A sphere with a dull or rough surface has a fuzzy highlight. A shiny sphere (like a living eye) has a sharp, clearly defined highlight, exactly reflecting what lit it. When the sun shines on an eyeball through the leaves of a tree, the highlight will show the leaf shapes. A light source from above casts a strong black shadow under the upper lid. Eyelashes may cast shadows and reflections across the eye.

The reflected light on the underside of the sphere is not as sharp, and makes an arc across the lower right quadrant of the eye – looking like a fuzzy banana. There may be a white line along the lower lid, the eye moisture reflecting light (see deer eye, lower right). STUDY THESE EYES.

Note other eye structures, too, such as eyelids, lashes and the deer scent gland (lower right).

Extra Credit – Illustrate Your Eye – 3 pts

Using a mirror, draw and shade your own eye 1x on smooth paper. Use scientific illustration lighting conventions. Write 150 words about what you observed and how your eye differs from eyes of other animals as shown at right. Apply a coversheet.

In scientific illustration, primary highlights are put in the upper left area. Reflections or "bounce" highlights, usually a long fuzzy arc, go in the lower right area. Leave reflection areas are white to avoid erasing later.

The pupil, whether round, elliptical or lozenge-shaped, must be symmetrical. Keep your lines and ellipses smooth.

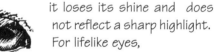

iris
pupil
lens
eyeball diagram

Notice the shadow cast by the upper eyelid on the eye at right. With its vertical pupil, this is probably a cat in low light conditions.

A gray pupil or a fuzzy upper highlight are signs of blindness or death. The gray of blindness is caused when the jelly-like liquid inside the eye turns opaque.

When the eyeball dries out after death, it loses its shine and does not reflect a sharp highlight. For lifelike eyes, avoid these errors.

dead

goat, sheep

Some animals have thick eyelashes that partly obscure the eye, cast shadows on the upper half of the eyeball, and make jagged reflections on the highlight.

The shape of the eye opening (slitted, wide open, etc.) may show such attitudes as suspicion, wariness, attention and sleepiness, or it may be a simple response to light intensity.

Eyes vary widely. Goats and deer have horizontal pupils (above left, with eyelashes), while rodent eyes seem to be mostly pupil and very protruding. Foxes and cats have vertical pupils. Deer have scent glands in their eye openings. Eye openings of many birds tilt forward, and have a beaded look.

bird

rodent

Birds active in daylight blink from below. Night birds tend to blink from above. A special *nictitating membrane* sweeps across from inner to outer edge to protect and clean the eyeball. Many mammals have nictitating membranes, too.

Nictitating membranes cover a beaver's eyes when it swims. They may partially cover a sick animal's eyes – you may have seen nictitating membranes on an ailing cat.

nictitating membrane

deer scent gland

Exercise #12 – Live Animal Sketching – 15 pts

The object of this exercise is to learn to sketch live animals, catch the fleeting gesture, and add details when possible. Complete two or more pages of sketches with an enlarged detail and field notes on each page. Review page 14 before beginning. Allow 2-3 hours for this.

piñon mouse *Peromyscus truei*

1x

For this Exercise you need:

1. .5 mechanical pencil with HB lead
2. kneaded eraser
3. 11" x 14" sketchpad
4. water bottle, binoculars, comfortable clothing
5. (optional) snack, folding chair, umbrella

Exercise:

1. Choose a nearby subject holding fairly still. Get as close as you can without alarming it — use binocs if needed. Sketchpad must be in shade — sunshine on your pad will make it hard to see your subject when you glance up.

2. Make ☐(1pt) one 30-second contour drawing (no peek), and a ☐(1pt) one-minute quick sketch to warm up. Make detailed drawings on the same page as the warmups, with field notes, questions and observations (see the list at the bottom of this page). ID the subject or make an educated guess. **When drawing a small subject, sketch it <u>at least</u> life size.**

3. First, watch for a still pose or repeated behaviors. Make a 5-second contour drawing in the air above the page, then do a light, quick, full-size quick-sketch drawing on your paper. Draw the entire pose before you start to do details, then make improvements.

4. If your subject changes position, start a different sketch (on the same page). Now you have two poses to watch for, and a much better chance of completing a sketch. Plan ahead so one sketch doesn't run into another. Start a third pose on the same page for even more options. Jot down notes and info between sketches.

5. Say to yourself things like:

"...the eye is directly above its feet when it stands,"

"...that negative space where the leg meets the body is shaped like half a mushroom...," etc.

<u>*Sketch the right-brain's observations.*</u>
<u>*Watch, and wait for a repeat pose.*</u>

6. Having problems? See page 14 for help — drop invisible lines from points on the body — what do they pass through or near? Look for angles, circles and negative shapes. Compare head length to body length. Is the body about three head-lengths? Four? Compare leg length to depth of body. Don't erase much at this point — draw lightly and remove try lines later when there is time. (Lighten up – this is supposed to be fun!)

7. ☐(2pts) Focus on single, clear linework. Avoid short, sketchy lines. Erase/replace only small sections at a time.

8. ☐(3pts) Show three or four sketches per page, in addition to warmups. If a page gets crowded, start another (or return to a previous page to add details).

9. ☐(2pts) Draw one 2x or 3x enlarged detail of your subject's head, ear, tail, foot, etc., on each page. Use binoculars if appropriate to the situation.

10. Check off requirements below for each page. Make sure you have enough notes and sketches to finish the exercise later without your subject.

11. When finished, clean up the page and apply a coversheet. Test the quality of your notes, by completing one of the rough sketches from your notes.

NOTE: Check to make sure you have:

☐(1pt) labels, ID, and scale (scale not needed for pets)
☐(1pt) pupils 100% black, with correct highlights
☐(1pt) correct information in upper right corner
  (name, date, location, conditions)
☐(2pts) thorough field notes
  (see below)
☐(1pt) your signature
  once on each page

Each page should include 2 quick sketches, 3+ drawings and 1 enlargement, plus:

info block, upper right

☐ your name
☐ date
☐ location (include site, city & state)
☐ conditions if outdoors (raining, warm, windy)
☐ subject I.D. (next to subject)

☐ signature (one time, somewhere on page)
☐ observations about subject's activity (10-50 wds)
☐ notes about color, markings, etc. for each drawing if appropriate
☐ measurements (tail about 3" long, etc.)
☐ scale (2x, 3x, etc. next to each enlargement)

Melinda Whipple-Smith 2000

77

Showing Action Believably

Before the invention of cinematography there was a lot of argument and guessing about how animals actually moved at high speeds. Old racing prints show galloping horses outstretched with all four feet off the ground, as in #13-#16 below.

Eadweard Muybridge devoted much of his career to photographing moving humans and animals, conclusively proving that galloping horses extend all four legs only when jumping over an obstacle.

Here is a redrawn illustration of a galloping cat from his book ANIMALS IN MOTION first published in 1887, then again by Dover in 1957. These poses

were drawn in a graphics program onto a "layer" superimposed over the scanned-in photograph.

The original photo (and many others in the book) are a great resource for the nature artist. Notice how some pictures in this series portray fast forward movement much better than others.

Examine this series, showing phases of a cat galloping (cats leap they way they thought horses did).

Which ones would you choose for "speed" poses? Do some poses look odd, perhaps even impossible? Figures #10 through #12 certainly would not give the impression of speed, nor would #18 through #21.

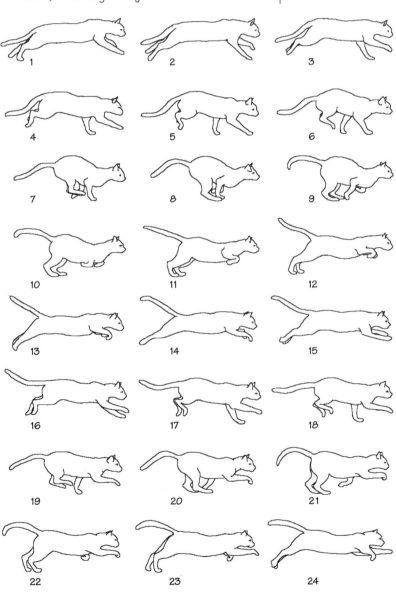

Some look much more like leaps than a gallop. You probably would NOT use those to portray an animal moving at high speed.

After looking at these, can you see how a "correct" pose might not be believable or appropriate in an illustration?

Regardless of how they look individually, if you are portraying a group or herd of moving animals you might include all of the phases in the illustration for a very effective and convincing group scene.

Think about this as you sketch. Choose the most appropriate pose or angle to express the idea you are trying to get across. Body language should always be considered when making a drawing, even if its probable end is not to "illustrate" a story. The wrong body language can distract the viewer's attention from the intended use or beauty of an illustration.

ANIMALS IN MOTION is also a great reference for finding natural-looking poses for such animals as buffaloes, raccoons, lions, ostriches, turkey vultures, pigeons, horses, kangaroos, elk, jaguars, humans, and several other exotic ungulates and birds. Just keep copyright laws in mind.

NOTE: *if you copy someone else's illustration, attribute credit as shown below.*

Drawn by Irene Brady from Plate 128, "Cat Galloping" (.017 sec.) from ANIMALS IN MOTION by Eadweard Muybridge, Dover Publications, New York (1957).

Chapter 9. Critiquing and Improving Illustrations

When you create an illustration, it is probably intended for other people to see. But when you work on a piece of art, you get so close to it and have looked at it for so long that you can no longer see its problems, imbalances, inaccurate lines and less-than-perfect composition. A critique from a disinterested third party is essential.

If you have the opportunity to be fairly critiqued, if you can find someone who can honestly appraise your work and point out, without bias, what you might do to improve it, you are extremely fortunate.

There is one way you **can** critique your own work, but it takes time — lots of it. If you can put aside your work for a week, two weeks, two months or a year, when you look at it again with fresh eyes you will probably see things to improve. The longer it is out of your sight, the better your critique will be. But what if you don't have the luxury of time to help you improve your work? A mirror can help.

If you take your art to a large, well-lit mirror and look at it critically, you **will** find trouble spots. But just as you became used to looking at your art while you created it, after a few trips to the mirror you will also lose the new insight. So look quickly, leave the mirror as soon as possible in order to retain the freshness of the backward image, then write down every observation you can remember about things to improve while they're fresh in your mind. Work from your notes until you are satisfied, then check the mirror again.

Still, there are things you won't see, simply because you are the artist. Without a critique by others, it can be difficult to move forward. How much you get from a critique depends upon how open you are to hearing what is said, and how hard you will work to follow the advice that is given.

A critique is not meant to embarrass anyone. In fact, if it does, it will lose most of its usefulness because an embarrassed person won't hear what is being said. Embarrassment is harmful on many levels.

The object of a critique must be to help the artist move forward from his/her own personal starting point.

No weight should be placed on anything but:

- the artist's own personal efforts to improve,
- how well the artist followed previous critiques, advice, and/or instruction designed to help them do that.

Illustrations are not created only for other artists to view. They are created for a broad audience of non-artistic viewers as well. So even people who don't feel their own skills can match those being shown still have a valid voice in helping to critique the work of others.

Scientific illustration has technical aspects, so technical requirements also need critiquing if possible. A classroom environment, or access to an actual scientific illustrator can be very helpful.

Taking part in a critique is an education in itself. Seeing the work of others and hearing the critique offered on their art helps you copy (or avoid) the technique or style being critiqued. You may gain valuable new insights, and perhaps you won't waste time and energy repeating others' errors yourself.

A critique is a great place to pick up pointers on good approaches, styles, and techniques.

When you join in a critique, it is important to not tear the artist down. Most people stop drawing when they're between the ages of about six and eleven — because someone rips their art effort to shreds (perhaps only verbally) and they give up in despair.

But a harsh analysis can pull even an adult down, so phrase criticism gently. There is, however, an obligation to say something if you see a way to help.

One effective way to critique is to make sure the illustrator has the first word. Given an opportunity to tell your critics what you do like and what you don't like about your own illustration takes the edge off a subsequent critique — it's easier to point a problem out yourself than have someone else do it — if you can see it!

After that, others can offer their observations. The object, of course, is to help the artist improve.

If you don't have the advantage of a scientific illustration critique, a friend might be willing to read pages 79 and 80, then critique your artwork using those guidelines.

When YOU critique:

- be kind (not, "that's a really crappy piece of art")
- be specific about the problem (not, "that's all wrong")
- be positive if possible ("that stippled area really works")
- suggest a solution ("Perhaps if you darkened this.....")
- don't be shy — you're providing a service

CRITIQUING A SCIENTIFIC ILLUSTRATION

WHAT TO LOOK FOR:

- **ILLUSTRATION meets the subject and media requirements for the assignment**

   That means _everything_ – medium requested, halftone or line art, subject, orientation, size...everything

- **COVERSHEET clean, smooth, attached at top of art, closer tabs, butt-taped on back of sheet**

   A rumpled, creased or dirty coversheet, overlapped butts, side attachment.....detract from its apparent quality.

- **FIRST IMPRESSION – a professional-looking illustration, rendered on good quality paper**

   High-quality paper gives a more professional look. Smooth, even linework and accurate details say "professional."

- **1″ MINIMUM FINGERPRINT BORDER, with no visible line, crop marks if necessary**

   A beautiful illustration with fingerprints on the art is unusable. Crop marks assure that art is correctly positioned.

- **CLEANLINESS – no leftover pencil lines, smudges, tears or blots; any repairs done neatly**

   Everyone makes mistakes, but neatly prepared artwork, even with repairs (if done well), is perfectly acceptable.

- **SCALE INDICATOR, bracket, text or numbers on the coversheet** (see page 117)

   This convention allows a publication to use its own fonts for the text/numbers. Coversheet notes will guide them.

- **ARTIST'S SIGNATURE, CORRECTLY SIZED, within the illustration's outline**

   Signature placed where it won't be thrown out with the trimmings if the artwork is cropped.

- **ACCURATELY shows what is there – and _doesn't show_ what is _not_ there**

   Inaccurate illustrations, no matter how well-drawn, foster misinformation. Scientific illustration must be accurate.

- **PERSPECTIVE principles have been applied**

   Misapplied perspective causes an illustration to look "odd", "skewed" or just "wrong."

- **LINEWORK clear, clean, steady; straight lines straight, hard edges continuous, no multiple lines**

   To create a crystal-clear illustration, the artwork must be meticulously rendered, with no extra or false lines.

- **ARTISTIC TEXTURE clearly represents original texture**

   If the chosen technique doesn't create the texture effect, the illustration will not be an accurate representation.

- **SHADING, good, even contrast, using scientific illustration lighting convention (from upper left)**

   Conventions simplify art, creating shorthand for understanding. Shading and contrast should be smooth and even.

- **DETAILS aren't obscured by shading, no shading on substrate except to clarify outline**

   Contrast can clarify confusing details, but shading applied to background may draw attention away from subject.

- **SPHERE, CYLINDER, and PLANE shading appropriately applied**

   Illustrating accurately requires a firm foundation and basic knowledge with regard to shading various shapes.

- **TONAL RANGE from white to black (in halftone illustrations)**

   While not always an option, the best halftone illustrations usually have tonal values ranging from black to white.

Problems can occur at <u>any</u> level of the illustration process. Learn how to sniff them out, prevent their recurrence, and make repairs. You won't be REALLY good until you can repair the inevitable errors you will create.

COMMON PROBLEM SOURCES:

<u>RESEARCH</u>: incorrectly interpreting or not getting enough information to draw or render the illustration accurately.

<u>EXPERIENCE</u>: not having enough knowledge or experience with the subject or medium to render it well.

<u>DESIGN & PLANNING</u>: forgetting to plan ahead for something – not leaving a highlight area white, for instance, or not leaving room for an element of the illustration. Forgetting to allow for margins. Failing to check the design in a mirror and/or have someone else critique it before beginning the final rendering.

<u>TRANSFERRING</u>: leaving out an item that was originally in the picture. Or transferring it carelessly so that the element is incomplete, inaccurate or confusing.

<u>FIRST DRAWING</u>: skewed perspective due to a tilted sketchpad. →

newt **a.** was accidently drawn on a tilted pad. When the problem was noticed and compared to a photo (**c.**) – it was computer-shortened (**b.**) to reproportion it correctly.

<u>RENDERING</u>: drawing or shading too dark or too light, so that details of the illustration are lost to the viewer during reproduction. Forgetting a convention, such as light direction, or neglecting to break background lines behind foreground parts as perspective breaks. Not perfecting a technique before rendering a pattern or texture. Or letting style get in the way of substance.

<u>CLEANUP</u>: not removing dead lines, fingerprints, margin lines, ink spills, or stains from the final illustration. Or removing more than you intended while trying to get underlying pencil marks out.

PREVENTING PROBLEMS:

Prevention, of course, is the easiest fix. And as for experience – practice, practice, PRACTICE!

• Find lots of research materials so that all the fundamental details are available.

• Research carefully so that you can begin with an authoritative foundation.

• Plan ahead so that everything gets into the picture in its proper place and proportions. Write notes while working, about things to remember: "don't forget whiskers," and "check ear length."

• Transfer and draw carefully so that the rendering starts out correct and clear. Double check.

• Throughout the rendering, keep hands clean and steady (some people can't drink coffee while working) and tape a piece of paper between hand and any part of the illustration being worked across. Use low-tack tape.

• Ask a friend for a critique – not about whether the work is "great," but whether the point has been gotten across ("Does this look like a foot?" "What do you see here?" "What could I do to fix this?"). Even a non-artist can see when something doesn't look right.

• Keep the workplace clear and firm to avoid rolling tools and spilling liquids. (Always put your soft drink or coffee mug on a separate surface.)

> Errors DO creep in. Here are some guidelines for damage control if they do.

REPAIRING THE DAMAGE:

<u>DO IT OVER</u>: It is important to know the difference between the fixable and the unfixable. If your design was faulty and a large part of your illustration is consequently the wrong shape, size or perspective – or inaccurate in any way – it may be better to start over again. If you didn't quite have a major texture worked out before you started and you can't fix it without removing half your picture, you may want to restart. But things aren't usually that bad. There are a number of things you can do to rescue an illustration.

<u>COMPUTER FIX</u>: If you have some experience in a graphics program, you may be able to scan in the artwork and fix the problem there. This will only work if you are experienced and know the program and *"original artwork"* is not required by the people you are illustrating for. Some publications won't take "copies" (printouts) and won't accept artwork on disk. If you want to take this route, always ask first.

cont...

Erasing, Retouching and Improving Artwork, cont...

KNEADED ERASER: Try the least destructive fixes first. Your kneaded eraser is the best first step for fingerprints and pencil lines. Stretch and knead it first to warm and shape it (see page 32), then try some gentle rubbing. It won't remove ink but it might work for pencil marks and smudges.

WHITEOUT: If you won't need to rework an area, you can dab on liquid whiteout to hide it. If you must rework an area, this isn't the best solution since it may leave a lumpy surface. It also leaves a different texture, and may yellow with age, so it doesn't work well for a pencil drawing. Dry correction tape leaves a smooth white surface, but its history is short, and it may flake off in time (or it may not). Press it down with your finger to ensure that it adheres tightly.

Small whiteout corrections may work on a pen-and-ink drawing. Since whiteout tends to clog a pen, using a *mechanical* pen over whiteout can ruin the pen. A flexible pen is cleanable, so that might work better. This is not your Fix-of-Choice for large areas.

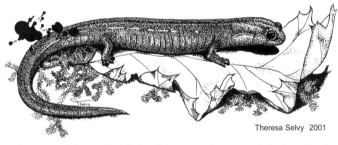

What would you do if this happened to your ink drawing?
(apologies to Theresa – the fake blot was added to her beautiful salamander via computer. Her original was returned to her spotless.)

Theresa Selvy 2001

WHITE ERASER: First, try your clickable eraser. If you have only a colored eraser, erase vigorously first on another piece of paper to make sure it won't leave colored streaks on your illustration. If the eraser is dirty or has been exposed to sunlight, it may make a really nasty smudge on your picture. First sandpaper the damaged eraser surface. It *might* work then, but test it first. Your white clickable eraser is best. To create a sharp edge, cut to shape with your X-acto blade. Use a metal shield for tight spots. Never use an "ink eraser." Its harsh abrasive will destroy the paper and reworking will be difficult or impossible.

ELECTRIC ERASER: Most professional illustrators use electric erasers (see page 85). They are easy to

use with a little practice, removing even ink quickly and well (unless it penetrated all the way through the paper). Be attentive and keep the tip moving in small circles so it doesn't drill a hole. Check by holding your art up to the light. Brush off erasures frequently (don't smear) so you can see your progress.

X-ACTO BLADE: You may be able to scrape away an ink mistake with your X-acto blade – if you hold it so that the entire edge of the blade is in contact with the paper and scrape lightly sideways. But if you tilt the blade, the point will rip into the paper.

When using scratchboard, this is an obvious fix. But it also works with smooth illustration board if used carefully. An X-acto blade can also be used on smooth paper to flick out a highlight in an eye. Then dab with a kneaded eraser.

MAJOR COVER-UP: If the messed-up area is large, it might make sense to redo the bad part on fresh opaque paper as thin as practical – a thick edge may photocopy as a line. Cut it to size and glue it over the offending area. You may need to redo a larger area to take advantage of natural breaks in the design (p. 113).

You must exercise more care with patches on a halftone than you would on a line-art pen & ink – in fact, it may not work at all on a halftone.

On line-art, carefully reconnect any broken lines or textures across the patched edge. While this might not be visually satisfying in its original state, a camera can't tell the difference and it should look okay when reproduced if you reconnect the lines carefully. Watch closely and be mindful when re-inking, so that the fresh ink doesn't crawl into the raw paper edge and make a blot. If it does, you may have to use one of the other methods to fix the blot.

SUCCESS?: Whatever "fix" you make, it is vitally important to make sure it will reproduce well when you are finished. Make a photocopy at about the intensity you expect your illustration to reproduce to make sure no errors remain visible. If your illustration is a halftone, make a digital halftone photocopy to make sure. On halftones, check patch edges carefully and examine for texture problems. Rework as needed, and re-photocopy until you are sure you can't see where the patch was made.

Exercise #13 – Correcting and Improving An Illustration – 15 pts.

By this point, you need to have finished and critiqued Project A (p. 117). The object of this exercise is to learn and use techniques for cleaning and removing unwanted areas from a finished illustration, correct errors or improve artwork on damaged paper surfaces, and to try other skills required to rework and save good artwork from the trashcan.

The Critique Basis – and Expectations

Creating the art for Project A (see page 117) and enduring a critique of it, will prepare you for the following exercise.

Ongoing critique of your work — your own, the mirror, and that of others, may have pinpointed areas of your technique, style, and processes which need improvement. No matter how good you are, there is always room for improvement. Take notes.

What's the best way to fine-tune your skills? You may find it helpful to collect art of illustrators you admire, and make an attempt to create work similar to theirs. As you approach their level of competence, you can diverge enough that you are not directly copying their style.

To fulfill the requirements of Exercise #13, you will need to improve or change your Project A illustration. **Completely redrawing is not an option since this is a practice run at cleaning up mistakes.**

If critique comments pointed out deficiencies in how carefully you observed your subject, review page 15 and Chapter 6 for ways to develop this ability. If you still have the original object you drew, go back for a closer look. If the object you illustrated is no longer available, find a replacement or research the subject and/or find other references to use.

> Knowing that you can repair your mistakes will increase your confidence in your abilities. This, in turn, makes your work freer and better from the get-go. It's an ascending spiral. So learn how to fix-it!

For This Exercise:

1. Before making **any** corrections, make and set aside two high-quality 1x digital photocopies of your **unimproved** illustration. Keep one to refer to as you work, and □(2pts) keep the other with the improved illustration for later comparison. Use a □(2pts) good digital copy machine for this step.

Make a second pair of high-quality photocopies of the art after you make the corrections.

□(2pts) Keep one of these with the illustration, and put the other in your portfolio (see page 135).

2. Read "The BooBoo Checklist" on page 84, and "Erasing, Retouching and Improving Artwork" on pages 81 and 82.

3. Examine your critiqued Project A illustration and study any critique notes and comments.

□(2pts) Copy the critique comments onto a sheet of paper to keep by your illustration as you work.

4. After each comment **and as you make those corrections**, □(3pts) jot down legible notes about problems you encounter and how you handle them.

While you are correcting something, it seems like you'll never forget how you did it. But most people DO forget after awhile, and if you take (and save!) notes it will help you find solutions next time you have similar corrections to make.

5. □(3pts) Make all the corrections to the best of your ability. Review previous chapters for assistance if necessary.

6. □(1pt) Apply a fresh tracing paper coversheet. If your illustration is larger and requires a butted sheet, remember that it will look much better with no overlaps, and with the joining tape on the backside of the sheet, extending to both edges. For tabbed closers, use sticky tape (not low-tack) and attach them directly on the corners.

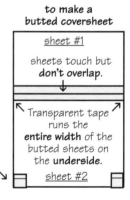

to make a butted coversheet

sheet #1

sheets touch but **don't overlap.**

Transparent tape runs the **entire width** of the butted sheets on the **underside.**

sheet #2

7. The finished exercise should produce:
- the improved Project A illustration
- protected with a fresh, neat coversheet
- "before" and "after" photocopies
- the critique comments by others
- your personal critique list, noting problems you encountered and the solutions you applied
- a much more confident illustrator — you.

Chapter 9. Critiquing and Improving Illustrations

The BooBoo Checklist

"If there is a 50-50 chance that something can go wrong, then nine times out of ten it will."

Paul Harvey, 20th Century newscaster

Scientific illustration is not a casual art form. It requires planning, research, careful execution, and the ability to emerge victorious when something goes awry.

Even experts have their bad moments, and the hallmark of a professional is the ability to:

- avoid the bad moment from the beginning
- recover successfully from inevitable slipups
- and remember to never set your coffee mug there again

> ### Post this checklist where you can check it before, during and after you do a project.

RESEARCHING:

- be sure you understand authoritative and correct written or photographic sources; check conventions
- use correct or sufficient information (be wary of web information, taxidermy mounts, hearsay, etc.)
- don't work from someone else's rendering — which could be inaccurate (or may infringe copyright)
- sketch and annotate your own sketches carefully and thoroughly for future use

DESIGN & PLANNING:

- get the illustration proportions and measurements right
- leave enough room for thumbprint margins
- make sure the paper (or whatever working surface) is big enough for the required size of illustration
- don't design an improbable, impossible, incorrect or just plain wrong scene or subject
- don't let style get in the way of substance
- remember to check the design in a mirror
- get the design approved by the person for whom you are illustrating before rendering
- carefully observe any scientific illustration and other conventions specific to the subject you are doing

FIRST DRAWING:

- draw the subject correctly, not skewed from a crooked or slanted artpad or viewpoint
- include all elements of the illustration

TRANSFERRING:

- double-check everything up to this point, before transferring the image to the finish surface
- transfer the design carefully, to avoid producing errors on the final drawing
- don't re-draw the transfer so dark that the rendering can't cover it — or so dark it can't be erased
- remember to check the transferred drawing in a mirror

RENDERING:

- choose the right medium for the subject and your skill level
- check out the technique first, so you won't find out that it is unsuitable — too late
- leave high-contrast highlight areas whitewhitewhite
- render the illustration dark enough that details won't drop out in reproduction
- render the illustration light enough that details won't close-in and blacken during reproduction
- use all conventions required by the field (botany, archaeology, etc.) in which you are illustrating
- never let technique overrule accuracy
- remember to check the final rendering in a mirror
- don't try to salvage a hopeless rendering (but be really certain it IS hopeless) — start over
- run photocopy checks for tonal values, use a digital copier for half-tone renderings

CLEANUP:

- entirely remove dead lines, fingerprints, ink spills, ketchup or squashed bugs from the final illustration
- during a correction, redraw the illustration correctly and cleanly with tidy repairs
- run a final photocopy check to make sure the repair is invisible
- deliver the illustration with a professional-looking coversheet and protection against other damage

DEADLINE:

- don't miss the deadline because you didn't allow time to do all of the above — plus time to deliver it

As Benjamin Franklin once said, *"Diligence is the mother of good luck."*   Be diligent — and good luck!

The Electric Eraser – The Professional Artist's Hedge

What they look like:

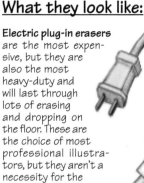
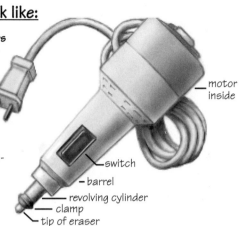

Electric plug-in erasers are the most expensive, but they are also the most heavy-duty and will last through lots of erasing and dropping on the floor. These are the choice of most professional illustrators, but they aren't a necessity for the casual artist.

motor inside

switch

barrel

revolving cylinder

clamp

tip of eraser

Cordless erasers are less expensive, and lighter, but they are not quite as durable as corded models.
Professional quality cordless erasers come with chargers in which you park the eraser to be recharged.

Student models, using batteries, are inexpensive – but not as sturdy or efficient as the more expensive cordless models. They drain the batteries fairly quickly.

If rechargeable batteries are used, this eraser is a good choice for people who are not SURE they want to be illustrators. **Nickel metal hydride** (NiMH) batteries are best.

What they do:

Electric erasers are not difficult to use, and their advantages make them essential if you pursue a career as a scientific illustrator. They make it easy to repair errors instead of trying to gloss them over. This makes the artist better, quicker and more proficient at the craft.

How do they work? The eraser is long and thin, ¼" wide by 6"-7" long and is gripped by a little motor at the rear end. The artist presses the switch and the motor spins the eraser against the area to be erased, "sanding" the blemish off and leaving the paper smooth and reworkable – a result not possible with hand-erasing. Of course, if the medium has permeated all the way through the paper, even an electric eraser cannot remove it.

Since you are applying an electric appliance to your precious artwork, there are things to know and practice before actually try it out on a piece of your art.

USING AN ELECTRIC ERASER: 1. Hold the eraser exactly as you hold your pencil or pen, because you will be using it on your art the way you use one of those tools. Grasp it solidly (a death grip isn't necessary) while you rest your forearm and the side of your hand on your worktop. Keep the side of your hand on the surface while erasing, to provide a solid base to work from. Before you begin erasing, tape a piece of protective paper between your hand and the art to avoid smudging it.

2. The switch is on the barrel next to your forefinger. It is pressure-sensitive and turns the motor on when pressed, off when you release the pressure. Become comfortable with the switch before you start to use it.

3. Switch it on and press the eraser lightly to an inked area (on something other than your art). The spin makes it pull slightly to the side, but it's easy to control if you expect it. If you press the tip hard against the paper, it will immediately dig a crater. Ooooopsy......

4. To erase, press the switch, then lightly rest the eraser tip on the blemish while you move it in circles about half an inch in diameter. Keep the tip moving in a circular (not back-and-forth) movement so it won't grind through the paper. Practice first on a scrap of paper.

5. When erasing something very black, the eraser tip may clog. Press it to a clean scrap of paper to spin off the black coat. If you need to erase shiny, dark graphite, first lift off most of the unwanted graphite that makes up the error with a kneaded eraser.

6. Every few seconds, blow away or brush off the erasures with a feather, paintbrush, or your sleeve so that you can check your progress. Hold it up to the light frequently to make sure you are not wearing through the paper. Don't hurry or you will ruin your artwork.

7. Stop and pull out more eraser occasionally so that the revolving barrel head won't scratch your art. About ³⁄₁₆" to ¼" is the ideal length for the emergent eraser.

8. After erasing awhile, the motor may get hot (you will feel it through the casing). Stop and let it cool down.

9. When you have removed the blemish, brush the paper clean and burnish the erased area. Burnishing presses the paper fibers down to create a smooth re-workable surface. The broad, shiny-smooth surface of the bowl of a spoon works well, but a tiny area may require something smaller. For a small spot, burnish through a hole cut in a piece of paper to protect the rest of the art. Test this first.

10. Once you've used an electric eraser, you will become more relaxed while drawing, knowing that mistakes can be easily repaired without much effort and trauma. This will raise your confidence, your skill level, your speed, and your enjoyment in being an artist. In short, you'll become a better illustrator.

Chapter 9. Critiquing and Improving Illustrations

Student Examples for Exercise #14 on page 89.

These student examples of Exercise #14 show many of the principles of a good microscope drawing. Each took about an hour.

Excellent insect specimens can often be found on windowsills in buildings. It is also possible (and very satisfying) to find and draw subjects in the field using a magnifying glass, plant loupe or, for higher magnification, the "wrong" end of binoculars. If possible, always carry binoculars on sketching trips.

The main drawback to using the binoculars or a plant loupe is that only an extremely small part of the specimen can be brought into focus without distortion. If you use either of these tools, work with care that you don't draw that distortion.

Make the source of the enlargement obvious (see enlargement at right and below). The close-up should be clearly set apart in a structure that can't be confused with any part of the subject. A circle looks good if it is carefully drawn, as in these examples. A square is also acceptable.

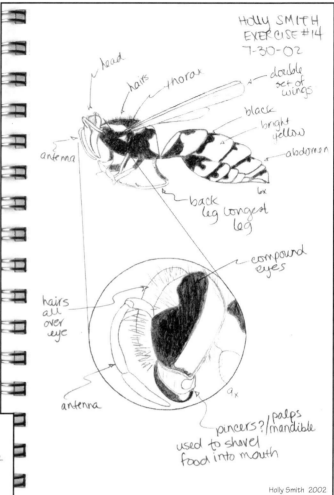

Holly Smith 2002

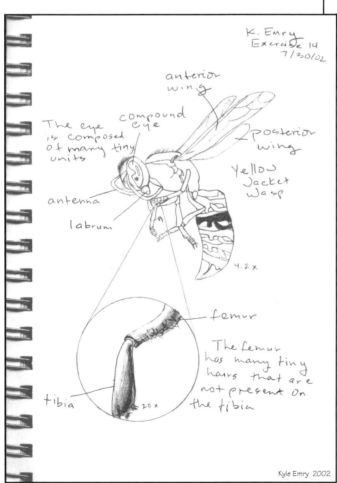

Kyle Emry 2002

The detail within the circle must show the structure exactly and in the same orientation, as the original – as though it were being seen through a magnifying glass. Fill the circle entirely.

If markings are an important aspect of the subject, as in the case of this yellowjacket, be sure to show them if possible. If there is not time to shade them in, or if it makes the structure appear too complicated, try to shade at least one of them to clarify position and intensity (at left), and label the colors (see above).

Thorough labeling is important, but those parts that are ambiguous or unknown can still be labeled with a "best guess" as long as a question mark is added to the label (see "pincers?" above).

Write legibly and practice the labeling conventions outlined on page 63.

It is acceptable (and useful) to return to a drawing at a future date if you find additional information to add to the drawing or notes.

Chapter 10. Drawing With Microscope & Magnifying Glass

If you are interested in drawing very small things – or just curious about the details of the natural world, a microscope can open up a whole new world to you. Often it stirs up more questions than it answers. If you think you know just about everything about something familiar, look at it through the lens of a dissecting scope! If you can afford to buy your own, it may be a wonderful investment for you. (It's also terrific for inspecting clogged pen points and removing slivers.)

ABOUT THE DISSECTING SCOPE:

Microscopes are expensive and delicate, but gently handled they will last for a long time since there are only a few moving parts. Look over the diagram at right and acquaint yourself with the names of the parts. The microscope shown is a dissecting microscope (the other kind, the compound scope, uses high magnification for cellular level viewing. Illumination shines up through objects on a compound scope.)

A dissecting microscope has two (binocular) eyepieces, and magnifies at a lower level, suitable for examining and dissecting larger items. Illumination typically shines down onto the subject on the stage from a built-in light source, although you can reverse this. A dissecting scope is necessary to complete Exercise 14. Your scope may look different.

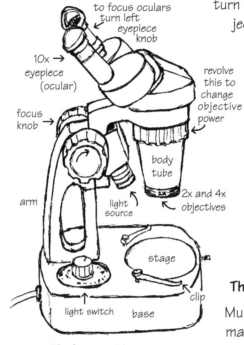

to focus oculars turn left eyepiece knob

10x → eyepiece (ocular)

focus knob →

revolve this to change objective power

body tube

arm

light source

2x and 4x objectives

stage

clip

light switch   base

What's wrong with the leaders above?

MICROSCOPIC TOPICS: (see drawing)

STAGE: Never put items directly on the stage. Always place them on a file card which you can push or pull around on the stage without having to touch the specimen (which may be delicate). The file card will also protect the stage from staining, and you can avoid having to clean off "ick & goo" when you are finished. To stabilize the file card, slide it under the clips.

ILLUMINATION: Turn on the light which shines on the stage. Items placed into the exact center of the light circle should be perfectly in view.

FOCUS: The focus knob is the largest knob on the scope. Revolve it to raise and lower the objectives and bring the specimen into focus.

BINOCULARITY: Look through both eyepieces and adjust the distance between them by pushing them apart or together until you have a full, clear view with both eyes.

ADJUSTABLE FOCUS:
The left eyepiece **may** have an adjustable focus ring. If so, close your left eye and focus on the subject through the right eyepiece, using the big focus knob. Then open your left eye and turn the left eyepiece until the object comes into the clearest focus. Few people have identical vision in both eyes, so be sure to make this adjustment for clear viewing if the option is available. If the eyepiece isn't adjustable, you may get better results by using only one eye.

OBJECTIVES: There are two objectives:

a **2-power (2x)** and a **4-power (4x)** lens.

The oculars are 10-power (10x).

Multiplied together, they produce magnifications of 20x or 40x:

10 times 2x = 20x,   10 times 4x =40x.

DEPTH OF FIELD: While you can see remarkable detail at 40x, the depth of field is very shallow, i.e. only a small portion of the subject will be in focus at any given time. For more depth of field, use the 2x objective. Revolve the knob at the top of the body tube to change objectives.

BACK-LIGHTING: Use the small knob at the front of the stage to allow replacement of the opaque stage with a clear or translucent stage. A different light knob setting lets you shine light up from beneath, which is useful for viewing transparent or translucent items, such as fly wings or tiny pond creatures in a clear glass dish of water.

BY THE WAY – The word "dissect" is pronounced **dih-SEKT**. It comes from the Greek root word **dis**, meaning "again and again", and **sect**, which means "to cut." **Di** means "two." If you DIE-sect something, you cut it into only two parts.

Student Examples of Magnifying Glass and Dissecting Scope Sketches

With A Magnifying Glass

At right is an illustration of a cranefly done with a magnifying glass. Field close-ups are fun with a magnifying glass. For greater magnification, look through the "wrong" end of your binoculars.

Notice the clean linework here. All tentative "try lines" were carefully erased and replaced. No lines have been left hanging. Clarity is essential. if you have trouble seeing how something connects, take the time to puzzle it out. Loose lines are not acceptable in scientific illustration. Your object is to "show the subject" for someone else to understand.

Take care to make each label clearly legible – not only to you, but to others as well. Many an illustrator has had to struggle later to interpret hastily scribbled labels and notes that seemed so obvious when written. Take the time to write and draw clearly for future reference. Use your kneaded eraser to clean up your drawing when finished.

body is light brown with black accents and looks hard and glossy.

This is a wing!

small hairs on head
eyes are almost as large as the head.
eyes are not glossy, they are a flat black

Heidi Soroken
17-24-01
Exercise #14
Cranefly

There are three segments to each of the six legs

1x

a little bit of hair on the end of the abdomen.

~8x

wings are iridescent and reflect several colors

Heidi Soroken 2001

With A Dissecting Scope

This lichen was drawn using a dissecting (dih-SEKT-ing) scope at a 20x setting, its lower magnification. The 1cm. bracket gives the viewer an idea of its actual size.

Note the *foliose* and *crustose* structures, plus one *apothecia*.

Refer to the *Lichen ID sheet on page 92* to identify parts.

If you are not sure what you are seeing, write a detailed descriptive note so that you can use a field guide later to identify it from your drawing – without having to go back and look at the specimen.

Note the size, texture, and any three-dimensionality that doesn't show up in the drawing. You may do a second or larger view to show any confusing aspect/s.

Stay curious as you draw. If something puzzles you, other viewers will probably wonder about it, too, so draw that part particularly carefully.

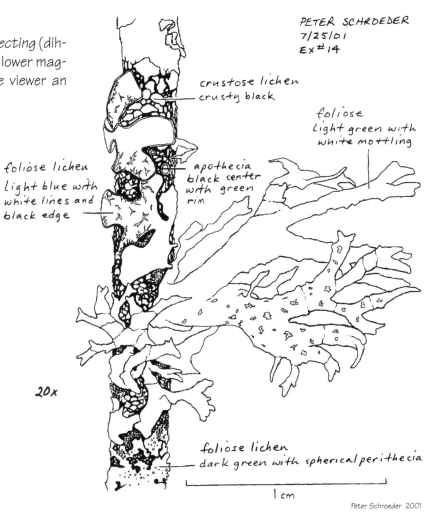

PETER SCHROEDER
7/25/01
EX #14

crustose lichen crusty black

foliose Light green with white mottling

foliose lichen Light blue with white lines and black edge

apothecia black center with green rim

20x

foliose lichen dark green with spherical perithecia

1 cm

Peter Schroeder 2001

Exercises #14 – Magnifying Glass OR Dissecting Scope Drawings – 15 pts.

The object of this exercise is to sketch specimens under magnification. Read pages 86, 88, 90 and 91 before you begin to draw. Use the lichen ID on page 92 (and the student example on page 88) to label lichens. Labels and notes about color, markings, structure, etc. are required, with leaders pointing to the features. SHADE only if/when entire outline and details are completed.

For this Exercise you need:

1. magnifying glass
2. dissecting microscope OR binoculars
3. one insect OR one lichen
4. small field sketchbook
5. .5 mechanical pencils, HB and 2B leads
6. kneaded & clickable eraser
7. ruler with centimeter markings
8. 1 file card or similar-sized piece of paper
9. compass for drawing a circle

Exercise: Draw either insect OR lichen, not both.

INSECT (MAGNIFYING GLASS): (see page 90.)

1. With your ☐(2 pts) small field sketchbook in a vertical position, draw an insect, using your magnifying glass for the main view and the scope's low power (20x) OR backward binoculars for the close-up. Lightly sketch the complete outline ☐(3 pts) 3"–6" long before you begin details. Add ☐(2pts) notes and observations (see page 86).

2. Draw a close-up 1½"–2" long or wide. Enclose it in a ☐(2pts) 2"–2½" compass circle and draw lines from the perimeter of the circle to the source (see below). ☐(2pts) Finish drawing everything that is inside the circle. ☐(2pts) Make notes and detailed observations for 6 or more structures (see pages 86 and 91).

3. ☐(1pt) Note scale on both. Now that you've sketched the subject close-up, the ORIGINAL source may not be as accurate as the detail. Erase what is wrong and ☐(1pt) **update the source.**

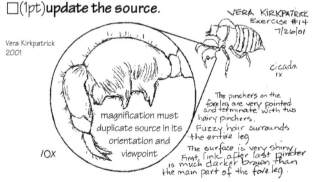

Vera Kirkpatrick
2001

VERA KIRKPATRICK
Exercise #14
7/26/01

cicada
1X

magnification must duplicate source in its orientation and viewpoint

10X

The pinchers on the fore leg are very pointed and terminate with two hairy pinchers.
Fuzzy hair surrounds the entire leg.
The surface is very shiny. First link after last pincher is much darker brown than the main part of the fore leg.

4. Shading is optional. Shade nothing until the outline is totally completed. After drawing the entire specimen, you may shade or apply texture to any confusing areas – but don't shade just to "pretty it up."

5. Apply a coversheet

LICHEN (MICROSCOPE): (see page 92.)

filecard

2cm.

moist lichen

1. Observe the lichen **in its dry state**, and ☐(1pt) write down its exact color. Then submerge it in water for 30 seconds. Remove and gently shake off excess water.

2. With your ruler mark off 2cm. on the file card. Place the lichen on the card.

3. BEFORE PUTTING FILE CARD ON SCOPE STAGE: on a sketchpad page, lightly draw a skeleton outline of the 2 cm. section ☐(2pts) 4"–6" wide into which you can draw details you see under the lens. Don't draw into the fingerprint zone. Shade only as suggested in the magnifying glass section.

4. NOW PUT THE CARD ON THE MICROSCOPE STAGE. Set your scope on low power (**20X, not 40X**).

☐(3pts) Draw the lichen, using right-brain techniques. Make linework medium weight, with clear, clean lines(no very-dark, doubled or sketchy lines).

If details are difficult to see, adjust the focus up and down as you draw – don't just gloss them over or skip them. If you cannot identify a detail, make a guess, along with observations, followed by a question mark. This can be useful later in making an ID.

☐(1pt) Draw a 40X detail of an *apothecia* if present

☐(2pts) Break lines to show perspective of more-distant/closer objects in unshaded areas. (In shaded areas the shading provides perspective.)

☐(1pt) Below the drawing, rule and label a horizontal 1cm. bracket – don't try to freehand the lines.

5. ☐(5pts) Include in your descriptive notes about the specimen:

• lichen colors before and after wetting
• growth form (foliose, fruticose or crustose)
• reproductive structures (apothecia, etc.)
• twig or substrate (anywhere it shows)
• observations (at least two, 10-50 wds)
• questions (at least one)
• correctly applied leaders (see p. 63)
• lichen name & scale of drawing. (see example on p. 88 and the lichen ID on p. 92.)

6. Apply a coversheet.

Arthropod Construction

Arthropods are, as Webster says: "...any of a phylum (Arthropoda) of invertebrate animals (as insects, arachnids, and crustaceans) that have a segmented body and jointed appendages, a usually chitinous exoskeleton molted at intervals..."

Sketching arthropods is endlessly fascinating. They come in an amazing variety of shapes and sizes.

You can use a magnifying glass or dissecting scope to see all the parts of the body and get them in the right place. But if you don't know what you are looking at, you might get something wrong without realizing it, so read this page before drawing.

Every naturalist should have a rudimentary knowledge of body parts, and the list below will help you sort them out. Read and absorb – so that you will get them right when you draw them, both under the microscope and in the field.

NOTE: When illustrating, show only the body parts normally visible from the viewpoint you select.

<u>INSECTS</u>: **have three body segments and six legs:**
(Insects include grasshoppers, beetles, bugs, dragonflies, butterflies, moths, flies, mosquitoes, etc.)

- head (to which antennae are attached)
- thorax (chest area, to which wings and 6 legs attach
- abdomen (with no legs attached to it)

<u>ARACHNIDS</u>: **have two body segments, eight legs, and two pedipalps:** *(Arachnids include spiders, scorpions, mites and ticks.)*
- cephalothorax (a combined head and chest area to which various appendages attach)
- abdomen (with no legs attached to it)

<u>CRUSTACEANS</u>: **have two chitinous body segments, usually 10+ leglike appendages, and two antennae, and are mostly aquatic:** *(Crustaceans include crabs, lobsters, crayfish, shrimp, etc.)*
- cephalothorax (a combined head and chest area to which the 10+ appendages attach)
- abdomen (often segmented and with leglike appendages attached)

<u>MILLIPEDES</u>: **are segmented and somewhat cylindrical, with two pairs of legs on each segment, and are herbivorous.**

<u>CENTIPEDES</u>: **are segmented, flattened, with one pair of legs on each segment, and are carnivorous.**

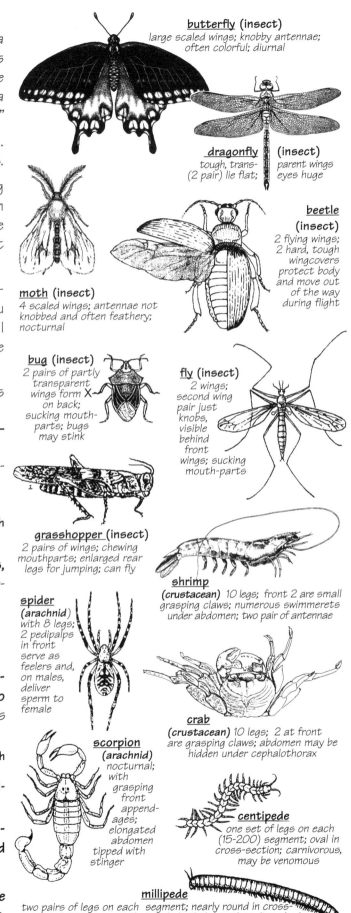

butterfly (insect)
large scaled wings; knobby antennae; often colorful; diurnal

dragonfly **(insect)**
tough, trans- (2 pair) lie flat; *parent wings eyes huge*

beetle (insect)
2 flying wings; 2 hard, tough wingcovers protect body and move out of the way during flight

moth (insect)
4 scaled wings; antennae not knobbed and often feathery; nocturnal

bug (insect)
2 pairs of partly transparent wings form X on back; sucking mouthparts; bugs may stink

fly (insect)
2 wings; second wing pair just knobs, visible behind front wings; sucking mouth-parts

grasshopper (insect)
2 pairs of wings; chewing mouthparts; enlarged rear legs for jumping; can fly

shrimp
(crustacean) 10 legs; front 2 are small grasping claws; numerous swimmerets under abdomen; two pair of antennae

spider (arachnid)
with 8 legs; 2 pedipalps in front serve as feelers and, on males, deliver sperm to female

crab
(crustacean) 10 legs; 2 at front are grasping claws; abdomen may be hidden under cephalothorax

scorpion (arachnid)
nocturnal; with grasping front appendages; elongated abdomen tipped with stinger

centipede
one set of legs on each (15-200) segment; oval in cross-section; carnivorous, may be venomous

millipede
two pairs of legs on each segment; nearly round in cross-section; herbivorous; coils into helical shape when disturbed

The yellowjacket is a carnivorous wasp with a short waist and yellow-and-black markings. Many other species of wasps are commonly mistaken for yellowjackets but the surest identifying feature is the short connection between the abdomen and the thorax — if it is long and thin, the wasp is *not a yellowjacket* and is probably mild-tempered and not to be run from with screams and hyperventilation.

In the United States, "yellowjacket" is a catchall name which covers wasps of the *Vespula* and *Dolichovespula* genera, and includes many species, some native and some European.

Some species of yellowjacket are strictly insectivorous, and eat flies, caterpillars, grasshoppers, etc.

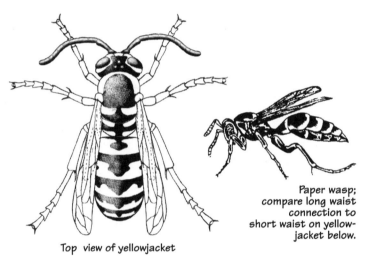

Paper wasp; compare long waist connection to short waist on yellowjacket below.

Top view of yellowjacket

Others scavenge for meat and fruits (they like soft drinks) and are likely to come into intimate and unpleasant contact with picnickers and, in fact, anyone who eats outdoors on a mild day where yellowjackets are scouting for food. Note: Honeybees are yellow and brown, and fuzzy. They won't fight you for food (yellowjackets do), and they are not attracted to meat. Yellowjackets may be called "bees."

Yellowjackets are equipped with a stinger and sturdy biting jaws with which they rip off bits of food to take home to their (usually underground) paper nest. European species make paper nests aboveground in trees or attached to protected surfaces. Occasionally the native yellowjacket builds aboveground, too. Yellowjacket nests are covered with a paper envelope. If you see wasps on a nest-comb which is *not* covered with an outer shell, they aren't yellowjackets.

Yellowjacket species are difficult to tell apart, but markings are definitive, so observe them closely. While they appear hairless, they do have fine fuzz on their bodies (not shown here). Look for dead specimens on windowsills.

Interesting areas to observe close-up on insects are:

- leg, including apical spurs and claws
- face from front, antennae, ocelli, and markings
- abdomen, including tip, segments and markings

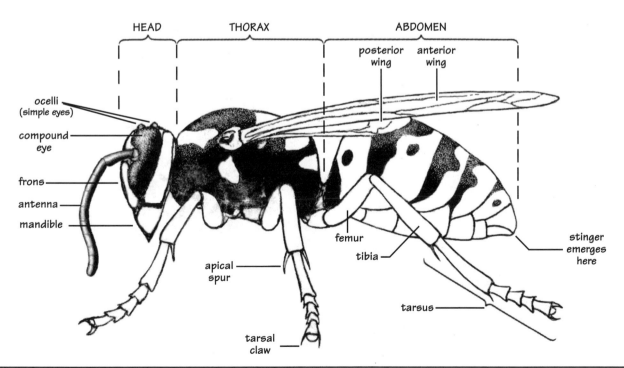

Lichen ID

A lichen is composed of microscopic green or blue-green algae and fungal threads called *hyphae*. Living and growing together symbiotically, they form a new body called a *thallus* which resembles neither of them.

The green alga in this composite plant photosynthesizes sugars to support the fungus, which makes up the bulk of the plant. Lichens grow on branches, twigs, rocks and sometimes on the ground. They can survive situations which would kill other plants. A long-dried lichen may be "brought back to life" by a good rain.

Lichens may be bluish, greenish yellow, lemon yellow, orange, brown, tan, chestnut, blackish brown, or grey. Fruiting bodies may be black, red, orange, maroon, white, brown, etc.

Most lichens are identified in the dry state, because when they get wet their chlorophyl may turn them green.

Lichens reproduce via spores, but their *soredia*, *isidia* and bits of *thallus* can all propagate vegetatively. A dislodged lichen may form a new thallus and continue on. Many lichen features may be seen only with a magnifying glass or microscope.

THREE MAJOR FORMS:

a. foliose (leaf-like)
b. fruticose (shrubby or hair-like)
c. crustose (crust-like)

rhizines
substrate

• **foliose lichens** *(leaflike):* are flattened and prostrate. The color and various features of the upper surface are different from those of the lower. The underside of the thallus is usually covered with hairy **rhizines**, which attach to the **substrate** (rock, tree bark or ground).

a. foliose

• **fruticose lichens** *(shrubby or hair-like):* are simple or divided, mostly cylindrical branches. They may be hairy, bushy, or even strap-shaped, but unlike the foliose lichens, they hang freely or stand erect. The hollow stem of a fruticose lichen is called a **podalia**.

b. fruticose

• **crustose lichens** *(crust like):* form a crust that is fissured or **areolate** (small discrete patches on the thallus surface). They are always firmly attached to their bark or rock substrate, and cannot be removed without destroying the lichen.

c. crustose

FURTHER DIAGNOSTIC FEATURES:

d. isidia
e. soredia

• **isedia:** are tubular, sometimes branching growths scattered fairly evenly over the lichen surface. Rising to only .5mm (or shorter) they may be simple or branched, spherical, knobby, dense or sparse. They may be brushed away, whereupon they break off and leave a scar.

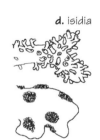

d. isidia

e. soredia, forming soralia

• **soredia:** originate below the surface and erupt on the surface as a powdery substance which may be brushed off. They consist of algae surrounded by **hyphae** (microscopic fungal threads that make up the lichen body) and may form miniscule round or linear clumps called **soralia** (see above).

REPRODUCTIVE STRUCTURES:

f. & g apothecia
h. perithecia
i. pycnidia

• **apothecia:** are cup- or disc-shaped structures (often in a contrasting color such as brown, black, orange, red or white) and contain spores.

f. apothecia

g. apothecia clumps on podalia (stem)

• **perithecia:** are bulb-shaped structures containing spores, and are buried beneath the surface with only tiny, dot-like openings showing.

h. perithecia

• **pycnidia:** are also bulb-shaped structures containing spores, but the structures are on the surface instead of buried beneath. They look a lot like bulbous **apotheciae (f.)**.

i. pycnidia

Chapter 11. Putting It All Together

Creating a scientific illustration can be difficult: The subject may be complex, straining the illustrator's capabilities, or it may be broken or partly missing, requiring some fudging. The deadline may loom impossibly close. There may be no original or live subject to draw from. Vital materials and information may be missing. Working conditions may be impossible. Available resources may be fuzzy or misleading. What to do? Here are some things you can do to get the picture.

WAYS TO GET THE PICTURE

If you have the subject (dead or alive) in hand:

• Sketch freehand using right-brain techniques.

• Sketch through a sheet of glass or rigid plastic onto acetate, transfer drawing to tracing paper or the finish surface and proceed from there (pp. 18–19).

• For hand-held subjects, do a controlled contour drawing, holding the object between eye and paper, and drawing around the contour (use one eye only, and brace your hand to hold it perfectly still). After the outline has been completed, the interior details can be filled in using right-brain observation and drawing techniques. See page 25 for details.

• For small subjects, use proportional dividers to transfer larger measurements to the paper surface.

Dividers are easy to make with cardboard and a clasp. Where you put the hole determines what the ratio will

• Start drawings with **left-brain templates** (p. 25).

• If sketching from a car (wild animal park or scenery), draw with a wax pencil or felt-tip pen on plastic taped to the window (see below). Then transfer the image to tracing paper for further work.

• Pose a stationary subject in a lifelike or natural position in whatever pose is needed (use blocks, clips, string, wire, pins, kneaded eraser, tape, bottles, etc.) so it won't move while you're trying to draw it. Use a stool as a scaffold for a larger animal. You can create quite lifelike poses,

distortions removed

correcting on paper the problems caused by the props. But make sure you don't possess or handle protected species without permission.

• Photocopy a flattish item by placing it on the photocopier glass. Surround it with white paper to avoid a mostly-black picture (it wastes toner) and be careful to not scratch the glass. A tracing can then be made from the photocopy for further work.

If you hesitate to use these methods because they seem too much like "tracing" or "copying," remember that such methods are an old and venerable tradition. Recent research has proven beyond any doubt that many of the Old Masters used lenses and other aids to help them transfer images to canvas.

cont...

Ways to Get The Picture (cont..)

If you can't sketch the actual subject due to time or access limitations:

• Photograph the subject from all conceivable directions. You may need <u>all</u> angles when drawing.

• Take photos with a digital camera, transfer to computer screen and print out (etc.).

• Trace your photos onto tracing paper using a light table or window.

• If you have slides, project them onto paper taped to a wall, outline, then photocopy to resize.

• If you have slides and access to a slide viewer/enlarger, sketch images onto tracing paper.

• Find photographs in magazines and books. Work from these or make photocopies if you need to preserve the magazine or can't take the book with you. Your "morgue" collection will probably be one of your most valuable resources. *Tearing pages out of library materials is a felony.*

• Find photos and information on the web, print them out and proceed from there (see page 98).

• Use stuffed specimens and dried parts (wings, feet, etc.) for reference, but never use them as your sole source.

You may use a combination of these techniques, depending on the circumstances and requirements of the job. You may even invent other techniques of your own. As they say, "Whatever works for you!"

In the end, the most important thing is to be able to meet the needs of the illustrative situation accurately without infringing on someone else's copyright.

When you use aids and material from various resources, be honest if asked — even though it may be tempting to downplay or deny it.

If someone wants to know where you sketched that mink, don't make something up — tell them you were forced by time, seasonal, locational (whatever) restraints to work from photographs.

If anyone gives you a hard time about it, point out the following:

Most illustrations are created from photographs. It would be pretty naive to think you could go out into the wild and find an animal to draw for a needed illustration **and**:

• expect to find one within the time frame you have available in which to draw the illustration.

• expect the lighting and weather conditions to make viewing and sketching possible.

• expect to have your sketchbook ready when it appears so that you don't frighten it off as you fumble around trying to get it out and opened up.

• expect the animal to get into the position you need for the illustration.

• expect it to stand there (or even remain in sight) for however long you need to draw it.

That should defuse any criticism.

Of course, as an artist, you'd rather go out and sketch the real thing, without having to compromise with such grimy truths. Alas.

So here's how to optimize probabilities:

Make a habit of sketching subjects anywhere you can, whether you have a particular need for it right now or not. When you go on a hike, take your sketchbook. A trip to the beach? A walk in the park? That's what your field sketchbook is for.

With the roadkill posed and sketched from all directions (spend as long as you can with it) you have illustrations of that subject for any need that may arise. You have sketched its feet, its nose close-up, you have moved it into poses you think you might be able to use later. You have done it outside, of course, because your housemates would give you a hard time about it (and besides, it smells better out there in the backyard, out of sight of casual onlookers).

There are plenty of magnificent nature photographs in magazines, so put out the word you need old nature magazines. The local recycle center may allow you to look for nature magazines in the bin — giving them an additional recycle. Cut out wildlife and habitat photos and start sorting and filing. A good "scrap morgue" is a priceless tool.

Drawing From Taxidermy Mounts

Drawing from a taxidermy mount is tricky. For example, mounts may be badly stuffed by beginning students; alligators stuffed for tourists may have neon red eyes; pumas may be mounted with hideously snarling expressions for boastful sportsmen; etc.

Mounts are mostly useful for checking features like fur, feathers, beaks, whiskers, ear or tail length, scale patterns, and details of feet. However, with age, fur fades, feathers fall out and become frayed, feet shrink, and beetles eat fragile ears. Beaks may be painted (sometimes incorrectly) by the taxidermist to simulate a color which fades after death. Mounted fish are usually painted, and may have fake parts.

As a drawing aid, taxidermy mount sketching can be useful. If you have photos of the living animal, obvious errors can be corrected. Still, you must practice extreme care any time you use a taxidermy mount as a reference.

In the drawing below, a taxidermy mount of a western grebe was sketched **(a.)**, then a photo was used to determine the actual shape of the head of a living bird. The head was traced from the photo **(b.)** adjusted to the correct size to fit the sketch, for trial placement on the sketch body then photocopied.

The same was done in the drawing at right, a stuffed taxidermy mount of a red-tailed hawk **(c.)**.

The head in the photo was traced onto tracing paper

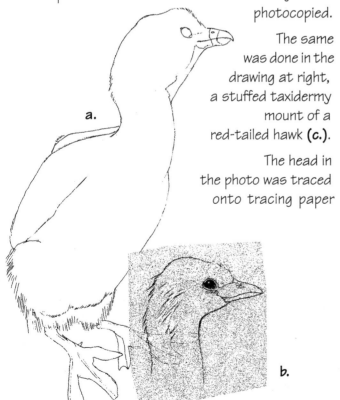

a.

b.

Allison Dew, 2001

(d.) placed over the drawing **(inset e.)** and shifted around until the head lined up on the shoulders. You can see that the stance and the fluff of the feathers on the sketched bird were greatly improved by this.

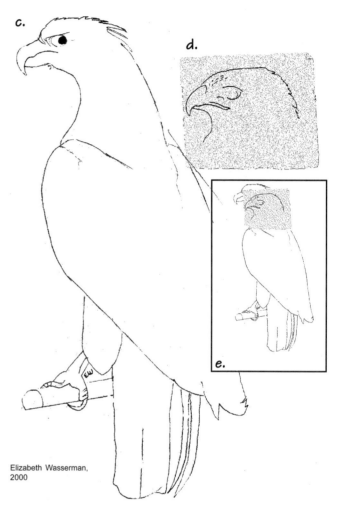

c.

d.

e.

Elizabeth Wasserman, 2000

Notice that by moving the tracing paper up and down, revolving it, and moving it from side to side, the bird's attitude can be changed. Be aware that a slight shift in position can alter body language. Use this knowledge to make the attitude of your subject match whatever is needed for the illustration you are doing — the hallmark of a good illustrator.

You can also use this technique if something about your drawing doesn't seem quite right. Trace the area in question onto tracing paper, then try the tracing in different positions, enlarging or reducing it if necessary. Do a mirror check. If the part you are shifting around is not correctly drawn, redraw it on tracing paper **first** to try it out, then transfer it back to your drawing if/when it works.

Problems With Drawing From Taxidermy Mounts and Photos

In many ways, it is harder to illustrate an animal from taxidermy/museum mounts or photographs than it is to sketch from a living specimen. Although it may seem as though a moving target would be tougher to draw than a mounted specimen or a photograph (which doesn't change pose if you sneeze or erase a line vigorously), different skills and study are required to make an illustration from a mount or photos look accurate and true-to-life.

The more methods and references you use in drawing your subject, the better your results are likely to be.

COMMON PROBLEMS WITH TAXIDERMY MOUNTS:

• **unrealistic stuffing** – bulges, lumps, stitches, stretched parts, enlarged or shrunken areas, etc.

• **uncharacteristic poses** – positions the animal seldom or never assumes in life.

• **misshapen/shrunken tissues** – nose, toes, legs, eyelids, ears, tails, etc.

• **lack of eyes** – commonly encountered on museum mounts – these "sausages" are only useful for basic "color and toe checking."

• **incorrect eyes** – may be the wrong color, filmed with the grime of ages, eyelids shrunken or missing, etc.

• **faded or ragged scales, plumage or fur** – age can fade specimens from dark brown to blond.

• **missing parts** – dermestid beetles chew off fur, ear tips and toes; legs or tails may fall off. On some specimens, you may mistake a naturally hairless spot for a damaged area, and erroneously add hair.

COMMON PROBLEMS WITH PHOTOGRAPHS:

• **undesirable poses** – no matter how many photos you have, you will seldom find just what you need.

• **parts hidden behind or under something** – don't try to fake it unless you know enough about that animal's anatomy. The missing part will have to be found on another source or hidden on your drawing, also.

• **obscured parts** – due to lighting or contrast, you may be fooled by shadows or contrasty photos into making mistakes on your drawing. Dark markings may be confused with shadows, and vice versa.

• **uncharacteristic specimens** – zoo or rehab animals often have misshapen or damaged feet, feathers or wings. They may be so fat or out of shape that they don't represent their species accurately.

• **uncharacteristic action phase pose** – may misrepresent what the animal is doing. For instance, some phases of running animals look very static (see page 78).

COPYRIGHT PROBLEMS WITH PHOTOGRAPHS:

• **copyright violation** – To avoid copyright infringement, especially if your work is destined for publication, your photo source/s must be unrecognizable. This goal can be met by using several photographs to produce a composite drawing.

But if you put the parts together in an anatomically incorrect fashion, you will not have a successful illustration. Extreme care must be taken. An understanding of anatomy helps, plus a careful study of the photos you have on hand, and a thorough critique.

> ### Don't try to fake it: RESEARCH.

SO, WHAT ARE THE BEST RESOURCES TO USE?

• **IDEAL** – **Live sketching.** Animals are drawn from life, with lots of details and field notes on behavior and anatomy. Wildlife is hard to find and draw; captive animals may be approached more closely for sketching.

• **NEXT TO IDEAL** – **Roadkills.** Terrific drawings can be made from a roadkill (preferably fresh) if it isn't mashed. Park safely off the highway right-of-way, nudge it off the road with a stick, photograph from all angles, and sketch on location. Remember, it's a felony to possess non-game wildlife, dead or alive. If you have a hunting acquaintance, ask about sketching opportunities.

• **OKAY SOMETIMES** – **Reference photographs.** Good photos may enable a careful illustrator to do the job. Use as many sources as possible, and always alter your drawing to the extent that your sources cannot be determined or guessed.

• **LAST RESORT** – **Mounted specimens.** Never use them as your sole source. See at left.

• **ALMOST NEVER** – **Other people's drawings or paintings.** If they made a mistake or copied someone else, you will, too, and it is also infringing copyright unless you get permission and/or clearly note "drawn from....." and quote your source – as in the captions on page 33. Use them to confirm a point, but never as a sole source.

Exercise #15 – Drawing From Many Sources – 15 pts.

The object of this exercise is to gain experience using various sources to create an illustration of an assigned subject. Using a one- to two-hour session with a bird taxidermy mount (or roadkill) and photographs of the subject, and working from client specifications (as in a typical illustration job), you will create a pencil illustration to meet those requirements. Before beginning, read this entire page and study the example on page 98. If a bird mount is not available, substitute whatever you have available and adjust instructions as needed.

For this Exercise you need:

1. 11" x 14" sketchpad
2. kneaded eraser
3. ruler
4. magnifying glass
5. taxidermy mount
6. .5 mechanical pencils, HB and 2B leads
7. photos of the same animal from various sources .

Note: a bird bill opens from this hinge point, **well behind** the eye.

Exercise: Your client has asked for the following:

"SPECS: We need a pencil rendering of a [taxidermy bird mount, your choice] perched or standing, in profile, alert, beak open as though calling. The body or head may be turned slightly. Either the height or width of the subject must be 6-8 inches. Light shading okay."

Look at the photographs of your bird to find parts you can use to create the illustration. Examine the taxidermy mount to see what you can use from that.

NOTE: Use both the taxidermy mount and the photos to create your final drawing.

In your 11" x 14" pad, make a quick sketch that meets the specifications for the illustration you will be drawing. Recheck the specs when done. **Use page 98 as a guide for sketches, notes, and final results.**

This exercise is designed as a typical real-life situation in which you might have limited access to a taxidermy mount (as in a museum), so after a 1-2 hour session with the taxidermy mount, you should have no further contact with it. Spend the time with the mount getting details that aren't available in the photos and might be useful in helping you create the illustration later.

Settle yourself squarely in front of the taxidermy mount, at the angle which you think would be the most useful. Place your sketch pad directly between you and the mount (see diagram above right).

1. In your sketchpad, warm up with one small 30-second contour drawing of the entire subject OR the specific part you intend to draw (don't peek). Sketch a small 1-minute contour drawing of the same area. Begin your sketching session.

2. You MUST use the taxidermy sketches in your illustration, so make detailed sketches, close-ups and notes.

Bill, nostril, mouth or gape length, feather direction and length on a taxidermy mount **should** be fairly accurate. Markings will *probably* be okay, although they may be faded. Refer to page 96 for parts that are most likely to lose their authenticity. Compare the mount with photos to help you avoid sketching badly mounted parts.

line up a prominent point on the subject with a **reference point**

body, sketchpad and subject **in direct line**

CAREFULLY NOTE:
- head and neck length and width, attachment to body
- bill length, width, gape if open (study bird skull above left)
- leg length and width, placement on body
- foot and toe length and width, number of toes
- scale pattern on feet and toes (use magnifying glass)
- feather detail and color, especially around eyes and bill
- special details specific to that animal

3. When your taxidermy sketches are completed, select what you plan to use from the photos. Read page 98 carefully to make sure your projected use won't violate the photographer's copyright.

4. Combine your taxidermy sketches and selections from the photographs to create your own, original rendering on a fresh sheet from your sketchpad (or on better paper if you wish). The final result should not be a recognizable copy of any of the photographs or the taxidermy mount. Shade just enough to indicate color/markings.

Check off this list to be sure your finished illustration meets scientific illustration **AND** the spec standards:

☐**(4pts) final pencil illustration meets all the specs**

☐**(1pt) shading conventions and highlights are correct**

☐**(2pts) linework is clean and clear, but not too dark**

☐**(2pts) well-proportioned parts are correctly assembled**

☐**(1pt) drawing is clean and spotless**

☐**(1pt) tracing paper coversheet is correctly applied**

☐**(1pt) all resources, photos & sketches have been saved**

☐**(2pts) make a good digital photocopy, 2/3 reduction, to ensure that the illustration will reproduce at the correct values. If some areas need to be darkened or lightened, do that and re-photocopy.**

☐**(1pt) put notes and arrows on the coversheet pointing out which sketches and photos were used and where.**

Student Example of Notes, Sketches and Final Rendering of Illustration for Exercise #15

Detailed notes answered potential later questions about feathers and proportions.

final rendering, at 66% from notes, sketches and photos

Lea Johnson, 2002

This foot was reversed and used as drawn, without further reference to photos.

correct head shape came from photos

OTHER PEOPLE'S STUFF ISN'T FREE

When referencing other people's photographs, written works, magazine articles and photos, or material off the web — IT ISN'T FREE — IT'S COPYRIGHTED. If you use someone else's work, you must either have written permission from them OR you must alter the end result so much that they wouldn't suspect you used their material as a resource.

When borrowing from photos, refer to several, at least six or seven, using only parts of each.

If you copy or redraw something exactly from a photo, you must credit the source (see a credit on page. 78. My own photo on page 33 didn't require a credit.).

If you use someone else's written material, you must either credit them fully (there are technical standards for this) or rewrite it in your own words. If you rewrite, it is your responsibility to understand and extrapolate the information correctly.

You never know where your work will end up. Be paranoid. Don't take chances — make sure your sources are not recognizable.

> CAUTION: Anybody can create a web site and put **anything** on it. He/she may be an authority with information that is 100% correct — **or** the information and photos could be bogus or inaccurate. Beware.

Chapter 12. Computer Art & Text

Competent illustrators are expected to take their artwork a lot farther along the reproduction path than their predecessors did. If you don't know how to scan your artwork to file and transmit it via email in PDF form to the printer, you may be passed over as an illustrator for someone who does. It has become crucial for the artist to be computer-literate.

Scientific illustration isn't what it used to be. Fifty years ago, there were few decent wildlife photographs to work from. There were a few published photos of pets or animals in zoos. Some photos could be found in National Geographics and in books, written by adventurers on safari to foreign lands.

There were no wildlife rehabilitation centers with native wildlife to draw. Cameras were unwieldy for taking reference photos, and film speeds were too slow to show much action, anyway. The only stop-action photos were Muybridge's (see page 78).

Artists spent a lot of time scratching out errors, covering them with white tempera paint, and trying to ink over the mess. The worst part was, they had no photocopiers to check results, and wouldn't know how good their fix-up job was until they saw it in print.

Final reproduction? Artists had little or no role in what finally happened to their illustrations during publication. It was a different world.

Now, to make an illustration, you can use photos and visit rehab centers and zoos with lifelike settings. You can check your results with a photocopy machine; you can go onto the web to look up photos of such obscure things as fairy shrimps.

But more than that, the computer has become a valuable artist's tool in its own right. It is possible to create entire illustrations in a graphics program — although it's not quite as easy as drawing by hand, scanning in, and tweaking the art to the *n*th degree. A troublesome hand-rendered piece can be cleaned up and improved remarkably in a graphics program.

Some things can be done easier and faster in a graphics program than by hand: stipple, scratchboard, some shading, cleanup, the second half of a symmetrical object, etc. Many printers/publishers are now requesting that artwork be submitted on CD.

So if you want to be an illustrator, it is important to add these skills to your repertoire in order to be on a solid footing in the field. If you don't, you may be perceived as a Luddite (the workers who threw their wooden shoes into the machinery in a futile protest against the Industrial Revolution). ☺

Actually, if you haven't tried manipulating images on the computer, you probably don't realize that (regardless of your current opinion) art on the computer is fun, rewarding, speedy, and can improve your end product by quite a bit. The most important criteria of doing art on the computer is *that it must not* look like it was done on the computer.

To that end, when you scan artwork make sure the number of dots per inch (*dpi*, a dot being one *pixel*) is high enough to not produce a pixelly product (below 150 dpi). Don't swing too far the other way, though. Gigantic files (1200dpi) can be very slow to work with. Here's what "the jaggies" do to a good picture:

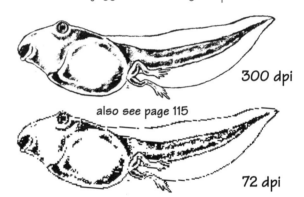

300 dpi

also see page 115

72 dpi

Don't bother making a 72 dpi scan for anything but web use. That's what it's designed for — fewer dots load faster and you don't really notice the jaggies onscreen.

Some low-end graphics programs produce pixelly text, so check a printout of the text before using. You may need to substitute text from a desktop publishing program.

18 pt.Text from a low-end graphic program.
18 pt.Text from a high-end graphics, desktop publishing, or word processor program.

The difference is pretty obvious, even if you aren't paying close attention.

Always scan at 150-600dpi, and check for jaggies before using text from a graphics program.

Scan A Graphic File To Use In Exercise #16

If you have a computer and scanner, and know how to use them, scan the Ticklebooty you made for Chapter 4, using whatever program you are most familiar with. This exercise is designed to give adequate results with even the lowest-quality equipment/program, but better and/or quicker results may be possible with better equipment and higher-end graphics programs.

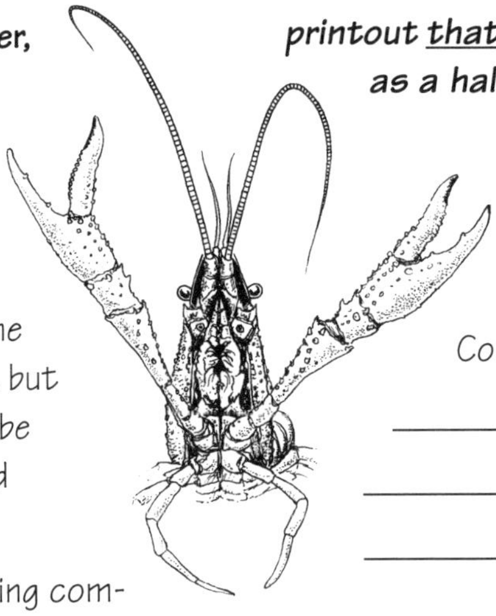

If you are well-versed in producing computer art, some of the following material may be elementary to you. But if you are not experienced, it will be essential. Whatever your skill level, you need to be able to produce the required results, so even if you are a whiz at computer graphics, work your way through this exercise for practice in fulfilling client requirements. If you don't have your own computer/scanner, try family, friends, copy shops, cybercafes, or, if you are a student, college computer labs.

Whatever your scanner or program, do the following:

1. START WITH 4" x 6" TICKLEBOOTY ART.

For this exercise, the scanned graphic must fit on the computer screen in the graphics program without causing you to scroll either horizontally or vertically. If it fits entirely on the screen, it's easier to work with. If it doesn't fit, photocopy a smaller version and scan that, or if possible, adjust the size within the scanner or graphics program (see box on page 104). Your Ticklebooty should be about the right size.

2. SCAN YOUR TICKLEBOOTY AT 150 – 300dpi:

If using a minimal graphics program, scan the art in at 150 dpi. If you don't know how, click on Help. If you're using a more sophisticated program, you may scan the graphic at 300.

3. SCAN AS LINE ART (NOT A HALFTONE):

Save the file in black/white only (not halftone) as ticklebooty.bmp or .tif, but not .gif or .jpg. The .gif or .jpg extensions are for web use. Since your graphic must not be a halftone, don't save it on a "photograph" setting. **If you see any kind of pattern on your** printout _that you didn't put there_, it was scanned **as a halftone.** Try again. SAVE.

If you are a novice at this, use the rest of this page to write yourself notes about your progress. Write down questions to ask someone later. Continue on page 101.

_____

_____

_____

_____

_____

_____

_____

_____

_____

_____

_____

_____

_____

_____

_____

_____

_____

_____

_____

_____

_____

_____

_____

_____

_____

_____

4. CHECK THE SCANNED FILE:

Save, then bring up the graphic in whatever graphics program you prefer. If the graphic doesn't fit in the window of the graphics program, either adjust its size if you know how, click on HELP, or start over with a smaller original (a photocopy may work.)

5. PRINT OUT A PAPER COPY:

When you have scanned in what looks like a good onscreen graphic, print out a copy to make sure everything is working properly and that your printout gives you results that resemble the original.

6. SAVE A COPY UNDER A DIFFERENT NAME:

Before you do anything to your new graphic, click on SAVE AS and save a copy of the file with a name like *TicklebootyCopy.bmp* (or *.tif*) or some other name that describes it well. Now you have two copies of the same file. Make changes on only ONE.

KEEP ONE FILE UNCHANGED SO YOU CAN GO BACK TO IT AND START FRESH IF NEEDED.

7. WHICH GRAPHICS PROGRAM?

For beginners, a low-end graphics program, the one packaged with the computer, is perfect. It is designed to be easy, relatively intuitive, and quick to learn. There aren't many commands, so you don't have to learn a lot of details in order to get results.

Such a program is quite adequate for learning, but eventually, if you want to perfect your skills, you'll want to graduate to a more sophisticated program.

A more complex program has more bells and whistles and you can do more things with less frustration — but the learning curve is steep and you will have to devote a considerable amount of time and effort to learning the program. The tradeoff is definitely worthwhile if you expect to become a professional illustrator. If you don't? Well, it depends on what you think is fun and worth working at.

Meanwhile, back at the ranch..... Open your copy and experiment on your illustration with whatever tools and commands are in the graphics program you are using. Even elementary graphics programs have a basic set of tools. Become proficient with as many tools as possible. Much of your knowledge can be transferred to a more complex program if you decide to get serious about it later.

8. EXPERIMENT (remember, commands may vary):

Shade some of your art with the **airbrush** tool. Erase unwanted lines with the **eraser tool** or **select** them and hit the **delete** button on the keyboard. Work your way through the entire "toolbox."

9. SAVE IT:

Save frequently — at least every five minutes. If you mess up the illustration, go back to the original, make a new copy and start over. If you like something you do, save it, then keep working on it. You can usually revert to the last saved version.

10. PRACTICE:

Anxious about tackling computer graphics (and lots of people are)? Practice before you start Exercise 16 to take away some of the apprehension. Cover the basics, then forge ahead and experiment with as many new techniques as you have time for.

11. WHEN YOU FINISH, PRINT YOUR WORK OUT:

Check out what you have done. Things may look good onscreen but not print out well; sometimes they look bad onscreen but print okay. Experiment.

12. WORD PROCESSING:

In Exercise 17, you will be importing a graphic into a document file, formatting the text, flowing the text around the graphic, and designing an article suitable for use in a newsletter, brochure or other publication.

Get acquainted with a word processing program if you aren't already. Familiarity with a word processing program is required for the Project B text, too.

COMPUTER NOVICE?

If you are a computer novice, all this may sound complex. But if you can follow the instructions as you would a pizza recipe, it's likely to turn out "edible."

Go at it in a spirit of fun, and try not to get frustrated. It's a learning experience. You'll need to know this stuff sooner or later, particularly word processing, to get along in our rapidly changing world.

> **Learning a computer graphics program takes time and concentration, so don't try to do it when you're in a hurry or stressed.**

Playing With A Graphics Program – Introduction

Altering an illustration with a graphics program can be very rewarding. You can improve the shading, clean up lines, add details, get scratchboard effects, multiply items, mirror-image symmetrical subjects, and so on.

Computers come with a basic graphics program already installed. As an artist, you should know how to use either that one or a more advanced one. You'll probably get hooked on the possibilities once you scan in a piece of your own art and discover all the interesting, time-saving things you can do with it.

In the following drill, you will get acquainted with the basic tools. Most graphics programs have similar tools in the toolbox.

Doodle with each tool off to the side before you use it on your picture – it will save a lot of UNDO time. Most of the tools are self-explanatory, but helpful descriptions will be given for each part of the exercise as you move through it. Remember, every graphics program has its own commands, and these instructions may not match that program exactly. You may have to tinker and experiment to get the results you need.

The illustrations on this page are similar to what you should produce, using your Ticklebooty graphic file

to try out the tools. If your ticklebooty drawing isn't available, you could scan in the kitten in this column and try to reproduce Printout Sheet #2 using the instructions in Exercise #16.

When you finish Exercise #16, you should have a solid foundation in beginning computer graphics, and know at least the basics of how to improve your artwork on the computer. And your confidence level will be way higher.

If you are already an accomplished computer artist, this assignment will be a snap. If you would like something more challenging, try the grasshopper exercise on page 112 (it must be done in a graphics program which allows variable rotation of _selected parts_ of the image).

Printout Sheet #1

Name
Date
Ex. #16

Printout Sheet #1 should show:
1. your original ticklebooty graphic scan.
2. your name, date and Exercise #.

The graphic above is the original bobcat kitten. Compare its eyes, teeth and raised paw with those of the altered illustration at left. Note the difference a short time spent scribbling finer fur marks can make. Imagine the improvements another hour of tinkering could achieve.

Printout Sheet #2

Bobcat Kitten At Play

cut and paste - moth and paw

pencil tool - scribbles around outline

fill tool   curve tool

airbrush

ellipse tool   line tool

brush tool - heavy lines under leg above

eraser - front of mouth and teeth, grass below

Name
Date
Ex. #16

rounded rectangle tool

Printout Sheet #2 should show:
your ticklebooty in a format similar to the one at left, complete with box outline.

As in the illustration at left, it should show:

1. the alterations you made
2. text added (title inside _or_ outside box OK)
3. lines pointing to where you worked on it
4. what tools you used to make changes
5. etc. (see page 105 for other requirements)
6. all enclosed in a box

The object of this exercise is to learn how to scan a piece of original artwork (black and white, but not a halftone) into a graphics program, alter it in a useful manner, save it to file and print it out. Please refer to pages 100-101 for scanning advice and other information. These instructions may not apply to the program you use, but they may be similar.

For this Exercise you need:

1. Your ticklebooty pen & ink drawing from Chapter 4. Use a 4" high photocopy of your Ticklebooty if necessary.

2. Access to a scanner connected to a computer.

3. A basic graphics program. Use a more sophisticated program **only** if you are already familiar with it or have LOTS of time to learn it.

Exercise:

1. Read and work through **Scan A Graphic File To Use in Exercise #16** and **A Practice Tour of the Graphics Program** on pages 100–101, then read **this** exercise all the way through before beginning.

For this exercise, you will be working in black and white only. Do not add any color to the art. **Do not do any part of it in halftone.**

This will take time, so don't skimp on the amount of time you allow for this exercise. Pages 102 and 105 outline what to do to complete this exercise.

> Note: The following instructions may only partially apply to the graphics program you are using. If they don't work, look for substitutes or alternatives. Experiment. In these instructions, the symbol > means "go to" or "click on."

2. Open the graphics program, wherever it may be on your particular computer. Start with a blank white screen on which you can learn how to use the tools that are displayed in the toolbox onscreen (see a toolbox example below). Browse through all the options in the bar at the top of the screen to get acquainted with your options.

3. Open a copy of your graphics file: >OPEN >LOOK IN: (drive) >"your file" and open it in the screen.

Until you get comfortable in a graphics program, always save a copy of your original to a different name and work on the copy, so that if something goes wrong you have the original to return to.

In a basic graphics programs, each time you change a graphic's size, pixels may be lost, making the image jaggy. It's better to start with the right

size illustration. You may not be able to UNDO back to your original copy.

However, if you must change the size of something and can't or don't want to rescan at a more useful size, >IMAGE, >STRETCH/SKEW and try percentages (use the same number for height and width to keep it in proportion.)

4. **Before you begin to experiment, print out a copy of your unaltered file** for visual comparison with your altered file. >Print Preview if this option appears. If the image doesn't fit on the vertical sheet >Page Setup and change orientation to Landscape. >Printer >OK. Review your print.

COLOR BOX: on the screen is the color box. If you are working on a black & white picture, all of the boxes should have gray patterns, no color.

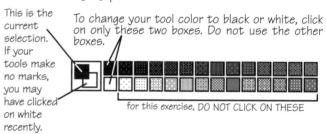

This is the current selection. If your tools make no marks, you may have clicked on white recently.

To change your tool color to black or white, click on only these two boxes. Do not use the other boxes.

for this exercise, DO NOT CLICK ON THESE

TOOLS:

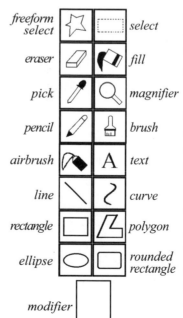

freeform select	select
eraser	fill
pick	magnifier
pencil	brush
airbrush	text
line	curve
rectangle	polygon
ellipse	rounded rectangle
modifier	

Compare the diagram and labels on the toolbox at left to what you see onscreen. Try them out.

If you can't figure a tool out, >HELP on the bar at the top of the screen. Click on INDEX, then type in the name of the tool.

If you goof, erase with the **ERASER** tool, or select with the **SELECT** tool and delete your error. If do something you like, SAVE, then continue. (>EDIT, >UNDO may undo your last move.)

Playing With Paint

If you are not familiar with the graphics program, read all the steps on this page all the way through before you begin.

NOTE: There may be a **DROPDOWN MODIFIER BOX** (or something similar) on the toolbox panel. It gives you ways to modify the tool that you have selected. For instance, if you have clicked in the airbrush section of the toolbox, spray pattern choices may be displayed in a modifier box (see at right). You can then click on your choice of spray pattern size. When using any of the tools, always check to see if any options are offered. The following instructions will assume you have a modifier box, so if you don't, you must discover what alternatives your particular program offers and translate instructions accordingly. A space has been provided at right for notes.

A line made with the **PENCIL** tool may be only one pixel wide. A pixel is the smallest dot you can make on the screen. To make a wider line, select **BRUSH** and choose the size and shape you want from the modifier box.

The **LINE** tool changes line widths in the modifier box. To use the line tool, click on the picture where you want the line to start, then drag to where you want the line to end. It makes only straight lines.

The **CURVE** tool is more complex, and different in each program. In some programs you make a line, then grab part of it and pull. When it has curved as much you want it to, drop it and double-click. Experiment if your curve tool works differently.

In some programs when you click on either the **SELECT** tool or the **TEXT** tool, the modifier box shows transparent and opaque background boxes They allow you to copy something, click on either box and, when you paste, it will have whichever background you selected.

Click on the **MAGNIFIER** to enlarge your view of the picture. The modifier box will give you magnification options. Choose one and click on your picture. To de-magnify, click on the magnifier tool again, then click on your picture.

Shade with the **AIRBRUSH** tool. >AIRBRUSH >the spray pattern size you want in the modifier box.

To copy, >**SELECT** tool. Click *near* what you want to copy and drag a rectangle around it. >EDIT >COPY, then >EDIT >PASTE. A copy of what you surrounded with the select tool will appear on your drawing. Click on it and drag it around.

> You can also resize it. Move your cursor around the graphic's outline until it blinks into an arrow. Click there and drag to stretch or shrink it.

If you need to copy only part of something, use **FREEFORM SELECT**. If you hit delete on the keyboard, everything inside the box will be deleted. If your copy is too big to paste onto the screen, delete it, stretch the screen bigger using the tiny handles located at the center of each side. Then paste again.

cont...

IF YOU DO SOMETHING THAT GIVES YOU AN UNEXPECTED BAD RESULT, FREEZE.

Without clicking ANYWHERE on your drawing, move the cursor up to the top of the screen to the word Edit near the top left.

>EDIT and when the drop menu comes down, >UNDO. This will undo the nasty surprise, and you can begin to work again.

But before you begin again, if you like your work up to that point, move your cursor up to File (beside Edit), > SAVE.

Save every time you make a major change that you want to keep, and/or every five minutes. This is a good habit no matter what program you are working in.

Always save before you print or open other programs so nothing will get lost.

The **FILL** tool will fill enclosed spaces with whatever color or pattern you click on in the color box. The area must be totally enclosed or your whole screen will fill. If this happens, >UNDO (see above) before you touch anything else. For this exercise, create a 1" circle (approximately) somewhere on your page with the **ELLIPSE** tool and fill it with **black**.

The **PICK** tool is for choosing colors. Don't use it for this assignment.

The **TEXT** tool is for adding text. Click and drag your cursor across the area where you want the text. You will be asked for font preferences and text size (if the **TEXT TOOLBAR** doesn't appear when you start to make text, >VIEW and click beside the text toolbar to activate it). In some programs, you can only work on a block of text as long as you don't deselect it. If you click anywhere outside the text box while working on the text, that text is finished. To make changes, you'll have to re-create the text. If your text box is opaque and covers a graphic, click on the **TRANSPARENT BOX** in the **MODIFIER**.

The four bottom tools help you create shapes. Use the **RECTANGLE** or **ROUNDED RECTANGLE** tool to make a box around your artwork. Use the **CIRCLE** tool to outline your sphere. Click on the transparent background box in the **MODIFIER** if an opaque box covers your picture. Try different **LINE** weights (change line weight in the **MODIFIER** box), and experiment with the transparent and opaque commands.

Save often, particularly when you reach a satisfactory point. If you make a lot of changes that you have not saved, and suddenly realize it's not what you

freeform select			select
eraser			fill
pick			magnifier
pencil			brush
airbrush		A	text
line			curve
rectangle			polygon
ellipse			rounded rectangle

modifier

wanted, you may be able to go back to the last time you saved it.

In **SOME** programs you can go back to the last place you saved by clicking FILE then NEW: When asked if you want to save your file, >NO and a blank screen will come up. Everything you just did is gone.

Now >FILE. The file you just exited will appear in the drop-down box under "File." Click on it, and your last saved version of that file will open. Now you can start over again. Changes will be faster this time because you'll know just what to do. But **test this before you need to use it**, since the process may be different in your graphics program.

When finished, you should have:

☐(½pt) One printout of the scan of your original drawing (not a halftone), just as you scanned it into the file — before making any changes to it, and

☐(½pt) one printout of the scanned drawing (see p. 102):

☐(1pt) framed in a **box**

☐(2pts) with a title created with the **text tool**

☐(2pts) a black sphere made with the **ellipse tool, filled**, then shaded with the **airbrush tool.**

☐(7pts = 1pt ea.) make changes with:
- **cut & paste**
- **pencil tool**
- **brush tool**
- **airbrush**
- **curve tool**
- **fill tool**
- **erase tool**

☐(1pt) label with the **line** and **text tool** to show where you have used tools to alter or add to the drawing.

☐(1pt) label with your name, date and Ex. 16.

Exercise #17 – Combining Text With Graphics – 15 pts

If you expect to be doing much of anything with respect to reproducing art, you will also need to be capable at combining text and graphics. While there are desktop publishing programs which make the task of combining text and graphics a snap, learning those programs is a rather steep curve. However, you can learn enough to get by in a word processing program. The left column on page 109 shows an example of what your end result for Exercise 17 should look like.

This exercise begins with the assumption that you have worked your way through scanning and computer-altering art in a graphics program. It also requires that you have scanned your Project B artwork and article (or similar materials) into their respective applications.

In the fast-changing world of electronics, computers, new inventions and applications, the following information could become dated very fast. If the instructions below don't cover your application or situation, aim for the end result and do what you need to do to get there.

For this Exercise you need:

1. Your Project B illustration (page 118) scanned into a graphics program as a .tif file.

2. Access to a computer word processing program.

3. Your Project B article (pages 119 and 123) of about 250 words in a .txt or .doc file (or whatever works in the word processing program you will use).

Exercise: Your client has asked for the following:

"SPECS: We need an illustrated article for our quarterly periodical. The article needs to be about 250 wds, and fit in a single colum 3½" wide by 9⅝" high. We would like a computer print-proof of the article/graphic. Please read our specs for complete details." [these may be found on page 120]

1. OPEN THE WORD PROCESSING PROGRAM:

When you have opened a new file, import your 250 word article into the workspace.

☐(2pts) Set text margins to give you a 3½" wide by 9⅝" long column (see example)

2. CHANGE THE PAGE MARGINS:

Switch to **print layout** view. It may look like this.

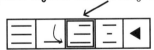

Move the cursor over the right margin boundary on the horizontal ruler (below). When the pointer changes to a double-headed arrow, drag the right margin boundary to 3½ inches.

Don't move the left margin – leave it where it is.

left|margin

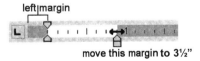

move this margin to 3½"

Your column must be 9⅝" long, so adjust top and bottom page margins in the same way to allow the article to fit on an 11" page (see example on p. 122).

Let's use the article below as an example. It is 248 words, not counting the title and credits. It is totally unformatted, and looks singularly uninteresting. Let's see what happens with a little tweaking. This illustration of a woodrat will be enlarged and given a text-free box to hold text at bay (not overlapping, as shown here).

Woodrats, Traders of the Wild
written and illustrated by Irene Brady

Woodrats, also called "packrats," are found throughout much of the United States. They are quite common in oak woodlands where they build big, volcano-shaped brushpile nests. If they live around cliffs, they cram sticks and twigs into caves or cracks in the rocks. This makes it next to impossible for a hungry coyote or bobcat to dig them out and eat them.

They may also scatter prickly cactus pads around their entrances so predators will get spines in their feet if they try to creep inside.

Most people think "ugh!" when they think of "rats," but woodrats are actually very pretty – like scaled-up deer mice, with soft gray fur, white underparts, and huge, shiny black eyes.

Woodrats are always looking for things to add to their nests. The list of things found in woodrat nests is enormous. There are sticks, of course, and grasses to soften their beds. Bones may show up there, too.

But that's not all. Would you believe socks, alarm clocks, spoons, coins, eyeglasses, matchbooks, compasses, and pocket knives? The list is mostly made up of things people go camping with, because that's usually when people and woodrats make contact. Woodrats especially like shiny things.

Another name for woodrats is "trade rats" because they often leave a stick or something else in return. It's not that Ratty wants to make you feel better about your missing wristwatch. She just doesn't have room to carry off both her stick AND your watch in the same mouthful.

A word processing program is not a very good desktop publishing program because it doesn't offer very many options. But it should work reasonably well for simple layout projects.

A desktop publishing program such as PageMaker, InDesign, Quark, etc., would give you more and better control of text block shape and size. However, the learning curve on such a program can be major, so if you won't be doing much desktop publishing, a word processing program will serve adequately.

3. MAKING THE ARTICLE FIT:

Once you have gotten your text block exactly 3½" wide by exactly 9⅝" long in a column on one page, you can insert a graphic as shown in step 8.

When you do, you'll create an invisible text-free box around the graphic, shaping it to fit the illustration – but a short distance out so that the text won't touch the art, as shown at right – then flowing the text around it. More about this later.

Remember, the text must extend the entire length of the column, but not past the bottom margin. If adding the graphic crowds out some of the text, you will have to find some way to get the text back onto the page. There are several ways to do this. You might:

this outline will not show on the printout

- **change font size**

  keep above 10 points for readability – this is 10 points.

- **move the graphic to change font flow**

  move it so that it falls at the juncture of two paragraphs – the extra room between the lines will help adjust for the graphic size. Try it – it really works. This text is 11 points.

- **change the graphic size until the font fits**

  grab a corner of the graphic with the cursor and drag it to a larger or smaller size. Maintain the proportions.

- **change the margin-width of the text-free box**

  make the margin wide enough that the text doesn't get close to the graphic, or it will appear cramped and crowded.

- **try a different justification or leading**

  a fully justified paragraph usually holds more words than a centered or left-justified one. You can also widen or narrow the space (leading) between lines.

- **change paragraph indent width**

  more words can be crammed into a line with a shorter indentation.

- **edit the article to be shorter or longer**

  as a last resort, you can add or leave out text. This requires great care, so proof it afterward to make sure it still makes sense.

NOTE: Never leave a tiny piece of text, like the last line or few words of a sentence "orphaned" on a page (that's an orphan at the top of this column).

4. FONT OPTIONS:

With a 250-word article, you have some options in the style and size of font you choose, and the leading. The word processing application may be limited on leading options, so other options may work better.

It's usually necessary to tinker with a paragraph to make everything fit. Each option will affect the final appearance of your article differently.

5. CHOOSING A TITLE FONT:

☐ (2pts) Select an interesting font suitable for your article title (see pp. 63–65). To grab the reader's attention, use a font large enough to extend the title to both margins:

Woodrats, Traders of the Wild

Notice how an interesting title font immediately grabs your attention. "Woodrats, Traders" and "Wild" are 30 points, while "of the" is 24 points. If you have options for the leading, you can control how much space that takes, too. The author's name should be next to and under the title, and much smaller, using the title font or the text font (this example is 8 points):

written and illustrated by Irene Brady

With the title and credits out of the way, you are ready to select an appropriate font for the text.

6. CHOOSING A TEXT FONT:

The paramount rule for picking the right font for a block of text is this: ☐(2pts)***The text font must be _easily readable_.*** Review pages 63-65, and 109 for guidelines. Also review your word processor's list of fonts to see which of them look usable.

Select the article text, then click on a font. If it:

- **is readable as a block of text** (in volume, the title font would drive our eyes crazy.) See page 109.
- **matches the subject of the article** (this is a slightly humorous article, so the font may be, too)
- **is a suitable size** (different fonts with the same point size may differ wildly in their letter widths, causing some fonts to take more room. See p. 109)

7. ☐(1pt) ADJUST THE TEXT FONT SIZE:

Unless through some quirk of fate your text fits the column precisely, you'll need to tweak it a bit. Click and drag with the cursor to select the text.

☐(2pts)This article is supposed to be around 250 words, but it can range from 240 to 260. Record the word count (e.g. "247 words") at the bottom of the page. **SAVE.**

A box at the top of the screen displays font size. Start with a 12-point font. After you add the graphic (see #8 below), adjust the font to a size that fits and completely fills the vertical space of the column.

The leading between lines should be at least the height of a lowercase letter. Adjust the font size and graphic size (and its text-free box – see #10 at right) until everything fits.

8. INSERT GRAPHIC:

Import your graphic from whatever file you had placed it. Insert it into the text about where you want it to appear. Click on it to select it, and sizing handles should appear. Grab a **_CORNER_** handle and move it to adjust the graphic's size. Be careful – moving a side or bottom handle may *distort* your picture.

correct   distorted   distorted

☐(1pt)Move the graphic around by clicking on it and dragging it. Keep it within the margins of the article.

9. ☐(4pts) WRAP TEXT AROUND GRAPHIC:

Word processing programs have varying methods of dealing with graphics and text. Learn how your program manages text wrapping. The default is usually a rectangular box at a fixed distance from the image, but a much more graceful look can be achieved by shaping the text flow (see woodrat and its surrounding text on the next page).

10. ☐(1pt) ADJUST SHAPE OF FLOWED TEXT:

The typical instruction is to click on the rectangular box to create edit points, then to drag the points to pull the border into a new shape. The text will flow around the new shape you create. See p. 107. **SAVE.**

*Use the space below to note any instructions or discoveries you make which you might find useful later:*_____

_____

_____

_____

_____

_____

_____

_____

_____

_____

_____

_____

_____

_____

_____

_____

_____

_____

_____

_____

_____

Woodrats, Traders of the Wild

written and illustrated by Irene Brady

Woodrats, also called "packrats," are found throughout much of the United States. They are quite common in oak woodlands where they build big, volcano-shaped brushpile nests. If they live around cliffs, they cram sticks and twigs into caves or cracks in the rocks. This makes it next to impossible for a hungry coyote or bobcat to dig them out and eat them.

They may also scatter prickly cactus pads around their entrances so predators will getspines their feet if they try to creep inside.

Most people think "ugh!" when they think of "rats," but woodrats are actually very pretty – like scaled-up deer mice, with soft gray fur, white underparts, and huge, shiny black eyes.

Woodrats are always looking for things to add to their nests. The list of things found in woodrat nests is enormous. There are sticks, of course, and grasses to soften their beds. Bones may show up there, too.

But that's not all. Would you believe socks, alarm clocks, spoons, coins, eyeglasses, matchbooks, compasses, and pocket knives? The list is mostly made up of things people go camping with, because that's usually when people and woodrats make contact. Woodrats especially like shiny things.

Another name for woodrats is "trade rats" because they often leave a stick or something else in return. It's not that Ratty wants to make you feel better about your missing wristwatch. She just doesn't have room to carry off both her stick AND your watch in the same mouthful.

RESULTS: Your finished layout should look similar to the one at left (but with your font choice). The text font used was Book Antiqua, at 10.7 points and 13.2 leading. Note the differences in the following fonts, all having the same text, font size and formatting. Oddly, the Tinkertoy font doesn't produce quote marks.

Woodrats, also called "packrats," are found throughout much of the United States. They are quite common in oak woodlands where they build big, volcano-shaped brushpile nests. If they live around cliffs, they cram sticks and twigs into
– Book Antiqua

Woodrats, also called packrats, are found throughout much of the United States. They are quite common in oak woodlands where they build big, volcano-shaped brushpile nests. If they live around cliffs, they cram sticks and twigs into
Tinker Toy (the title font)

Woodrats, also called "packrats," are found throughout much of the United States. They are quite common in oak woodlands where they build big, volcano-shaped brushpile nests. If they live around cliffs, they cram sticks and twigs into
– Arial or Helvetica

Woodrats, also called "packrats," are found throughout much of the United States. They are quite common in oak woodlands where they build big, volcano-shaped brushpile nests. If they live around cliffs, they cram sticks and twigs into
– Times Roman

Woodrats, also called "packrats," are found throughout much of the United States. They are quite common in oak woodlands where they build big, volcano-shaped brushpile nests. If they live around cliffs, they cram sticks and twigs into
– Century Gothic

Woodrats, also called "packrats," are found throughout much of the United States. They are quite common in oak woodlands where they build big, volcano-shaped brushpile nests. If they live around cliffs, they cram sticks and twigs into
– Maiandra

Woodrats, also called "packrats," are found throughout much of the United States. They are quite common in oak woodlands where they build big, volcano-shaped brushpile nests. If they live around cliffs, they cram sticks and twigs into
– Verdana

Before & After: Font Choice, Text Flow, Illustration, and Viewer Level

This is an actual newsletter, before and after a make-over. The BEFORE format is *adequate*, but not very compelling. Even at a casual glance, it is clear that the AFTER format, with a more readable font, illustration, text-wrapping, fun-font title and table of contents would probably be more attractive to children and consequently more likely to be read and enjoyed.

before

THE Pacific Explorer

The Pacific Northwest Museum of Natural History Publication
WINTER 1994, Vol. 5, No. 3

by Laurie Red

Museum Winter Hours, November 1 through March 31, 10 AM – 4 PM, closed Christmas Day

Fabulous Fakes
and how they are made

Dear Explorer,

It's really hard to tell the difference between what's real and what's fake in the exhibits at the Pacific Northwest Museum of Natural History. For instance, the Rocky Intertidal Zone was made by artists, but parts of it are actually real. Here's the true story of how the tide pool scene was made.

First, some people from a company called FORMATIONS Inc. went to the Oregon Coast near Newport and took pictures of a rocky Intertidal area. Then they painted a latex coating (like liquid rubber) on the rock surface. While it was still wet, they pressed nylon fabric Into the latex to make it strong. After it dried, they peeled the latex and nylon off the rocks. This became a mold which they brought back to the museum. *You could make a similar mold of something - like an acorn - by just pressing an acorn into some clay that you could harden by baking.*

Using the pictures that were taken as a guide, ACADEMY PRODUCTIONS of Hollywood built a *set* (the base of the exhibit) out of plywood and a steel mesh like chicken-wire. A person with a spray gun sprayed a fiberglass mixture onto the set to cover the wood and wire. Next, plaster, sand and other materials were patted onto it to form the shape of the tide pool. While the final layer of plaster was still wet, the mold made at the coast was pressed onto it to make the realistic looking surface. *If you pressed some soft clay or silly putty into your hard clay acorn mold, the silly putty would come out shaped like the acorn.*

Finally, barnacles, seaweed and other tidepool things were fastened onto the molded surface with glue or wire. The barnacles are fake, made by filling a latex barnacie mold with resin, letting it harden, then removing it from the mold and painting it. But the seaweed is real seaweed which has been dried and dipped in a preservative so that it won't rot or dry out and crumble. It still even smells like seaweed.

When you visit the Museum, take a close look at the other exhibits and see if you can figure out what's real and what's not. □

In This Issue

after

THE Pacific Explorer

The Pacific Northwest Museum of Natural History Publication
for Curious Kids of All Ages WINTER 1995, Vol. 5, No. 3

by Laurie Red
illustrated by Darby Morrell

Fabulous Fakes

It's really hard to tell the difference between what's real and what's fake in the exhibits at the Pacific Northwest Museum of Natural History.

For instance, the Rocky Intertidal Zone was made by artists, but parts of it are actually real. Here's the true story of how the tide pool scene was made.

First, some people from a company called FORMATIONS Inc. went to the Oregon Coast near Newport and took pictures of a rocky intertidal area. Then they painted a latex coating (like liquid rubber) on the rock surface. While it was still wet, they pressed nylon fabric into the latex to make it strong. After it dried, they peeled the latex and nylon off the rocks. This became a mold which they brought back to the museum. *You could make a similar mold -- of an acorn, maybe -- by just pressing an acorn into some clay that you could harden by baking.*

Using the pictures that were taken as a guide, ACADEMY STUDIOS of Novato, California, built a set (the base of the exhibit) out of plywood and a steel mesh like chicken-wire. A person with a spray gun sprayed a fiberglass mixture onto the set to cover the wood and wire. Next, plaster, sand and other materials were patted onto it to form the shape of the tide pool. While the final layer of plaster was still wet, the mold made at the coast was pressed onto it to make the realistic looking surface.

If you pressed some soft clay or silly putty into your hard clay acorn mold, the silly putty would come out shaped like the acorn.

Finally, barnacles, seaweed and other tidepool things were fastened onto the molded surface with glue or wire. The barnacles are *fake*, made by filling a latex barnacle mold with resin, then resetting it harden, then removing it from the mold and painting it *(see above).* But the seaweed is real seaweed which has been dried and dipped in a preservative so that it won't rot or dry out and crumble. It still even smells like seaweed.

When you visit the Museum, take a close look at the other exhibits and see if you can figure out what's real and what's *fake.* □

In This Issue

Magic Tricks with Computer Graphics

You can scan a line drawing into a graphics program, add shading, and turn it into a halftone (see below). It helps to have a pen tool and tablet for this, but it is possible (although difficult) with a regular mouse. Some of the adjustments on this page might not be possible in a basic graphics program.

If you have a heavily shaded (stippled, crosshatched, whatever) line drawing you'd like to turn into a halftone, scan it in, hit it with a blur filter, smudge it in places with a smudge tool, improve some highlights and your halftone art can be ready to go in short order (with a bit of practice).

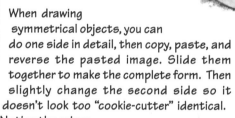

hatching woodducks

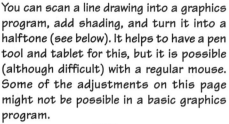

cougar covering scat

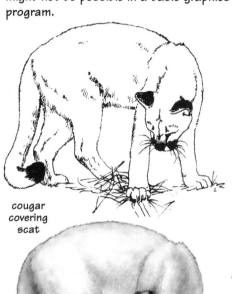

When drawing symmetrical objects, you can do one side in detail, then copy, paste, and reverse the pasted image. Slide them together to make the complete form. Then slightly change the second side so it doesn't look too "cookie-cutter" identical. Notice the minor differences made to the antennae and wings on this butterfly.

spicebush butterfly

In a graphics program you can resize and combine elements from two different drawings, such as reversing and revolving the egg and chick illustrations at left as needed for the new layout below.

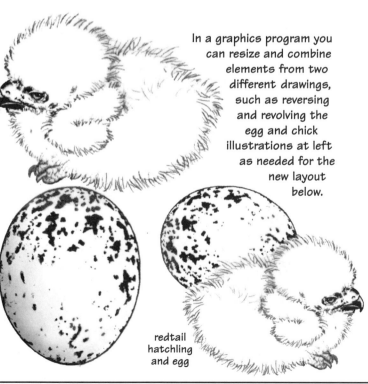

redtail hatchling and egg

Need black/white line art when all you have is a halftone? Heighten the contrast, remove some gray tones manually, and DING! a black and white line drawing in minutes.

pink shrimp

Extra Credit – Grasshopper Graphics File Manipulation – 10pts | (only possible in some graphics applications)

Here's the scenario: You have been hired to create an illustration of a particular kind of grasshopper, but they want it tomorrow — you already created an illustration of this species (below) for someone else, but copyright issues will not allow you to offer the same illustration to the second party.

The client wants a line illustration (not halftone) to show the grasshopper vertically grasping a stem of barley or wheat with all six feet as shown in the rough. This species of grasshopper is about two inches long, so you will only need to show about three to four inches of the barley or wheat.

They want the final printed-out image of the grasshopper to be about □(1pt) 4" high. Your original file is not available, so scan in "your" big illustration below. The final printout should be non-pixely, at about 300 dpi. Use a graphics program which allows variable rotation of _selected parts_ of the image.

□(1pt) In order to avoid copyright problems, change enough of the grasshopper to make it unrecognizable to the original party, but still

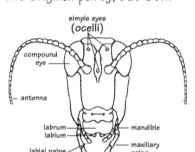

client's rough

like this

the same species. This is actually not an uncommon situation. For guidance, review Chapter 11.

Do not redraw this grasshopper by hand. Make all your manipulations on the image within the graphics program. **You MAY draw the barley or wheat stem off-screen**, scan and paste it into the illustration, or you may draw it on-screen if you can do it well.

Don't make anatomically impossible changes. To avoid that, study resource photos of grasshoppers clutching grass stems. Look online for resources.

Make printouts of the process at three or more pertinent stages, where you have made changes, added or moved things in a major way. Number them in sequence for later reference.

IMPORTANT:
□(1pt) do not change the grasshopper species
□(1pt) remove all signs of text or leaders
□(1pt) research and show the correct wheat or barley
□(1pt) pose grasshopper as the client requested
□(1pt) change the image sufficiently to avoid copyright infringement. This is subjective — you decide.

Suggestion: for starters, change at least seven things, such as reversing, moving legs, curling antennae differently, etcetera.

□(1pt) produce a finished printout AND printouts of the image at three or more stages of the process.

□(1pt) the image must look like an original pen-and-ink illustration, and not show pixels at a casual glance (examine illustration below for allowable pixelization).

□(1pt) write 150+ words describing your process **as you do it**.

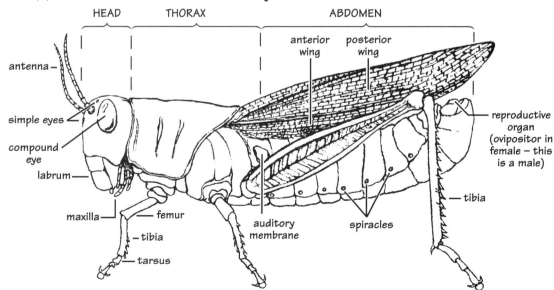

Chapter 13. Final Rendering

The object of this chapter is to increase your skills in correcting problem areas of your illustration. If it doesn't meet the client's criteria in even one area, it is not acceptable. Refer to pages 81–82 and "The Booboo Checklist" on page 84 before beginning improvements.

For this Exercise you need:

1. Project B artwork, critiqued
2. correction tape and/or liquid correction fluid
3. X-acto blade
4. kneaded eraser, white eraser
5. access to electric eraser
6. possibly some paper to make a repair
7. tracing paper and tape for coversheet
8. pen for redrawing

Exercise:

1. ☐(2pts) On a sheet of notebook paper, make a list of the corrections that were suggested by your critiquer/s (as you did with Project A).

2. ☐(2pts) Before making corrections, photocopy the original illustration 1x. Since the art is not a halftone, be careful you do not set the digital photocopier on "halftone" or "photo" when copying.

3. Examine the entire illustration for dead lines that need removal, then go on to errors and blotches.

4. Begin corrections with kneaded and white erasers.

5. If the least-destructive erasers don't work, consider pros and cons of other methods before trying.

6. Test a correction method **off** your illustration first, to determine the best way to do it.

7. Practice in another area until your skills are good enough (or you gain enough confidence) to do it well enough so that your repair won't show. When erasing, don't grind a hole through the paper.

8. The error must be totally removed. When this is accomplished, burnish the area smooth. The bowl of a clean spoon works well, but make sure that the gray patina won't come off on your picture (try it first on another area). Use stainless steel not silver.

9. Redraw any part of the illustration that was lost or removed in the cleanup. If you use liquid or tape whiteout, test before burnishing – tape whiteout may come off; dried liquid whiteout may collect smudges from your burnishing tool.

10. Match the redrawn area of the illustration exactly with the original, with no obvious seam. Use the size and type of pen point needed to give the same appearance to the correction; use the same strokes, and ink in the same direction as in the original drawing.

WORK SLOWLY AND CAREFULLY. DON'T TRY TO RUSH.

11. If the correction fails, you may have to redo that part (not the whole thing) on a different piece of paper and glue it carefully into place. Pick a place where the joining of the new piece onto the old won't be obvious. Redraw the damaged area and glue into place. Connect all lines carefully.

This exercise is about learning how to make good corrections. Do not replace the entire illustration.

12. When you have finished with improvements, the illustration must be:
   ☐(3pts) clean and camera-ready
   ☐(2pts) all problem areas removed or replaced
   ☐(2pts) corrections indistinguishable from the surrounding illustration **when photocopied**
   ☐(1pt) clean coversheet attached at top
   ☐(1pts) with no wrinkles or partial tape, etc.
   ☐(½pt ea = 3pts) On the back are: • date, • name, • address, • phone number, • email address and • the subject's common and scientific names.

13. ☐(4pts) Open **your critiqued Project B article** in the word processor and choose fonts, spacing, etc.

14. Scan and import your **improved art** into the article, flowing the text around the art (see page 109). Make sure the **entire article** fits into the column (leave off the bibliography) and that the facsimile article/art meets all the requirements of "the client" and Project B.

15. Print it out and coversheet the facsimile.

WHERE'S THE PATCH?

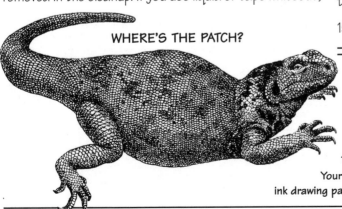

When it was discovered that the scales on the midsection of this chuckwalla were incorrectly rendered, the offending section was "corrected" by redrawing and inking more accurate scales on a piece of high-quality paper, cutting it to shape, and pasting it onto the drawing to cover the original mistake. Then the edges of the patch were carefully inked to join them seamlessly to the drawing. Can you tell where the edges are? Turn the page to see if you guessed right.

Your corrections should be this invisible, too. If your correction on an ink drawing passes the line-art photocopy test, you have succeeded.

Away and Beyond — A Partial Listing of Career Possibilities

SCIENTIFIC ILLUSTRATION IN A UNIVERSITY SETTING, FOR PUBLISHING INSTRUCTORS AND STUDENTS

environmental education, botany, zoology, geology, forestry, anthropology, archaeology, medicine, dentistry, electron microscopy, etc.

ENVIRONMENTAL EDUCATION

college and university outreach programs
elementary school district outdoor education programs
privately-endowed environmental institutes
government-endowed environmental education—national, state, community

ENVIRONMENTAL ACTION and EDUCATION GROUPS

spot art, brochures, flyers, displays (Nature Conservancy, etc.)

NEWSPAPERS AND NEWSLETTERS

environmental reporting and illustration
stringer, free-lance opportunities

MUSEUMS, NATURE AND ENVIRONMENTAL CENTERS, REHABILITATION CENTERS, ZOOS, AQUARIUMS, ETC.

promotional graphics, brochures, advertisements, newsletters
interpretational displays and trail guides
exhibit design
models

MAGAZINE ILLUSTRATION, DESIGN & LAYOUT

adult science and nature magazines (Audubon, Natural History, scientific journals)
children's science and nature magazines (Ranger Rick, Cricket, etc.)
trade magazines with science sections (Time, Newsweek, Discover, etc.)
product catalogs

WILDLIFE ILLUSTRATION, FINE ART

free lance and commissioned, personal or group studio
open-air markets, art fairs and street faires

MEDICINE AND DENTISTRY

facial and other body reconstruction for prosthetics
biomedical sculpture for educational purposes
anatomical models
computerized anatomy

PARKS, REFUGES AND RECREATIONAL AREAS

brochures, trail guides, site displays, etc.

COURTROOM AND FORENSIC MEDICINE

courtroom displays
forensic reconstructions

BOOK ILLUSTRATION, DESIGN & LAYOUT

trade and independent publishers
textbook publishers
specialty publishers

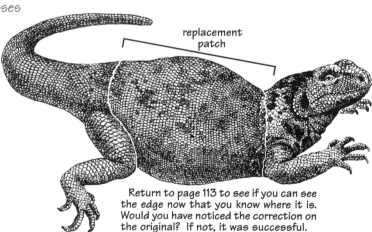

replacement patch

Return to page 113 to see if you can see the edge now that you know where it is. Would you have noticed the correction on the original? If not, it was successful.

FREE-LANCE WHATEVER YOU WANT TO DO

books, magazines, brochures, business cards, posters, field guides, greeting cards, clipart, whatever strikes your fancy. You may even stray from scientific illustration to other more commercially oriented art and design fields. It's always good to have a number of arrows in your quiver.

WEB PAGE ARTWORK AND DESIGN

TEACHING — ALL AGES

OTHER THINGS YOU HAVEN'T EVEN IMAGINED. . . .OR WHICH DON'T EXIST YET. . . .

Appendix I. Projects

Skulls of Carnivorous and Omnivorous Mammals by Irene Brady
showing various styles, techniques and states of enlargement/reduction

Carnivores and Omnivores

Carnivores are meat eaters, with teeth designed for catching and shearing. The molars are pointed and cannot grind food (which is why a dog "wolfs" its food down). Carnivores aren't designed to chew their food up into little bits.

The coyote and red fox represent canid (dog-type) carnivores. The bobcat and domestic cat represent the felids (cats), and the weasel, mink otter and badger are all mustelids (so is a skunk).

Raccoons (none of the above) are omnivores. A raccoon does eat meat, but it also eats many other things — like fruits, seeds, nuts, roots, etc. Its teeth are more generalized, with additional grinding molars to accomodate the omnivorous diet.

Bats may be insectivorous or frugivorous (fruit-eating). The one shown below eats insects and has large, sharp teeth to help it pierce through insect carapaces.

Carnivores have large, long, sharp teeth on the front corners of the upper and lower jaw. These sturdy tools, the canine teeth, are designed to pierce, grab and hold. The rear molars are sharp and jagged, and their main use it to shear off meat pieces so they can be quickly swallowed and carried off in the stomach to be digested later (or regurgitated for young at the den.)

Canids and mustelids have a lot of sharp teeth to help them catch, hold and eat their prey. Felids have fewer sharp teeth, maybe because they have claws to help them catch and hold their food.

weasel

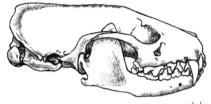

mink

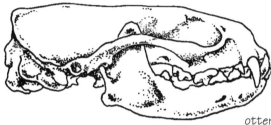

otter

badger

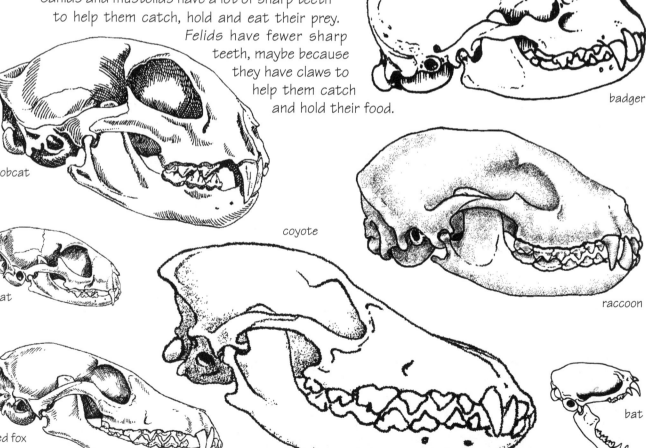

bobcat

cat

coyote

raccoon

red fox

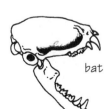

bat

Enlarged too much, this skull becomes very pixelly. See how bad it looks?

Skulls of Herbivorous Mammals by Irene Brady

Can you find the three halftone skulls? All drawings on this page are inked line art. When line art is reproduced as a halftone, its crispness blurs.

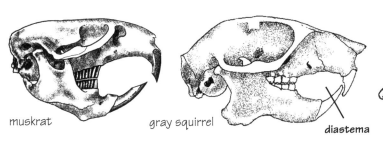

muskrat   gray squirrel

diastema

beaver

Herbivores

Above are skulls of plant-eating herbivores — rodents (muskrat, squirrel and beaver) and below, a *lagomorph* (jackrabbit). The rodents have large front incisors for gnawing woody twigs, and a large *diastema*, the space between the front incisors and the chewing molars. They also have comparatively large areas for muscle attachment on the sides of the lower jaws to power their heavy-duty chewing.

Like the rodents, a jackrabbit at left has a large diastema. Its upper front incisors are smaller, but they are backed up by a second set, peculiar to *lagomorphs*, which brace and strengthen them (see detail at left).

The grazing herbivores below have no upper front incisors. Instead, the tongue and lower teeth press grasses against a leathery plate where the front incisors would be, and pinch them off. Antlers, sported only by buck deer, attach to a disklike pedicel found only on the buck's skull (bottom right).

jackrabbit

second set of front incisors

The difference between antlers and horns can be seen at bottom.

Antlers are shed from the pedicels every year, and new ones grow from the pedicels the following season.

Horns are much different. The core of a horn remains attached to the skull while the horn itself, made of the same material as finger nails and hair, pushes upward from the skull to lengthen the horn. A horn is never shed.

Aside from sexual dimorphism (variation between male and female), notice the differences between the white-tail and mule deer skulls.

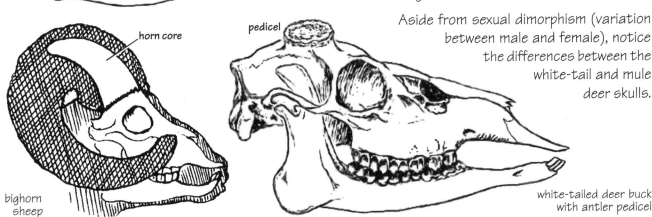

mule deer, doe   domestic sheep

horn core   pedicel

bighorn sheep

white-tailed deer buck with antler pedicel

116

NAME:_____ | **Project A – A Pencil Halftone Biological Illustration – 50 pts**

Use this list to check off steps as you complete the objectives.

Project A is designed to be very similar to a real-life illustration job. It may take you awhile to research and draw, so be sure to allot enough time to complete it without undue stress. If you haven't had much drawing experience, this may look daunting. But taken step by step, you may discover talents you never dreamed you possessed. In scientific illustration, accuracy is the key, so pay attention to details. Be sure to follow instructions exactly.

Proposal for a client ☐(3pts):

A proposal helps you formulate what you plan to do and to determine whether you have chosen an appropriate subject for the assignment and your skill level. It contains:
- your subject
- the medium and tool you plan to execute it in
- any questions you have about it.

At right is a typical proposal for Project A.

Rough ☐(3pts):

A rough need not be perfect – that could waste time since your plan may change when you begin the actual illustration. At right are student rough and finished illustrations for Project A. See p. 139 for more on how to make a rough.

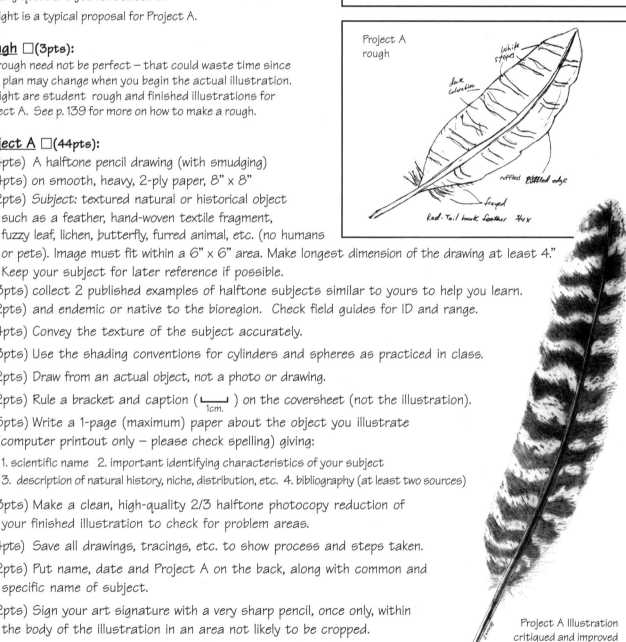

Project A Proposal:

My Project A drawing will be of a red-tail hawk feather, in HB and B lead, with mechanical pencil and smudger.
Robert Sweeney

Project A rough

white stripes
dark coloration
ruffled tattered edge
frayed
Red-Tail hawk feather 3/4 x

Project A Illustration critiqued and improved

Robert Sweeney 2002

Project A ☐(44pts):

☐(4pts) A halftone pencil drawing (with smudging)

☐(4pts) on smooth, heavy, 2-ply paper, 8" x 8"

☐(2pts) Subject: textured natural or historical object such as a feather, hand-woven textile fragment, fuzzy leaf, lichen, butterfly, furred animal, etc. (no humans or pets). Image must fit within a 6" x 6" area. Make longest dimension of the drawing at least 4." Keep your subject for later reference if possible.

☐(3pts) collect 2 published examples of halftone subjects similar to yours to help you learn.

☐(2pts) and endemic or native to the bioregion. Check field guides for ID and range.

☐(4pts) Convey the texture of the subject accurately.

☐(3pts) Use the shading conventions for cylinders and spheres as practiced in class.

☐(2pts) Draw from an actual object, not a photo or drawing.

☐(2pts) Rule a bracket and caption (⌷) on the coversheet (not the illustration).
1cm.

☐(5pts) Write a 1-page (maximum) paper about the object you illustrate (computer printout only – please check spelling) giving:
1. scientific name 2. important identifying characteristics of your subject
3. description of natural history, niche, distribution, etc. 4. bibliography (at least two sources)

☐(3pts) Make a clean, high-quality 2/3 halftone photocopy reduction of your finished illustration to check for problem areas.

☐(4pts) Save all drawings, tracings, etc. to show process and steps taken.

☐(2pts) Put name, date and Project A on the back, along with common and specific name of subject.

☐(2pts) Sign your art signature with a very sharp pencil, once only, within the body of the illustration in an area not likely to be cropped.

☐(2pts) Apply protective tracing paper coversheet, neatly attached at the top only, with tape closers at bottom corners (see page 138).

| Project B – A Biological Illustration Suitable For Publication – 50 pts | NAME:_____

Use this list to check off steps as you complete the objectives.

Project B is a true-to-life line art illustration job for a natural history publication. Your success is measured by how well you meet the stated needs of the publication. Project B also includes researching and writing a short article and a submission letter to accompany the illustration, and creating a facsimile page on computer using your illustration and article, as it would appear in the publication (Ch. 12). Study pages 118-124 in depth before beginning Project B.

Proposal for a client ☐(2pts):

- choose a subject appropriate to your skill level.
- use pen and ink, either flexible or mechanical pen.
- pen/ink shading must be stippled.
- you may attempt a faux pen & ink (pages 44-45), **but the illustration will not be acceptable if it reveals any clues of its pencil/photocopy origin.**

Rough ☐(3pts): See page 117. Indicate the medium.

Project B ☐(45 pts): *(READ DETAILS ON PAGES 119-120)*

At right are student examples of Project B.

☐(6pts) Create a clean illustration, ready for publication.

☐(3pts) Do artwork 150% of its proposed published size (see page 122).

☐(4pts) Subject: a wild plant or animal (mammal, bird, reptile, insect, etc.) native to the area, and posed against a natural background.

☐(3pts) Work from at least four photos or personal sketching sources (not other peoples' art), and a stipple example by another artist (not from this book). Keep all drawings and tracings used to create the illustration together with the illustration.

☐(3pts) Do art on heavy, smooth 2-ply paper, 1" margins. Maximum paper width or height 10," minimum 8." For horizontal subjects, maximum paper size is 8" x 13."

☐(5pts) Follow the publication's format and instructions for artwork exactly.

☐(3pts) Lightly print your name, date, address, phone, email, common & scientific name, and "Project B" on the back.

☐(1pt) Ink your artist signature within the body of the illustration.

☐(2pts) Apply protective coversheet, appropriately attached (see page 138).

☐(4pts) Write a 250 word article about your subject suitable for use in the proposed publication (see pages 119 and 123).

☐(4pts) The article about the illustrated subject must match the publication's style, and include:
- scientific and common name of subject
- important identifying characteristics,
- description of natural history, including niche, distribution, surrounding habitat, etc.
- bibliography (2 sources minimum, at least one NOT from the Internet).

☐(2pts) Write a submission letter to the publication to accompany the illustration and article (see page 124).

☐(2pts) Make a clean, presentation-quality 2/3 reduced photocopy of the art.

☐(3pts) Using your article and art, create a facsimile page using word processor and graphics program.

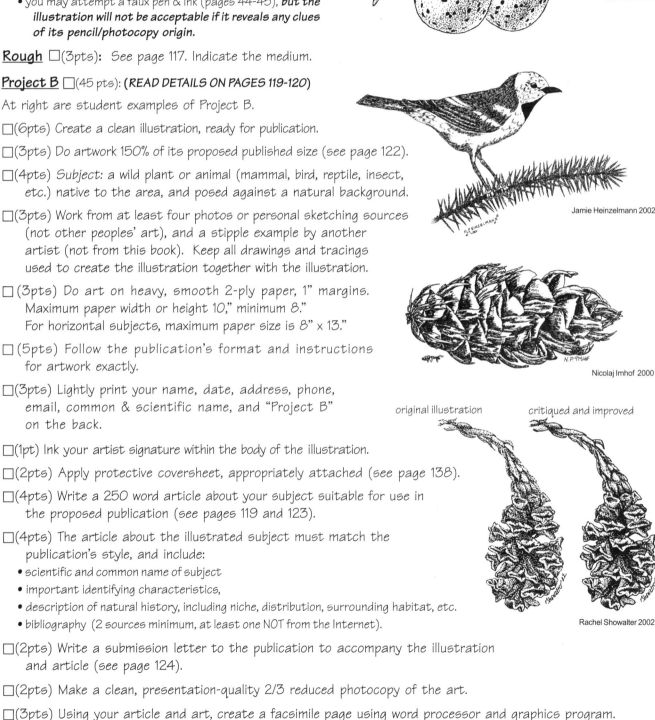

Lin Roden 2001

Jamie Heinzelmann 2002

Nicolaj Imhof 2000

original illustration   critiqued and improved

Rachel Showalter 2002

NAME:_____

Read this and the next page carefully before beginning Project B.

The Illustration:

• Create an illustration at 150% of its published size on a heavy, smooth paper 10" maximum, 8" minimum width or height, (13" for horizontal illustration) and suitable for publication in a specified periodical. When reduced, it must fit, with the article you write, into one column on that periodical's page.

OR...A mainly horizontal subject, such as a lizard, may not exceed the width of two columns, and must be situated across the **bottom** of the two columns.

• Art must meet the format and artwork requirements for the periodical exactly.

• Do not design your illustration directly on the surface upon which you plan to do the finished illustration. Do not do the final illustration on tracing paper.

• Correctly position your art signature.

• Attach a protective tracing paper coversheet.

• Indicate scale with a bracket and the "cm." measurement on the coversheet (not on the artwork).

• On the back of the illustration include: name, address, email, phone number, date, illustrated object's common & scientific name, "Project B."

The Resource Materials:

• Save drawings/tracings used to create the art.

• Photocopy any photographs, sketches and the stippled illustration by another artist that you used as resource materials. Note the parts you referenced, staple them together and save them with the drawings and tracings.

• Use your sketches from actual objects or photo resources whenever possible – they can be your most  important resource. Use at least four photos (or sketches _you_ have made) as references.

The Article:

• write an article (250 words in a word processing program) about the subject you illustrated. Techniques for doing this successfully are covered in Chapter 12.

The Article: cont...

• write in a style similar to the selected journal's style.

• include scientific and common names.

• include important identifying characteristics.

• describe natural history, niche, distribution, etc.

• attach a bibliography containing at least two sources, at least one NOT from the Internet.

The Computer Mockup:

• As practiced in Chapter 12, create a computer mockup of the periodical page, using your article and art the actual size it would appear in the periodical.

The result should resemble the **left-hand column** on page 109.

The Submission Letter:

• Write a submission letter to the journal to accompany the illustration and article. Follow the Business Letter Example on page 124 closely.

• The letter must be computer-generated.

• Start everything flush with the left margin.

• Address it to the periodical, and to an individual if you know the the name of the right person.

• Begin with a salutation "Dear (fill in correct name):" then write the body of the letter.

• Be brief and businesslike, stating what is enclosed and why. Compliment the journal on its looks and mission. Say you hope they can use your work. Tell them where to contact you for future assignments.

Note: Do not sound apologetic or over-modest; don't offer (even if true) that you are thus far unpublished. Sound competent but not egotistical.

• Follow with the closing "Sincerely" ("Sincerely yours" is slightly more formal), space down about an inch to make room for your handwritten signature. Insert your full name (and title if indicated).

• After your name, on the left margin, insert the following: "Encl. (2): One illustration of (insert name of subject)" and "One article about (insert article subject)." These two enclosures are the artwork and the article printout, as shown on p. 124.

• Sign the letter with your real signature (not your artist signature) in the space above your name.

Solution to the puzzle on page 38. Squint if you still can't see what the subject is.

Hills & Streams
A Journal of Natural History for the State of Jefferson-Montane Region

Submission Guidelines

Focus: all aspects of natural history in the Jefferson-Montane region, including: flora, fauna, geology, scenery, and local Native American lifeways.

At this time we are looking for accurate representations, not cartoon, fanciful or diagrammatical art (unless otherwise specified).

Please note that all submissions to Hills & Streams are non-stipend (nonpaying).

General subjects for Hills & Streams include:

- field sketches of plants and animals in their actual habitat, not floating
- formal illustrations of flora and fauna characteristic of the region
- field sketch pages & notes, attractively arranged on one page
- local prehistoric artifacts (pottery, projectile points, clothing, etc.)

Line Art Requirements:

- media: pen and ink, scratchboard, or other line art techniques **(no halftones)**
- size: artwork to be submitted 150% of printed size
- illustrations must be one vertical column width (one-column size is 3½" wide x 9 ⅝" high) or no more than two columns wide if horizontal. Measure width of sample page (on page 122).
- height variable, but no illustrations wider than one column width will be accepted except in the case of typically horizontal subjects (snake, lizard) which may extend across both columns within the outside margins, and only at the bottom of the page.

Artist's signature:

- signature must be clear, large and crisp enough to reproduce clearly.
- signature size must not overwhelm artwork.
- illegible or too-large signatures will be removed because they detract from the illustration.

Captions:

- identify all subjects on the back of the illustration, with correct spelling (common name, genus and species names are required for flora and fauna)
- scale bracket shall be ruled and labeled on the coversheet, not on the art, with scale notation (2x, ¼x, etc.) or metric measurements.

Identification:

- artwork must be clearly marked on the back with artist's name, address, telephone number, e-mail if any, date, subject identification, and any other information important for writing a caption AND the return of the artwork.

A Collage of Tear Sheets of Student Art which Appeared in an Off-Campus Periodical
(a tear sheet is an actual page or clipping removed from the printed publication)

Of the Klamath-Siskiyou's ten species of
orn-producing plants, it appears so far that
oak and California black oak are the ones

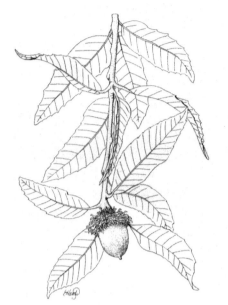

Tanoak
by Heidi Soroken
Mountains & Rivers
Fall 2001

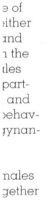

Yellow-breasted Chat
by Andrea Fraga
Mountains & Rivers
Spring/Summer 2002

about programs and volunteer opportunities with the
Klamath Bird Observatory, see their website at
www.klamathbird.org.

Yellow-breasted chat
(Icteria virens auricollis)

*"When the
bird and the
book disagree,
always believe the bird."*
James Audubon

Feather
by Wendy Olson
Mountains & Rivers
Spring 2001

Mortar & Pestle
by Matt Paroulek
Mountains & Rivers
Spring/Summer 2002

ably from season to
constant, as long as
tured and burned or
ance against starvat

e related lineage of breeding
ers or a father and his sons),
e of
either
nd
n the
les
part-
and
behav-
ynan-

nales
gether
d the
s
n
ers,
s
e the
ings,
l
ting is
cies of
ding
rood-

Acorn Woodpecker
by Peter Schroeder
Mountains & Rivers
Fall 2001

ing and enjoy what remains of this beautiful
season of change. 🍂

-- Evan Frost

Oregon White Oak
by Vera Kirkpatrick
Mountains & Rivers
Fall 2001

The image on the cover is an oil painting
by Teresa Stark Giacomini entitled "Two

A Treasure of Triads

by Noelle Jordan

As winter days grow longer and winds become gentler, those who hike the moist woods await the coming the Western Trillium (*Trillium ovatum*). When these large, white flowers are in full bloom, rest assured, spring is here.

Also called Wake-Robin or White Trillium, this member of the Lily Family is commonly found in mesic forests from western Canada south to Colorado, throughout the Cascade Range in Oregon and in the California Coast Range as far as Monterey County.

The name trillium is a reflection of the plant's morphology – three leaves, three sepals, three petals, and a three-parted stigma. The six stamens echo the theme in a multiple of three.

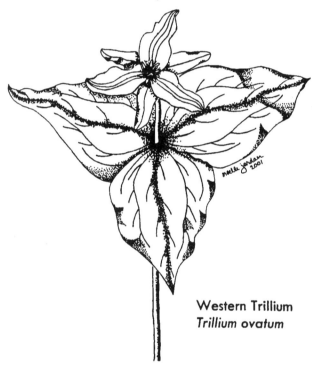

Western Trillium
Trillium ovatum

Several different beetle species, bumble bees, and honey bees ensure that pollination occurs, producing up to 150 seeds. After the seeds mature, they are dispersed by ants and yellow jackets. Trillium has devised an ingenious incentive for dispersers: each seed has an oil-rich food body attached. The ants and yellow jackets eat the food-body after delivering the seed to a new area, doing the plant a favor and being rewarded at the same time.

This spring, keep your eyes open for this showy wildflower, but remember – take only pictures and leave only footprints.

Poetry

in a redrock canyon

In this narrow canyon, vertical and red,
I slowly come to know
that I am of no account –
   of less use than a flowering buckbrush
      less use than a small red stone that holds
         the soil in place awhile.

I only am two ears to hear the sighing wind
   the tittering swifts,
      the thunder growl.
I only am two eyes to see the towering walls
   of ancient dunes crossbedded now for far
      too long to count.
I only am a nose to breathe the incense, past
   the amber bee-wing blur, of
      honey-scented Berberis flowers.

I only am a questing mind to wonder
   at this most incredible and
      boundless muchness:
            red beyónd red
            time beyónd time
            air beyónd pure
            sun beyónd infinity
         and know that in this endlessness
      beyond all being
I am just a tiny pulse
of no account
on any scale –
and knowing this
I feel exaulted
to be
barely
anything
at all.

Irene Brady
Talent, Oregon

Writing An Article – Some Ground Rules

Writing a good paper or article is an important element in communicating with your audience. The following guidelines can be applied to any writing project. In writing the article for Project B, use the following guidelines:

1. The 250 wd. article should have at least two bibliography entries, closely related to the subject. Any on-line reference should contain a complete web address, and should give the title of the web page.

2. Be consistent in your reference terms – pronouns and plurals must agree: i.e. If you choose to write "they, them, their," etc. in the initial sentences, do not change to "it, its, and it's" in later sentences in the piece. Maintain a constant reference throughout the piece both within sentences and between all paragraphs in the piece. Below, the sentences in paragraph **a.** are inconsistent. References which **should** agree have been placed in bold italics:

---

a. The acorn *woodpecker pokes acorns* into holes which *it drills* into ponderosa pines. The **acorn fits** exactly into the **hole** <u>he</u> **excavates. They retrieve their** acorns later when **they** can't find other food.

Correctly written, it could read either of two different ways:

b. The acorn *woodpecker pokes* <u>acorns</u> into holes which *it drills* into ponderosa pines. The <u>**acorns fit**</u> exactly into the **holes it excavates.** **It retrieves its** acorns later when **it** can't find other food.

OR

c. Acorn *woodpeckers poke acorns* into holes which **they drill** into ponderosa pines. The **acorns fit** exactly into the **holes they excavate. They retrieve their** acorns later when **they** can't find other food.

Use the pronoun "he" or "she" only when referring to a known individual, as in "**he** is my parrot, Joe," or an individual of a specific gender, as in "**he** knows when the female is receptive".

You'll notice the word "acorn" was changed to "acorns" because the beginning sentence refers to holes, and it take more than one acorn to fit into more than one hole. Additionally, several woodpeckers won't excavate the same hole (although they may enlarge it), so the correct form is "holes" not "hole."

This concept may sound complex, but if you read your paper through with pronoun and plural agreement in mind, it should become clear very quickly. Use this concept in every paper you write.

3. Scientific names, called "specific names," are italicized. They are underlined only if you cannot italicize them (as when writing by hand). The initial letter of the *genus* name is capitalized, but not the initial letter of the *species* name, e.g. *Lynx <u>rufus</u>*. Written by hand, <u>*Lynx rufus*</u>, is underlined because italic handwriting is not recognizable as such.

Your article for publication must be produced with a word processing program. Handwritten articles are not acceptable for submission.

4. If you illustrate only part of an entity, your article should be mostly about what you illustrate.

For instance, an illustration of a fir cone would concern that cone's structure, with only a passing reference to the fir tree. If you illustrate a pheasant feather, your subject is that feather, with only a short reference to the type of pheasant. There are many ways to make a good article about a feather: where it grows on the bird, uses of the feather (flight, warmth, etc.), the parts of a feather, types of coloration (iridescence, ultraviolet function, etc.), utility of markings, any recent research done on feathers, etc.

You might even refer to its human uses, such as fly-tying.

Make it interesting!

5. Try to aim your style, content and reading level to fit your audience. Look up the Flesch-Kincaid Reading Level guide online and use it.

The Wall Street Journal is written for a 6th grade reading level.

If you have time, try out your finished article/ illustration on someone of the appropriate age and education level.

Barred Owl Feather
Strix varia
2003
Bianca Tapia

Project B Business Letter Example

Below is a reduced facsimile of a well-written business letter showing the way it should be formatted and the information it should contain. It was created by a student on an 8½" x 11" sheet. One-inch margins all around are minimum. Use a 10- or 12-point font. Use this same format for an email business letter, but don't worry about the margins in an e-mail.

While an e-mail does not require a written signature, a mailed or hand-delivered business letter always does. Sign it between the words "Sincerely" and your typed name (about four spaces or "enters" – roughly ¾"–1").

There are several acceptable business letter formats, but the easiest to remember is this one, in which everything butts up against the left margin. A longer letter can be continued on the back of the sheet, but beware of "orphans" (bits of text alone at the top of a column or page) and "widows" (bits of text abandoned at the bottom of a column or page). A single, one-sided one-page letter is ideal in today's busy world.

Use this format for a formal business letter any time you want to make a good impression.

More details about business letter requirements for Project B are outlined on page 119. Follow those instructions.

More details about business letter requirements for Project B are outlined on page 119. Follow those instructions.

Jan Phillips
171 Wightman Street
Ashland, OR 97520

March 15, 2057

Mr. John Doe
Hills & Streams
55 5th Street
Science City, UV 55555

Dear Mr. Doe,

Enclosed is a pen and ink drawing of a Western Trillium (*Trillium ovatum*) for possible publication in the spring issue of Hills & Streams. I am aware that your organization does not provide payment for artwork submissions, and that you are constantly reviewing artwork from many sources, but I would be delighted if you can use my work.

Hills & Streams is a quality journal, and I am pleased that it is published by a local organization. The articles are creative, informative and pertinent to the beautiful wildlands that surround us here. It would be an honor to be associated with a journal of such regional importance.

If you are interested in using this drawing, or would like to contact me for future assignments, I can be reached at 555-555-5555, or you can contact me via email at janp@students.oou.edu.

Sincerely, (or Sincerely yours,)

Jan Phillips

Encl. (2): *One illustration of a western trillium (Trillium ovatum)*
One article about the western trillium

APPENDIX I. PROJECTS

Project C (<u>for advanced students only</u>) – A Comparative Illustration – 50 pts

Project C is designed to fulfill the requirements and expand the horizons of the advanced student. The project includes a comparison drawing of two or three similar items, simulating a real-life assignment from a professor of one of the sciences asking a student to illustrate his/her article in a periodical. This project will bring into play the information you have learned about objective observation, right-brain techniques and other aspects of scientific illustration. Project C should not be started until after Chapter 4 has been completed. This project requires a critique before the final cleanup.

For Project C you will illustrate two or more similar specimens, using an art technique that best shows their characteristics, in a manner that clearly illustrates their differences. Many publications require line art, so research carefully. Choose a scholarly or natural history journal, using their art specifications. This illustration may be drawn from specimens, photos, or combinations of these. If you have questions, see Projects A and B, and see the examples on page 126. Make the illustration 150% of the size you would expect it to appear in the periodical.

Write a 250-word minimum paper describing the variation between the specimens and detailing the processes used during the illustrating process to try to get the effects you wanted. Write a summation paragraph explaining either why you are satisfied with your results, or what you would do differently if you had time and the inclination to re-do it. Be planning this paper as you illustrate, as this will trigger thought processes that will help you throughout the project.

<u>Proposal</u> ☐**(2pts):** Write a very specific proposal stating what you plan to accomplish. Describe the intended medium/technique fully. Page 126 shows good Project C examples. Only two subjects are actually *required*.

<u>Rough</u> ☐**(3pts):** Follow instructions for the Project A rough, but show how the subjects will be oriented to showcase their differences. In your rough, indicate with arrows and notes the comparisons being made between the subjects.

<u>Project C</u> ☐**(45pts):**

☐(10pts) Create a clean illustration, ready for publication, with all blemishes and errors completely erased, scraped away, patched, or treated with whiteout, making the correction invisible when photocopied.

☐(3pts) For this project, make artwork about 8" at its widest or highest dimension.

☐(5pts) Choose a view and rendering techniques which clearly highlight the differences between the subjects. Take care to clearly compare those differences, placing all subjects in *exactly* the same pose and orientation.

☐(3pts) Do art on heavy, smooth 2-ply paper, with 1" margins. Maximum paper width or height 10."

☐(5pts) Follow the periodical's format and instructions for artwork exactly. Avoid backgrounds if possible.

☐(1pt) Sign the art within the body of the illustration.

☐(2pts) Apply a protective coversheet as shown on page 138.

☐(3pts) On the back of the illustration, lightly put your name, date, address, phone number, email address, the scientific and common names of the subjects, the scale of the subjects, and "Project C."

☐(7pts) Write a 250-word (minimum) paper as outlined above. The paper must include:
- the scientific and common names of all the subjects
- all important identifying characteristics, and comments about the comparison
- an observation or hypothesis about the significance of the differences (think about this while working on it)
- a summation paragraph as outlined above
- a bibliography (3 sources minimum, only one of which may be from the Internet)

Try to show evidence of **insightful and keen personal observations** in your paper and summary.

☐(3pts) Collect and keep with the illustration photos and/or photocopies of all resources used, with each source clearly indicated. Preserve any actual objects illustrated. Also save all drawings and tracings used to create the illustration. These resources will be invaluable for later reference while making changes or improvements.

☐(3pts) Make a clean, high-quality photocopy of the art, reduced to 2/3 its original size to show it as it will be printed in the journal. Make changes and improvements to the original until you can achieve a quality photocopy of publishable quality. This photocopy is the equivalent of the plate that will be made for reproduction from your work by the printer, so the less touch-up it requires by a third party, the better your printed results are likely to be. Don't take chances on someone else's judgment or artistic capabilities.

Project C Comparative Illustrations

Red Fir / White Fir

The fir cone comparisons at right are a good example of a student rendering for Project C. Notice that the cones are drawn in identical views and in their actual relative sizes to make comparison easier. The differences in needle size, curvature and growth habit are clearly shown.

This cone illustration would be suitable for use in a field guide or any other publication used in identifying trees and cones. With these drawings, the viewer would be able to compare cones in the hand and make a decision as to their identification.

The coversheets for this illustration and the illustration below showed brackets with measurements, and identified the species.

This illustration was accepted for inclusion in a publication.

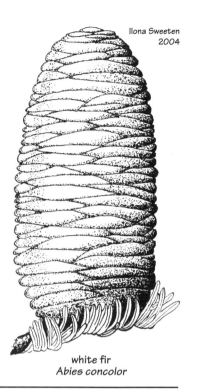

Ilona Sweeten
2004

red fir
Abies magnifica

white fir
Abies concolor

Bullfrog / Spotted Frog

spotted frog
Rana pretiosa

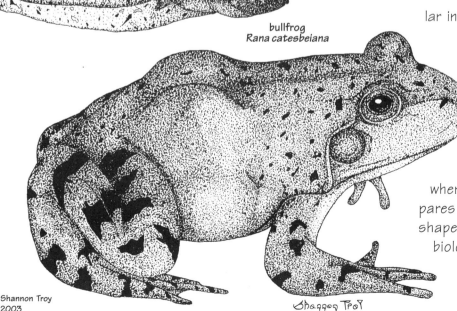

bullfrog
Rana catesbeiana

Shannon Troy
2003

These frog comparisons are also a good example of a student rendering for Project C. The illustration compares the physiology of adults and tadpoles of the spotted frog and bullfrog.

This comparison is of particular interest since the bullfrog is an alien intruder in many Western ponds, taking over the habitat and crowding out native species, such as the spotted frog, which would normally live there. This guide could help biologists identify bullfrogs in ponds where they don't belong. It compares sizes, markings, and general shape, useful things to know to a biologist charged with trying to restore a pond to equilibrium.

The illustration was accepted for inclusion in a publication.

Appendix II. Field Sketchbook & Portfolio

A good field sketchbook is small enough to carry easily – 5" x 8" is ideal – is unlined and spiral bound to open up and fold back on itself, and has a pencil and eraser attached. Sketching is instant entertainment and extraordinarily rewarding.

WHAT TO SKETCH IN A FIELD SKETCHBOOK:

Sequences: Examine plant development, animals courting, insect life cycles, plant successions, etc.

Large sites: Become familiar with a specific place (your yard, a mountain) and note what happens during a season, or on the same date throughout the years. As a rule, focus on details, not scenery.

Small sites: Study a 1-meter plot. How many different plants and insects live there? What's happening now? What happens over a space of time? Who eats what? Who eats whom? Sketch and take notes.

Comparisons: How many kinds of plants can you find in a given area? How are they the same or different? Compare what lives on them. Compare how they propagate. What else can you discover and compare?

Details: Choose an item and sketch it broadly. Now sketch it again in more detail. Take it apart if possible and sketch the parts. Draw close-ups. How are parts attached? What is special about this species?

Time of day: What is happening at one particular time of day? What changes as the day passes? What flowers are blooming? What birds are singing or active, and what are they doing? What about lizards? Insects? Mammals? Sketch!

Rehab center, museum, zoo, or arboretum: This may be the only way to sketch some subjects. Sketch movements, phases, growth habits, fruits, activities like eating, scratching, grooming, courting, etc.

Roadkills: Most wildlife is shy and difficult to sketch, but details can be easily seen on a roadkill (see pages 55, 93 and 96). No need to touch – move it with a stick or rubber gloves to a better place for sketching.

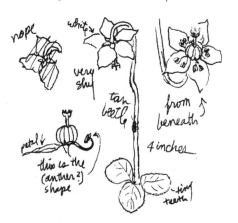

> ### ON UPPER RIGHT CORNER OF EACH RIGHT-HAND PAGE:
>
> Your name, date, location, weather, time of day, observations like bird songs, drought conditions, leaves turning color, habitat, etc. Do not sketch on both sides of pages. If avoidable, do not turn the book sideways to sketch.

MAKE SPECIFIC NOTES TO GO WITH SKETCHES: such as the color of a bird's beak, length of an antenna, scale (1x = same size. Estimate or measure). You may record size as inches or centimeters. Note color gradation on a flower petal, fuzziness of a seedpod, behavior of a subject, comparisons, observations, questions – whatever you notice.

PLAN AHEAD: Decide what you might draw, then plan where to put it on the paper. Your first strokes are most important – start too large and you'll go off the paper (can you do the missing part as a detail elsewhere?). If you draw too small, you'll need to make enlarged details. Make written notes a part of the design. Write neatly enough that you can read it later.

BE ACCURATE: Don't spend your sketching time looking through guide books. If a subject interests you, draw it with enough detail to allow identification later. On the sketch (below left), I later confirmed identification of the One-flowered Moneses, *Moneses uniflora*, by the beetle crawling up the stem – unlike most flowers, it's pollinated by beetles. If you have only a pen, don't be too timid to use it. If you make a mistake while sketching in ink, start over. (Note the false start in upper corner of ink sketch at left.)

LOOK A LOT: Spend as much time looking as drawing. Glance at your subject every five seconds or so. If there's no opportunity to draw, study the details and draw from memory at the first opportunity.

LEARN SOMETHING: If you don't learn something from your sketch, you probably aren't being curious enough. Make notes on your sketch about the things you learn.

ENJOY: You surely won't have a chance to sketch daily – just do it when the urge strikes, or if you're stuck someplace with nothing more urgent to do. The more you draw, the more proficient you will become at putting your visual notes down on paper.

Field Sketchbook – Student Example

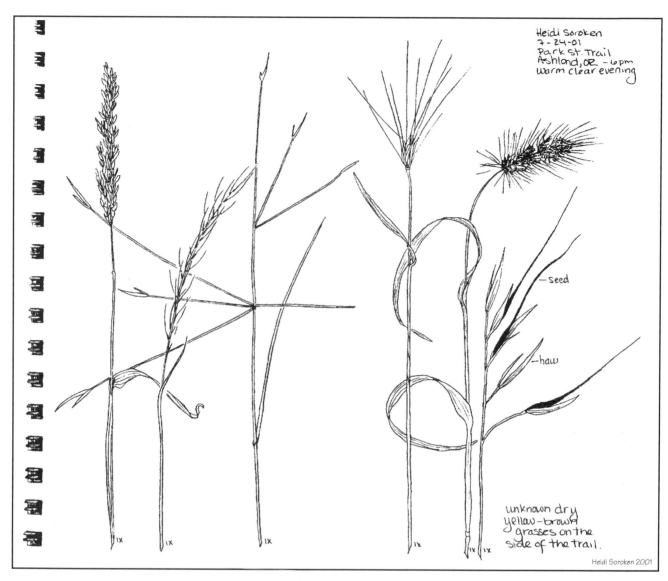

Heidi Soroken
7-24-01
Park St. Trail
Ashland, OR – 6 pm
warm clear evening

—seed

—haw

unknown dry
yellow-brown
grasses on the
side of the trail.

Heidi Soroken 2001

A good newspaper article, according to the newspaper reporter's credo, contains the answers to The Five W's – "Who, Where, What, When, & Why." Add "How" ("Wow"?) to that list, just to hit all the bases.

If you consider those questions as you sketch, you will discover much more than if you are just drawing shapes. Your curiosity will be piqued, and you will experience a far more interesting encounter with your subject than you may have anticipated.

Consider the grass drawings above. How many times have you walked past (and totally ignored) a clump or stalk of grass? What if you had taken as close a look as Heidi did? Try it and see what discoveries you can uncover. That's the hidden reward a non-sketcher will never encounter. Such riches!

But what about the "W's"?

Consider.....**Who** is living on that plant? **Who** eats it? **Who** uses it as a nest? **Where** did you find it? **What** caused it to grow there? **When** does it bloom (or visit the area, or have young, etc.). **How** did it do that? And **WHY**? The "WHY" is the kicker. That is what science is all about. Few answers are found without asking "**Why**?" And all those other questions, too.

The purpose of a sketchbook page is to learn and to teach. If you are drawing for yourself only, you are still learning and teaching yourself. When you return to your sketchbook months or years later, you may be astonished at what you did, what you recorded, what you asked and what you learned.

If you ever share your sketches with other people, you will introduce them, also, to the wonders you encountered. That's good for the environment and the earth – a good enough reason for anyone.

A page from a 4-Holes Swamp sketchbook

Here's a page of field sketches from a practicing naturalist's sketchbook, warts and all. When you see published "naturalist's sketchbooks" (and there are several excellent ones available) don't be misled into thinking the pages started out looking the way they do in the published books!

Sometimes a sketchpage done "on location" does turn out perfectly, but the format usually falls prey to the excitement of the sketching moment. Notes are scribbly and sometimes illegible, sketches may be just a little bit sketchier than one might like, or the drawing is inaccurate, requiring notes that say things like "shorter than this."

Since this page was originally done in ballpoint pen (a major oversight when heading out the door) there was no choice of erasing, and booboos are right out there in plain sight. The two butterflies originally "malted" in the shrub, and the hawks' heavily barred tails started out being "barded" — which may be halfway between banded and barred. Who knows how the brain works when we take quick notes!

The "ichneumon" insertion was added later when the wasp was identified in a field guide. But one could seem a lot wiser (and tidier) by hiding the fact that it was an afterthought.

The page has no name or date, making possible problems if it becomes detached from the rest of the sketchbook. And it might someday be useful to know that it was sketched near the canoe launch at 4-Holes Swamp (in the Beidler Forest Audubon Sanctuary) in South Carolina on a warm, sunny day in late March, just after a rain.

1:06 p.m. I may have spotted a hawk nest. I've been hearing them call: "Eee yughk! Eee yughk!", two of them back & forth in the trees across the lake, then the two came together on a tree across the way, with a broken crotch, one left & the other stayed & seemed to settle down. Heavily barred tails, reddish heads, hard to i.d. properly, medium size, maybe slightly smaller than redtails. —Yeah! Barb says they're red-shouldered hawks!

tufted titmice overhead. "tut-tut-few, tut-tut-few"

out in the sunny grass — a white butterfly about 1½"

orange
white
½"

2:15 p.m. then, 3 black waltzing swallowtails, fluttering, circling, one flew away, two fluttered into a shrub & mated.

longer & higher
2½-3"
more like this

ichneumon.
wow! I just saw this huge wasp (yellow, red & brown) inserting its eggs into a rotten log! When it was done, it stood on its head with abdomen straight up & pulled until it freed its ovipositor, (3-part) then pulsed until it had slacked down to a single 3" tail, and flew away. I sketched from @ 12" away — no more than 3 minutes total, but I don't know how long it had been laying.

Try to get it right the first time, but if you meet with obstacles don't let them paralyze you. Just go out and sketch! (To see how this sketch looks when "cleaned up" a bit, turn to page 60.)

Field Sketching Strategies

WHY SKETCH?

A field sketchbook may serve a number of purposes: from simple pleasure, to personal improvement, to basic research. Whatever your reasons, take pride in doing it as well as possible.

Since we never know the eventual fate of a sketch page and its accompanying notes, it may turn out to have been important to take the time and effort to do it well – in your choices of subject, the answers you sought, the information you noted, and the care you took in observing and recording your subject, both visually and in your notes.

Who knows? Your field sketchbook could some-day be the basis for an article you write, or it could serve as the only baseline study for some obscure but important species.

Certainly it is a tool you can use to better understand this world and share the knowledge you gain. Take this responsibility seriously. It could be one of the most important things you ever do.

MAKE ACCURATE OBSERVATIONS:

Observe carefully, then sketch and note what you see as accurately as you can. Check details with your magnifying glass. Draw close-ups, then details of your close-ups.

MAKE, IN-DEPTH, LEGIBLE NOTES AND CAREFUL I.D.S:

Write what you know, question what you don't, and most important, don't draw something you can't see properly. Don't make assumptions. For instance, every "cone" isn't a "pine cone" – it may be a spruce, redwood, or cedar cone. So unless you are certain of its identity, instead of "pine cone," only write "cone."

Research and add clarification later if you aren't sure about something. Use specific names when you know them, common names otherwise. If you don't know any name, describe the item or make a guess, followed by a "?". Write neatly for others (not just yourself) to read without confusion.

For more information about notes – how much to write and about what, read page 131.

INDICATE SCALE:

Include an accurate scale next to each view. Use the 1x style, or brackets, as shown here, to relate the size of the original to your sketch. ⊢——⊣
5"

PLAN ATTRACTIVE PAGES:

When possible, plan attractive pages with ½" margins. They will look more professional, be a pleasure to read, and the open 8"x 5" sketchbook will photocopy with maximum ease on 8½" x 11" paper.

USE CLARIFYING PERSPECTIVE TECHNIQUES:

Break any lines that pass behind others, lighten distant lines, reduce size with distance to establish perspective. Lessen details in more distant areas. Review page 27 for more information.

DEVELOP CONSISTENT, APPROPRIATE LINE WEIGHT:

Put simply, your drawings should be tidy and reproducible with little touch-up and no major loss of visual information. A good line-weight is clear, but erasable if necessary. Avoid multiple, sketchy "try lines." You will just have to erase them later for the sake of clarity, and this can greatly complicate drawing.

How do you know what line weight to aim for? Photocopy a page of your sketchbook at a setting that retains all the lines but doesn't fill in the background with gray. If you draw so that the lines are clear but no background appears, you have the right line weight. For more details, read page 15.

APPLY SHADING JUDICIOUSLY:

Shading can clarify markings, coloring, shapes, and textures. Keep it minimal for clarity and for line-art reproduction. Pages 29-30 have more details.

DEVELOP YOUR RIGHT BRAIN:

ALWAYS sketch with right-brain techniques. When stumped, look for negative shapes; drop imaginary lines through and past prominent features; compare shapes, sizes and positions, as shown on page 14. Talk to yourself as you draw.

BE OPEN TO IMPROVEMENT:

Artists are too close to their art and notes to evaluate whether or not they have created the intended information. If someone (particularly a professional) asks for clarification of something, or points out an improvement, be open to adapting, changing or adding information to your drawing or notes.

You should try to add to your field sketchbook on a regular basis. If you need to meet a deadline but have left the sketching until the last minute, you can get really stressed trying to find subjects and hastily draw them. You lose much of the joy and benefit of observing and learning. So watch for and collect good drawing subjects – things you might like to draw for future use. The sketchbook exercises in this section are designed to be done in the order presented, so pay close attention to the different emphases and tasks covered in each exercise. Read pages 22 and 23 again, so that you will tackle your field sketchbook sessions in the right spirit. These assignments assume you are using an 8" x 5" pad.

SUBJECTS TO _AVOID_: (also known as "NoNos")
- _pieces_ of things – such as sticks, chunks of bark, etc. except as a detail, done in conjunction with the entire item.
- mineral specimens – rocks are much too difficult to illustrate without a great deal of practice.
- man-made articles – except archaeological specimens (this IS scientific illustration, after all).
- scenery – except to show habit or habitat of a close-up subject you are rendering.
- distant views of small subjects – such as a bird-shape in a distant tree or shrub (except to show habit or behavior).
- do not work from photographs, preserved or mounted specimens (mounted or specimen _insects_ okay, if whole).

The object of the field sketchbook is two-fold. One object is for you to learn how to draw, the other is to share what you have learned with others.

Try to combine the two in a show-and-tell format. Sketch and write as though you were sharing a country ramble (via letter) with a friend in a foreign country – find something interesting and convey the excitement. What questions would an interested observer ask about your subject? Answer with close-up drawings and detailed notes.

For ease of reference later, create only right-hand pages with the sketchbook in an upright position. Draw in the sketchbook horizontally only on the rare occasion when you can't make a horizontal illustration fit the vertical page.

Also for ease of reference, and to observe good field notebook etiquette, write your name, date, location, (and weather conditions if appropriate) in the upper right-hand corner of each page.

Each sketch should have a caption to identify it and a scale to indicate its size. The "times" indicator is usually used (2x, ½x) or you may note an actual size ("3 inch stem"), or use a bracket/measurement. Sketch close-ups on the page next to their sources.

When using a bracket, don't make it the entire length of the subject; rather, select a small measure like 1cm. or 1in. and make a line **the length it would be if held against the subject.**

Sketches, not notes, should predominate the page. Notes should be close to their subjects and as thorough as possible without being wordy. To avoid confusion, place leaders (lines) from captions to the parts they indicate. Check for ambiguities.

Field Sketchbook #1: Objects   12 pts.
2 or more pages, 2-3 drawings per page

Subjects: 2-3 small, handheld natural items like: leaf, feather, acorn, lichen (see NoNos above).

Technique: line drawing only with HB lead. Don't shade unless it is absolutely needed to show form. Work on right-brain techniques.

The reduced image of the page below is an example of a good field sketchbook page. While the jay was not "hand-held" it is small and presented a good opportunity to record behavior. Shading was avoided in order to concentrate on shapes. Spend your time in the field sketching; shade later.

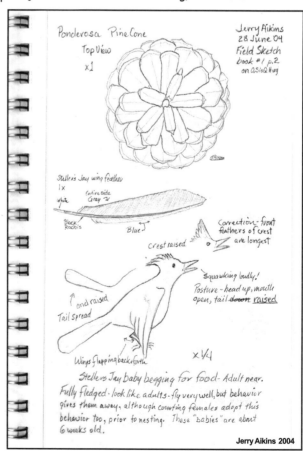

cont...

Field Sketchbook Assignments

Field Sketchbook #2: Textures   12 pts.
2 or more pages, 2-3 drawings per page

Subjects: 2-3 small, handheld natural items with HB lead as in first assignment, but shade with 2B lead to show texture, markings and form. Pick subjects with interesting textures. Draw one 3x magnification (or larger) **of each** subject, using the exact view in the detail that you showed in the source.

Technique: Shading is required for this assignment. Focus on textures on the surface AND as they appear on the outline contour of the subject (see Chapter 3 for shading techniques). Show markings, but don't let dark shading obscure details.

A magnification is *measured against the original.* If the original subject is one inch wide, a 3x magnification would be three inches wide. Choose an interesting area to magnify, one that is difficult to understand or see — flower parts, places where parts join other parts, etc.

Create two or more pages like the one below.

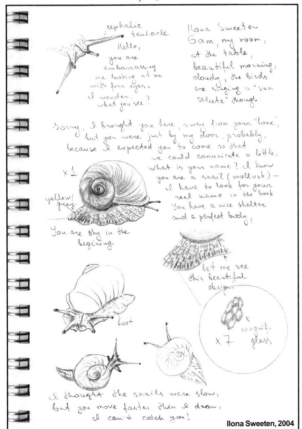

Ilona Sweeten, 2004

This illustration of a snail, plus a 3x detail of the mantle pattern combines views with observations, telling a great deal about the snail in a minimum of space. If a subject makes your imagination soar, go with the flow. Just be sure to keep your drawings accurate!

Field Sketchbook #3: Plants & Habits   13 pts.
2 or more pages, 2-3 drawings per page

Subject: 2-3 plant subjects at 1x, and a 3x or higher magnification of some aspect for each page.

Technique: Work on right-brain techniques. Focus on correct line weight and accuracy. Do not shade extensively. Please use no more shading than was suggested for Field Sketchbook #1. Concentrate on pointing out structural details with your drawings and detailed notes. Create two pages similar to the following, including a *habit* for each plant.

Ilona Sweeten, 2004

At left is an example of how to use a "habit" to set the scene for an illustration and make it more understandable.

You may not know all the names for parts, but you can describe with drawings and words what you are seeing, and you can add notes later.

If you're not sure about something, make it a question.

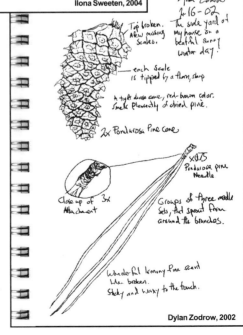

Here is another example of a Field Sketchbook #3 (the habit was drawn on the next page).

The detail on the cone is not only accurate, but is beautiful as well.

Notes include scent, feel, and texture, as well as growth pattern.

But use a lid, or compass to make a clean circle around a detail. Add it later if you don't have one handy while drawing.

Dylan Zodrow, 2002

Field Sketchbook Assignments

Field Sketchbook #4: Animals / Textures — 13 pts.
2 or more pages, 2-3 drawings per page

Subject: 2-3 different types animals (mammal, bird, amphibian, reptile, fish, insect, etc.) and one enlargement of each.

Technique: work on right-brain techniques. Focus on correct line weight and accuracy. Use conventional shading to indicate skin, hair, scale, or other coat/skin texture. Point out structural details within your drawing, and make detailed notes. Indicate scale or measurements. (Look for insect subjects on dusty windowsills.)

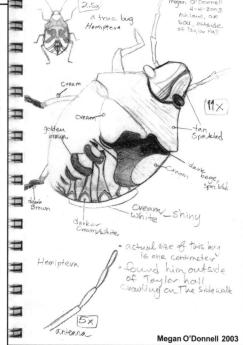

Hillary Hulen 2003

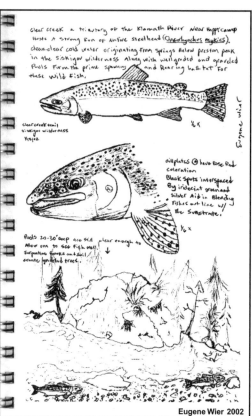

Eugene Wier 2002

Eugene's steelhead trout sketches at right show good details, texture and markings. The notes could be a bit larger, but they contain excellent observations. The page has a good habit drawing as well.

The scrub jay, below right, was sketched from a road kill. This gave Lisa the opportunity to examine closely all aspects of the jay at length and in detail. The fresh tissues were not shriveled as they would be in a taxidermy specimen.

There are federal penalties for possessing many species of wildlife (or even parts of them, such as feathers). Be aware.

The page above shows Hillary's detailed study of a chickaree (Douglas squirrel) foot. Careful examination turns up interesting details, such as the cupped palm of the paw, and the fact that the toe pads don't exactly correspond with the toes. These excellent observations are all signs of an alert naturalist.

Megan's bug, at right, was sketched in a hurry, and demonstrates how to get all the details when you only have time to draw half of them.

The notation "a *true bug*, *Hemiptera*" was made later after consulting a field guide.

Megan O'Donnell 2003

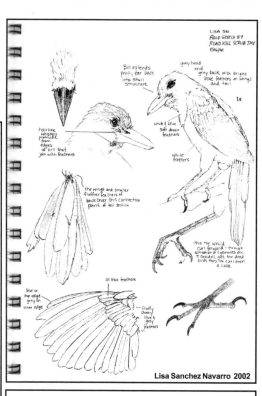

Lisa Sanchez Navarro 2002

3pts Ex. Credit – Missing Items: Some of these field sketch pages are missing important items (close-ups, notes, origin, etc.). Find three or more things missing from these field sketch pages. Always check your own field sketch pages, too.

Attaching a Pencil Loop and Ruler To a Sketchbook

DON'T GO OUT TO SKETCH WITHOUT A PENCIL AND RULER.

To make sure you always have a sketching pencil available, use 2" wide tape to make this handy loop inside the back cover of your sketchbook (or any notebook), designed for a mechanical pencil with a clasp. See also some ways to make sure you can keep a ruler and eraser handy.

Start with an 8" piece of tape, laid **sticky side up** on a table. Cut a new 2" piece, and carefully place it face down onto the 8" piece, 2" in from the left end (**a.**).

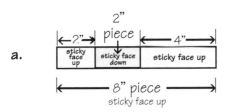

Hook your pencil over the doubled tape (**b.**), then fold the short end back over the pencil and press the sticky sides together (examine **c.** closely to see how far to go), forming a loop for the pencil (**c.**). It should slide freely up and down.

Turn the assembly over and press it inside the **back** cover of your sketchpad. Place it far enough down from the top that the pen won't poke out past the top edge (**d.**).

Also make sure it is positioned so that
- the cover will still close
- the pencil snugs up firmly against the sketchpad.

Close the sketchbook to make sure. You may have to pull the assembly back off to reposition.

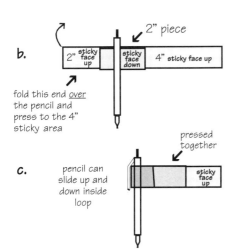

Anchor the assembly inside the cover with another long strip of tape (**d.**). If you don't, the attachment will be floppy.

ADD A RULER: Your sketchbook needs a carry-along ruler with inch and centimeter markings for specimen measuring. Photocopy one at 100%, cut it out, and paste it along the inside or outside edge of your sketchbook's front cover (below).

The sketchbook below is folded open to show **the _inside_ of the _back_ cover.**

Sketchbook from the front, closed and ready to carry.

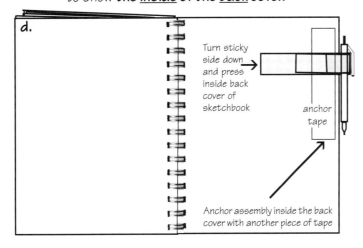

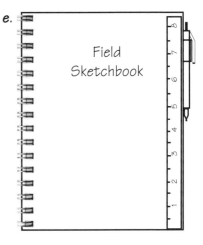

It's also a good idea to carry along a kneaded eraser. Flatten a small chunk (as big as the end of your finger) and press it between two pages near the rear, or tape an envelope inside the back cover, into which you can slide it.

Artists looking for employment have at least two advantages over almost any other type of job seeker. Instead of just *telling* prospective employers about their abilities, illustrators can offer visual proof. Furthermore, a diploma isn't the most important thing — the portfolio and resume are. So once you put together a collection of art images and achieve functionality in basic computer programs, you are ready to offer your services.

YOUR PORTFOLIO:

Your illustration portfolio should contain good quality, clean photocopies or scans of at least four of your best scientific illustrations. A portfolio designed for actual job seeking really needs at least fifteen to twenty pieces, but this will get you started.

Good-quality presentation books may be found in many office supply stores. For this practice project, you may begin with an inexpensive six-page (12 faces) presentation book.

You have several options for producing a stylish and attractive portfolio:

• Produce it entirely on the computer, including designing pages, scanning in illustrations, and importing them onto the pages for printout.

• Design the pages on the computer up to the point of adding the artwork, then print out the pages and cut and paste trimmed photocopies or printed pieces (like a business card) to the pages.

• Figure out a way to get equally attractive and accurate results with a photocopier, attractive backing pages, and cutting and pasting.

YOUR VISUAL RESUMÉ

Whatever method you choose, don't put original artwork in a portfolio that you will be handing around — use photocopies or scans.

Caption all illustrations, noting subject, medium, and date (the date is optional).

Decide on a format — style, size for elements, justification, relative positions on pages, etc., and stick to that format.

Attach art so that it won't shift position in/on the pages. Two related illustrations may be placed together on a single page.

If you elect to scan in artwork and print out pages complete with art, captions, frames, etc., the pixels must not be visible. That means the art must be scanned at 300dpi, at least.

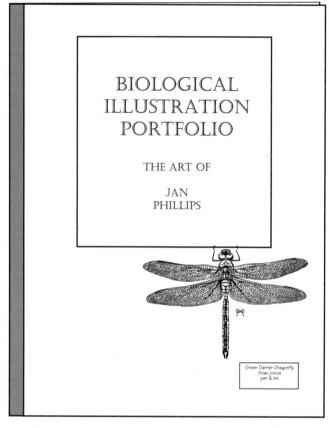

BIOLOGICAL
ILLUSTRATION
PORTFOLIO

THE ART OF

JAN
PHILLIPS

Green Darner Dragonfly
Anax junius
pen & ink

A good-looking design is essential for the cover of your portfolio. It should be designed to make someone want to pick it up and look inside (design tips in Chapter 7).

For this project, the cover should be computer generated and have your name on it, using an illustration that you produced during the course of working through this book, and the word "portfolio" so that its contents are obvious (see above).

If the illustration you use on the cover is also used inside as a portfolio piece, place the label on the inside illustration only. The above illustration was not used inside, so its label was applied here.

PHOTOCOPYING:

If you photocopy halftone portfolio pieces, use a digital photocopy machine that makes excellent, clean copies. You may have to search to find a good one, but it is important for the end quality of your portfolio. It may use a "text" setting for line art.

cont...

Examples of Portfolio Cover and Inside Pages

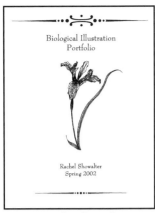

**example of student
portfolio cover design**

Make clean black and white non-halftone copies of ink line drawings. Make digital halftone copies of halftone or color pieces.

Cover any specks with whiteout, and re-ink any lines that dropped out.

When possible, display illustrations vertically so that you don't have to turn the portfolio sideways to view them. If you have horizontal pieces, group them together in the portfolio to minimize the need to switch from upright to sideways and back.

Tape or glue small pieces (such as business cards) onto contrasting paper to frame them (see at right).

Keep any tape or glue invisible. Choose one neutral color (gray, beige, tan) for background insert sheets.

Handmade papers with subdued color and texture make good backgrounds. They are a bit expensive — but they can look nice. If you choose to use (and can afford) handmade papers, don't select a style so conspicuous that it draws attention away from the art. Use consistent color and style throughout — they give a portfolio a more professional look.

If you computer-design pages with boxes to frame your art, avoid wide, black frames, which can overwhelm a drawing. Measure the illustration, then create a box onscreen big enough to frame it on the page, along with a caption, perhaps in a matching box (see below). Leave ½" between the artwork and the graphic box.

This is how a computer-designed page might look.

Art was measured, then correct-sized boxes and captions were printed out on the insert sheet.

Photocopy art was trimmed and pasted to the sheet. Art could also be photocopied or scanned and printed right onto the insert.

Items look neatest when aligned with one another.

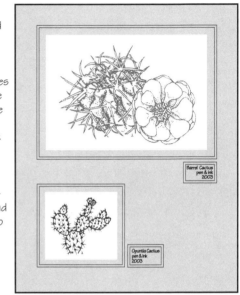

A word processing program has the capability to make your portfolio look good, but you have to use good design principles. Create a layout plan in order to avoid a haphazard look. If you don't know how to begin, review Chapter 7.

SOME POINTERS

• Choose one, pleasant, non-distracting font for use throughout the portfolio.

• Although the inside font should be easy to read, the title may be more dramatic. Don't get too carried away, though. A "FRIGHT FONT," for instance, would not be a good choice.

• Leave **at least** ¾" of background between the artwork and the edge of the sheet it is printed on. Leave a minimum of ¾" on top and sides between the sheet the art is on and the insert edge (see gray area at left) and a full inch on the bottom. These margins are important — see at left.

• If you trim anything, cut it neatly and perfectly square. Take your time. Chewed or crooked edges look painfully amateurish. If you're trying to display your capabilities as an artist, this is an entirely avoidable, drop-dead gaffe.

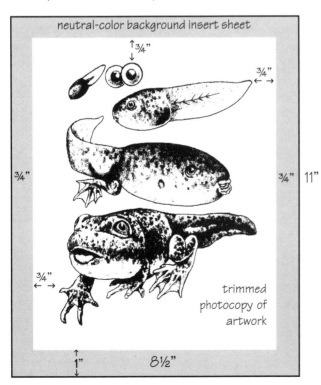

neutral-color background insert sheet

trimmed photocopy of artwork

Appendix III. Useful Things & Career Tips

HOW TO ENLARGE AND REDUCE:

Artwork that will be reproduced is usually drawn 1½ times (150% of) the size it will be when reproduced (its "final size"). This gives you plenty of room to work on detail. Reducing the finished artwork tightens and tidies it up for reproduction. It's amazing how much better it looks. But some people get hung up on how to figure the enlarged dimensions — especially when the measurements involve fractions.

Quick, now, multiply 4 $\frac{7}{16}$ x 1¾!

THERE IS AN EASIER WAY: To get a handle on the concept, look at the diagram below:

In this case, a 4" x 5" area must be enlarged 150%, to 1½ times or "half again" what its final reproduced size will be. To find the new size:

- Draw a 4" x 5" rectangle →

- Run a diagonal line (**ab**) through the opposite corners and extend it well beyond the upper corner.

- The bottom measurement is 4." Half of that is 2." So extend a line (**ac**) out 2" or "half again" further.
  The math: 4" + 2" is 6"

- Extend a new line (**cd**) up from **c** until it intersects **ab**. Where they meet is the height of the new area (shown as a gray tone here), 150% enlarged.

- You can reduce the size of things this way, too.

- **Practice:** Use the information above to enlarge the box below by 1½. It's possible to find the measurements without any math at all – using a strip of paper. Do you see how?

enlarge me
150%

PROPORTIONAL SCALE: Of course, with a proportional scale, you can effortlessly calculate a reduction or enlargement to the exact size you want. You can buy a proportional scale at an art supply or stationery store, or you can ask to use the proportional scale at a copy shop (they usually have one behind the counter).

PHOTOCOPY: Another method is to use a copy machine and enlarge to 150%. A copy machine can also make your job easier by enlarging and reducing individual design elements, too.

If you have drawn something and decide it should be larger or smaller (or just want to try some variations) you can photocopy several sizes of each element, cut them out, and move them around on your layout until you find a combination of element sizes and positions that look good (see page 67).

A visit to the copy shop will cost you some loose change and a bit of time. Go prepared to make several different sizes of each element so that you have materials to play around with.

COMPUTER USE: Another alternative is to enlarge or reduce in a computer program. If you are familiar with desktop publishing, graphics or word processing programs, combining art and text can be relatively simple.

- Scan your illustration into a graphics program to create a graphic file (Ch. 12).

- If text is needed on the art, be sure your graphics program has a good text capability. Some of the low-end graphics programs give pixelly results. To get better results, import the file into a word processing or desktop publishing program, then type up a block of text and tinker with text and graphic size until it looks good (see page 107).

> NOTE: Using a computer program does not guarantee expert results. You must know and apply design principles (then practice them) to be able to design a layout effectively. Basic principles of design and layout may be found in Chapter 7.

Apply A Protective Cover Sheet

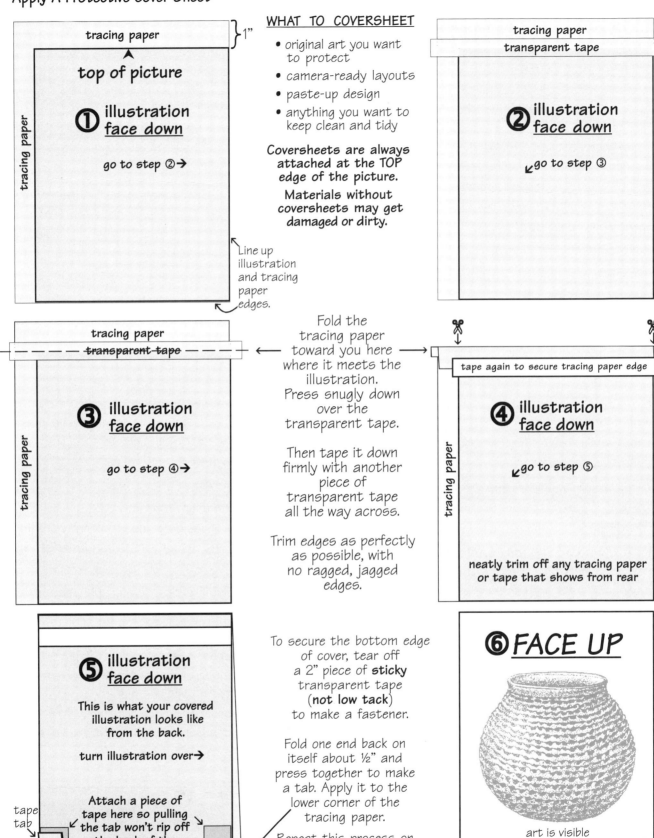

WHAT TO COVERSHEET

- original art you want to protect
- camera-ready layouts
- paste-up design
- anything you want to keep clean and tidy

Coversheets are always attached at the TOP edge of the picture.

Materials without coversheets may get damaged or dirty.

tracing paper

① illustration face down

top of picture

go to step ②→

Line up illustration and tracing paper edges.

tracing paper
transparent tape

② illustration face down

↙go to step ③

tracing paper
transparent tape

③ illustration face down

go to step ④→

Fold the tracing paper toward you here where it meets the illustration. Press snugly down over the transparent tape.

Then tape it down firmly with another piece of transparent tape all the way across.

Trim edges as perfectly as possible, with no ragged, jagged edges.

tracing paper
tape again to secure tracing paper edge

④ illustration face down

↙go to step ⑤

neatly trim off any tracing paper or tape that shows from rear

⑤ illustration face down

This is what your covered illustration looks like from the back.

turn illustration over→

tape tab

Attach a piece of tape here so pulling the tab won't rip off the back of the illustration

To secure the bottom edge of cover, tear off a 2" piece of **sticky** transparent tape (**not low tack**) to make a fastener.

Fold one end back on itself about ½" and press together to make a tab. Apply it to the lower corner of the tracing paper.

Repeat this process on the other corner.

press together

Leave at least ½" sticky surface to adhere to back of illustration.

⑥ FACE UP

art is visible through coversheet

Tape tab is placed all the way to the side, then folded down over the bottom edge and pressed tight.

WHAT IS A ROUGH?

- A rough may be a sketchy drawing, with doodles in the shape of the subject, and boxes filled with squiggly lines to indicate text.

- It may be a drawing so complete that it could be mistaken for a finished illustration.

- It could be anywhere between those two extremes, depending on its proposed use, who asked for it, and why.

a rough

ANSWERING QUESTIONS

So what should your rough look like? Ask your client what is needed. If you can't find out, be as thorough as possible without actually doing the illustration. If you are making it for yourself, it should answer some questions you need to clear up before you begin. Here are some questions that roughs answer:

1. What are the spatial requirements for the illustration?

If you are creating the illustration for a specific place with known dimensions, your rough should reflect the proportions of that space: if the space is 3" x 9," your rough may not need to be that size, but it must have those proportions, 1:3. And they must be the right orientation: horizontal or vertical. You may be asked to make the rough full size.

- *Knowing the dimensions will help you choose your subject appropriately, including the pose and other necessary components of the illustration. A standing giraffe in a long, narrow, horizontal space, for instance, would have to be very far distant. If the illustration is very small, you should avoid an elaborate treatment in which the details would be too small to see.*

2. What style of illustration is required?

Is it formal, as for a scientific paper; or informal, as in a regional journal or a nature center educational brochure? Is the illustration to be a simple outline or a complex and intricately-shaded rendering?

- *If a complex rendering is expected, it may be a good idea to show a small part of the rendering completed — such as, one finished leaf on a sketchily rendered branch. Observe all scientific conventions.*

3. What are the subject requirements?

A rough is useful for defining the subject and the amount of it to be shown. In the case of a chipmunk, for example: should it be the whole chipmunk; only its head; head and forefeet; etc. If it has markings, are they to be shown? All of them? These are choices that should be worked out in the rough stage.

- *Can you find the necessary subjects you need to draw? You may want to illustrate a snowshoe hare, but can you find one? Is there one at a local Wildlife Rehabilitation Center, for instance, or can you find enough good photos to glean details from? Find a subject for which you have models. Then decide the best way to orient it, to best illustrate what you need to say about it.*

4. What views are needed?

Is the animal doing anything specific? What orientation would show it best? In the case of a potsherd, what view would show all the required qualities? If a plant, what angle would show off all the important features of that genus and species? What other features are important?

- *Research it. What are the requirements for this particular subject. Have you chosen the best subject to show what you want? Have you considered the best way to display that characteristic or trait? Will one view do, or will you need two? If you need two, should you treat the illustration as two subjects in different poses or as two views of the same subject? Does it matter?*

5. Is any text to be included?

If a title is part of the illustration, try to rough-letter it in a style similar to what will appear on the illustration. Blocks of text should be indicated by a printout of text, or blocks of lines (see page 142). Include captions.

- *If you will be doing the text as well as the illustrations, remember that different fonts have very different sizes, uses and functions. See Chapter 7.*

Transferring a Rough Drawing to The Final Drawing Surface

> **TERMS:**
> - A ROUGH is a preliminary sketch usually made on tracing paper to plan the design and try some effects.
> - The FINISH SURFACE is the paper upon which you create the final illustration for reproduction.
> - RENDERING is the process of illustrating the final drawing.
> - TRY LINES are lines you "tried," but which weren't quite right (they must be removed).
> - The FINAL DRAWING or ILLUSTRATION is what gets reproduced for publication.

CREATING THE ROUGH ON TRACING PAPER:

Draw your rough sketch on tracing paper so you can easily see how to transfer all or part of it to the finish surface. **NEVER design or sketch your illustration directly on the finish surface.** You can't do it without erasing and messing up the paper.

Trying to preserve the clean, smooth finish surface while sketching and erasing on it slows and inhibits your work. You won't be creative if you're struggling to keep the paper clean and white.

Tracing paper also lets you check out how things look in reverse. You can move things around by tracing them and repositioning them under the tracing paper. You can add things to the drawing by tracing other objects into the design. The picture on tracing paper can be cut into pieces and taped back together in different configurations.

PREPARE THE SKETCH FOR TRANSFER TO THE FINISH SURFACE:

If your rough sketch is in pieces or not on tracing paper, bring your design to its final configuration. With an HB (medium) lead in your mechanical pencil, trace the images onto tracing paper.

When the outline (no shading at this stage) is complete, remove all try-lines so that only the actual outline you want to appear on the final illustration remains on the single sheet of tracing paper.

TRANSFER THE OUTLINE TO THE FINISH SURFACE FOR RENDERING:

If you want the illustration reversed (flopped), place the outline face down on the finish surface and burnish the outline onto the finish surface.

REDRAWING THE IMAGE:

If your image will not be reversed, turn the outline face-side-down on a piece of white paper (for visibility) and trace the image **onto the back** of the tracing paper. Redraw all the lines — sight across the surface to make sure all lines are complete. Now turn it face up, place the redrawn side against the finish surface, and burnish.

BURNISHING TECHNIQUE:

To burnish, rub the paper with a smooth, hard surface. The bowl of a spoon or the flat part of your fingernail, not the point, works well. (Don't impress or flatten the finish surface with excessive pressure as you transfer the image). The graphite image will be ghostly and temporary, so it must be preserved.

PRESERVING THE TRANSFERRED IMAGE:

To keep the transferred graphite image from rubbing off as you draw, VERY lightly redraw the image **on the finish surface** with a light (H or 2H) lead. Now pinch the edge of your warmed-up kneaded eraser until it is paper-thin and flexible. Erase the ghostly graphite image with light feathery strokes of this kneaded eraser flap. This will keep it from smearing as you draw. The faint H pencil line should remain visible until your rendering is complete. To keep the drawing clean, cover any part that you aren't actively working on.

squeeze out a flap on your kneaded eraser and wipe with it

CLEAN YOUR ART:

When your art is finished, the last, very important step is to erase away the working outline and any dirt or smudges on the paper. Be careful not to mar the finished art. Since you have no control over the reproduction process after it goes to the printer, stray marks may end up as black blots on your published illustration. A printer may notice and remove artifacts for you, but it is **your responsibility** and **your problem** if an artifact, blot, or smear **you** left on a drawing appears on the reproduction.

Kneaded erasers are great for cleanup, but for darker problems use your white eraser or an electric eraser to get everything perfectly clean. Try the eraser elsewhere first to make sure it won't make smudges. *Ultraviolet from sunshine degrades erasers, making them smear; dirty erasers increase the problem.*

What Is a Rough? – Some Examples

Making roughs can help you see problems with your design – and figure out what to do about them.

Due to a miscommunication, the roughs above on the left didn't meet the needs of the illustration's client – they were the wrong orientation and too crowded. Several more roughs were tried before the artist produced the final acceptable illustration above.

> A rough can try out ideas and suggest solutions. It can be covered with notes, or not; it can make suggestions, ask questions, note sizes and captions. Its purpose is to resolve major issues in the rough stage.

The dragon below was an art school assignment "to make a 'texture monster' with at least ten textures," (an advanced form of the Ticklebooty in Chapter 4). Compare the rough with the finished illustration and you will see that some anatomy changed and much detail was added to the final illustration.

The proposed textures are numbered on the rough. But when the illustration was being rendered, other textures suggested themselves and were added, making the original whimsical and eye-catching concept into an even more interesting rendering.

If your art or style is well known and you have a reputation for producing consistent work, you may be able to get away with fairly crude roughs like these.

However, a client might request that at least part of the rough be more (or completely) finished, or ask to see a similar example of your work, hoping to avoid unpleasant surprises.

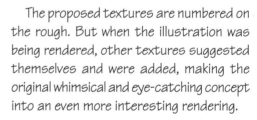

Irene Brady

Preparing a Rough Layout for Client Review and Reproduction

Rough layouts may be prepared on computer or as outlined below. The procedures below apply with either method — except that using a computer you can replace the tape-and-T-square routine with the computer printout rough.

CLIENT'S ROUGH LAYOUT: For a foundation sheet, measure a piece of heavy paper or illustration board 150% of the dimensions of the to-be-printed piece plus a 1" margin all around. Indicate margins with crop marks (see crop-mark instructions on page 152).

TAPE ON PHOTOCOPIES OF THE ART AND TEXT ELEMENTS: Using removable tape, fasten the elements in place where you feel they should go. Everything should be arranged exactly as it will appear on the reproduced piece (see **a.**). The edge of the foundation sheet is your guide, so make certain it is exactly square.

a.

Apply text and captions, if any, using a T-square or a grid to make sure they are perfectly level.

APPLY TRACING PAPER COVER-SHEET WITH TWO CLOSER TABS: (See page 138). Don't use an opaque cover sheet — the art cannot be seen without lifting the cover. With a cover sheet of tracing paper, the illustration can be located in a file and examined without getting damaged or soiled with fingerprints. Although this isn't original artwork, you still want to keep it as clean and presentable as possible. Notes may be jotted on the cover sheet if needed.

MAKE 2 COPIES: Take two photocopies or printouts, the size they'll be when reproduced, along with the layout (see **b.**) when you go see the client. Both should be clean and presentable. Give one to the client, and keep one. Make notes on yours to take back with you.

To look really professional, put a cover sheet on the client's photocopy printout. This will give it the appearance of finished art, a professional touch.

If the art is to be in color, make a color copy for the client, since it is difficult for most people to infer from a black/white copy what a colored piece will look like. With a colored copy, the client will have everything needed to continue to work with you via email, telephone, fax, etc.

Carry the original layout, the client's copy, your business card (and a brochure if you have one) in a clean folder to visit the client. The brochure, show-casing examples of your work, will serve as an advocate for you if the client becomes anxious while waiting for the work to be completed. It says *"This person is an established illustrator. Trust this person."*

MEET WITH THE CLIENT: Dress professionally and be on time when you go to present the rough layout.

CHANGES: Your rough may be accepted exactly as is by the client. But by paying for the art, the client has a right to request changes. If the client doesn't like your layout, it may not be a reflection on your work, but merely a difference in opinion. Move items around on the rough layout and try out variations. When the client is satisfied, write down and discuss the changes to make sure you understand what is wanted. Get a deadline for the final layout.

Leave your business card with telephone number, fax, or email where you can be reached. Exit with the layout, your photocopy and notes.

MAKE CHANGES IMMEDIATELY: Do the work before you forget exactly what is wanted. Don't put it off, thinking you will remember. If you run into unexpected difficulties, the client's words and intonations will still be fresh in your mind, and you may be able to deal with it without having to call and ask.

FINAL APPROVAL: Lay-out and make copies of the approved design, and present it with the original artwork to your client BEFORE the deadline. Keep extra copies of everything you give the client for your own files and portfolio.

b.

A ROUGH LAYOUT

GETTING PAID: Let the client know before you start when and how much payment you will require. Don't be embarassed to ask for your fee. You would expect to pay someone who did work for you, right? And you certainly wouldn't be offended if someone required **you** to pay for something you had ordered. Be assertive in a professional manner.

One easy approach is to say, pleasantly, *"You can make the check out to ...."*

Charts, Graphs and Diagrams

Charts, graphs and diagrams describe material more clearly and quickly than written or spoken descriptions. Visual information usually sticks with the viewer better than written or spoken information. Charts, graphs and diagrams can be made quickly and easily in computer programs. Check for simplicity, clarity and accuracy before presenting them.

THE FUNCTIONS OF CHARTS, GRAPHS AND DIAGRAMS ARE:

- to get the greatest number of ideas
- into the smallest space,
- with the least time and ink possible,
- without distorting, confusing or misrepresenting data.

CHARTS AND GRAPHS COME IN VARIOUS FORMATS. HERE ARE EXAMPLES OF THE MOST COMMON:

XY GRAPH (SEE DETAIL AT RIGHT)

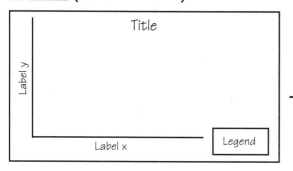

XY GRAPH DETAIL

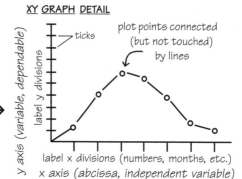

An XY graph is a common type of graph, showing what happens to something over a period of time. It is frequently used to show the results of scientific research.

PIE CHART

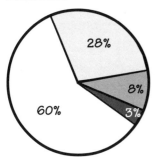

A pie chart shows percentages of elements which, all together, equal 100%. Tints are often applied to the wedges of the "pie," to make them stand out or to differentiate them clearly. Always check to make sure the total equals 100%. ☺ If you don't, somebody else **will**.

HISTOGRAM

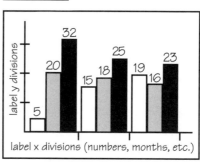

A histogram is characteristically used to show time vs. number of individuals or items. Some power companies use histograms to show the comparison of the current month's fuel usage with usage during the same month in the previous year.

DIAGRAM

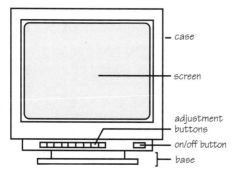

Desktop Computer Circa 1999

A diagram is usually a stylized drawing which shows an object, its parts, (labeled) and their relationships (spatial) to each other.

A QUICK FLIPCHART AND BLACKBOARD TOOL:

Here's a simple way to mark off a series of **EVENLY SPACED TICKS** for a chart or graph. The only tool needed is a measuring stick with regularly spaced increments. The slant of the ruler determines the spacing: a steeply slanted ruler spaces the lines more closely together. This makes impromptu marking of any size easy.

Mapmaking Guidelines

MAKING A MAP WITH COMPUTER MAP-MAKING GIS PROGRAMS:

Map-making used to be the illustrator's standby. There was only one way to acquire a map – hire an illustrator/cartographer.

With the advent of GIS (Geographic Information Systems) computer mapmaking programs, it has become possible to produce maps without having an art or drafting background. There may not be a lot of control over the map's final appearance, but the results are quite usable. However, if a GIS program isn't available when you need it, you should know how to proceed without one.

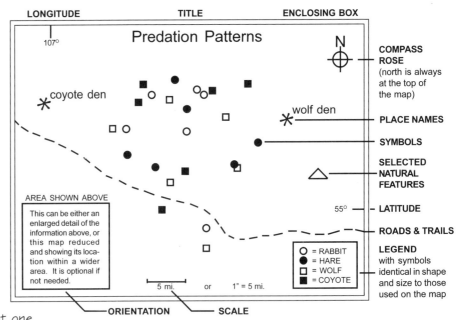

SOME TYPICAL MAP FEATURES

MAKING A MAP *WITHOUT A GIS PROGRAM*:

If you have a basic map to start with, you can add the features that make the map do what you need it to do, and say what you need it to say.

USGS (United States Geological Survey) maps are uncopyrighted and free for use. To find good free sources for USGS topo maps, search the web under "USGS topo maps." There are topo maps for every mapped area in the US.

Other map sources may also be found on the Web, and "hard-copy" topo maps are available in outdoors stores, bookstores, etc. There are some good state topo map books available, as well. **However, all maps except USGS maps are copyrighted.**

If you use any other kind of map, you must completely redraw, change, add or omit things. Drop or add road names, leave out creeks, abbreviate "Road" to "Rd.", etc. Add or omit shading patterns if this doesn't change the definition of a feature.

One method used by map-makers to detect "map theft" is to add a small bogus item to the map – a non-existent mountain, a jog in a road, etc. If the same fake item is found on a re-published, unchanged map, copyright has been infringed and the map cops may come and get you. So if you were thinking of a little map-napping, don't do it. Redraw.

THE PROCESS:

Cover a base map or aerial photograph with tracing paper and trace lightly with pencil. Then ink over the graphite, erasing the pencil lines when the ink is dry since you don't want them to appear on the final map.

Scan the map and pull it up onscreen in a program that will let you add the title, boxes with legends and details, a compass rose (see above), a scale, and latitude and longitude lines if needed (maps for scientific journals usually need two coordinates).

Computer fonts may have symbols you can use. Take advantage of draw toolbars to manipulate text and add freehand drawings. Create names and symbols and move them to their correct places on the map. Complex maps may require textures or tones for clarity. A graphics program may enable you to add shading patterns. Or you could apply press-on patterns bought in a survey supply or art store.

If necessary, you can make your own patterns and print them out on transparent label paper, then peel-and-stick.

Observe any applicable conventions related to the subject matter and scientific field.

All maps should be surrounded by a border, but the map's title may be placed outside the border.

Designing A Display

The function of a display is to make people stop and look. But what makes people stay and learn? Whatever your field, you may be called upon to produce a poster or a display.

The hallmarks of a good poster or display are similar to those of other types of presentations.

ATTRIBUTES OF A WELL-DESIGNED DISPLAY:

- **BREVITY:** The message must say the most with the least words.
- **READABILITY:** The text font must be easy to read, particularly from a distance.
- **INTEREST:** The graphics and layout must hold the viewer's interest.
- **CLARITY:** The message must be clear, easy to digest, and uncrowded.
- **EMPHASIS:** The most important elements must be larger or brighter than less important elements.
- **SIMPLICITY:** The graphics and text must present the message with a minimum of fuss.
- **ATTRACTION:** The display must appeal to the esthetic senses.

DESIGN:

When designing a display it is important to plan and create text and graphics with the whole display in mind. Consider ways to present the message and graphics to best suit the situation and purpose — including things like projected audience, traffic direction, and lighting.

Conference or poster exhibits usually have strict guidelines about the poster dimensions and whether it is to be wall-hung or a table display, etc. Follow these closely — all other points being equal, a non-conforming display might be rejected for what seem to be insignificant technical reasons.

Be alert to the overall appearance. Colors should be coordinated. Blocks of text and illustrations should be consistent but varied in size and positioning to keep a viewer engaged. Flow should lead the viewer from one area of content to the next without sending them off your display.

Sketch out ideas for your entire display before you decide on the style and number of panels.

TEXT:

Words by themselves tend to be boring. You can improve matters by choosing a clear and pleasant font, by not crowding text, and by highlighting important words or ideas with larger size or color.

Build the text blocks in a computer program. A simple word program will do the job reasonably well. **Don't try to hand-letter unless you're an expert.**

You can be creative with the title — an eye-catching title font may draw attention to a less-than-riveting subject. But don't try to use a fancy font for the text of the display. Instead, use a simple, easy-to-read font that won't place hurdles between reading and understanding.

Choose a single font for the body of the display — although you can vary the size, use italics, bold or underline it, or use all caps (for short important sections). A simple san-serif font like Helvetica (also called Arial) is good. If you have lots of information to include, a narrow font like Times Roman might work well (see page 109). Strive for simplicity.

Create your text in blocks, one or two paragraphs being about the right length (posters must be quickly read, so don't get wordy). A text block can be printed on colored paper, then mounted on a slightly larger sheet of complementary or contrasting colored paper to give it a thin border before being positioned on the display. This makes the text block into a graphic element and catches the viewer's attention.

Review Chapter 7 for more tips. Be consistent in all usages, and spell-check (then check spelling of) all text before printing it out. Test on scrap paper first, to avoid an expensive mistake.

The Theory Behind A Successful Display

MARGIN RULE OF THUMB:

To avoid a crowded effect, don't jam text right up against the edge of its block (see below). People don't like to read crowded text, and will move away without bothering to see what you have to say. Here are two quick measures to make your job easy:

1. *Leave about the width of an average letter of that font size (an **a** or **k**, not an **i**) between text and sides.*

2. *Leave about the <u>height</u> of a letter (like a **k**) of that font size between text and the top or bottom.*

A quick visual check is the only guide you'll need.

•This much margin between the letter and edge is ideal for a poster or large display, but a bit wide for a small label.

•The margin here would be fine for a small label, but barely passable for a large display.

•This margin is not acceptable for a large display; it is too crowded for even a small label.

A 2" border around the elements of a large poster or display makes the display look roomy and easy to read. A 1" border is the MINIMUM allowable.

TEXT BLOCK BORDERS:

Once you have established the size for adequate margins, put a single-line box around each text block at that distance and print it out on white or neutral-colored paper. Carefully cutting just outside the line will create professional-looking text blocks, ready to attach to the poster. Heighten the effect by backing each text block with a slightly larger rectangle of colored paper. Subtle cream, grey, tan, light blue or green may be suitable, but avoid pinks, oranges and bright, hot colors.

Mount charts, photos, artwork, etc. on the same colored border paper for consistency. This improves the professional effect of the display.

If you don't print a border around the text block, mount each text block on a complementary-colored paper to form a border.

IT NEEDS A BORDER TO LOOK ITS BEST.

GRAPHICS:

Graphics attract interest. Graphics can be logos, photos, drawings, paintings, graphs, diagrams — or even blocks of text, as mentioned above — creating visual sparkle on the display.

Each graphic should serve a definite purpose on the display (no fluff), and must be designed to be as interesting as possible. For instance, a diagram can be used in place of a description.

A simplified treatment can substitute for a complex idea. A successful graphic transmits the idea without distorting it, in a simple, easy-to-understand manner.

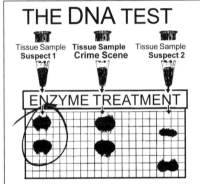

"The DNA Test" at right was designed as a TV graphic, with an expected eight-to-ten-second airing. While it is very simplistic, it gets the complicated concept of DNA matching across to the layman quickly. Color can also improve clarity.

3-D EFFECTS:

A 3-D effect can be achieved by attaching additional *Fomecore-based graphics with velcro (see p. 150 for construction details). Mount a photo or piece of art on fomecore display board, cut out the shape, and sculpt it by indenting it with a blunt object.

Burnish down the edges with a hard, smooth object for a beveled, rounded look. Attach velcro to the back and press the 3-D graphic onto a velcro piece fastened to the display. Such attachments may extend out past the edge with good effect.

ARRANGEMENT:

For best results, print out everything that will go on the display, then spend

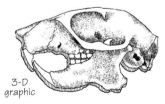

3-D graphic

some time arranging pieces and trying alternate positions before sticking things down. Sometimes last-minute rearrangements are serendipitous.

cont...

Fomecore is the brand name for a type of light-weight display board.

Anything that extends beyond the outside border of the poster should be firmly anchored so it can't slip during display – but detachable so that the poster can be easily coversheeted and carried.

Fasten nothing permanently until you're sure.

BUILDING THE FOUNDATION:

Simple wall-hung and free-standing displays should be constructed of sturdy, light-weight materials for ease in handling and shipping, and security in hanging. They are less likely to detach and fall, or to be damaged if they do. Here are some options:

• Fomecore is a light-weight poly-foam, covered front and back with a smooth white or colored paper. It is easy to work with and available in art and office supply stores. Easily cut with a blade, this display board can be taped together in panels to make freestanding displays. It can be faced with colored matboard or paper for striking effects. Multi-panel displays can be constructed using 2" transparent tape as hinges. Pre-fab hinges, available in office supply stores, are an option, but they create a space between the panels, so be sure to check out the effect before making a decision.

• Fairly inexpensive three-panel corrugated cardboard table displays designed for school science fairs are also available in art and office supply stores. Some are designed as portable classroom "blackboards" with a slick surface for dry-erase markers. Things can be glued or taped to them to make a more permanent display, but care must be used in removing tape, since the fragile surface detaches rather easily. Remove the tape on disassembly.

• Some photocopy shops can produce large posters from small originals. Some will even work from disk if you have designed a display on the computer. However, there is some expense involved.

• A tight budget may make it more feasible to produce text blocks via computer printer, cut them out, then glue them or tape them onto the display board with 2-sided poster tape. You can also print them onto 8½" x 11" label paper for press-on labels.

COLORED BACKGROUNDS:

Fomecore is the standard building material for posters. It comes in white, black and primary colors. White can be boring, so it's good to give your display a bit of *pizazz* with a LITTLE color – but avoid the bright primary colors for professional-looking results.

FACINGS ON DISPLAYS:

Facings of colored paper or matboard, with subdued complementary tones, are a good choice. To face the display with colored matboard, place a large piece of colored matboard face up on a cutting surface.

Place the display board also face up on the matboard and lightly line around it. Set the display board aside. With a metal straightedge, cut the matboard with an X-acto blade or matboard cutter. Glue the matboard to the display board.

DISPLAY CONSTRUCTION:

A three-panel display will stand by itself. Before attaching any of the text or graphics, butt the panels together (face-up) and press a 2" strip of clear tape the entire length of each seam on the front of the display. The taped seam is not conspicuous once the display is assembled, but you can face the display with paper to disquise the tape if you prefer.

Use a simple, hinged wing-stand to prop a single-panel display upright. It can be attached with 2-inch tape and folded flat for transporting or hanging on a wall. See page 149 for a step-by-step instructions on how to create a small display.

PROTECTIVE COVER:

The protective cover on your display is the first thing people see when you arrive to set your display up. If it is sloppy or ugly, you're off to a bad start.

The protective cover should be designed to remove or tuck completely out of sight when the poster is on display. You may have to butt pieces of paper together (see p. 17) to make it large enough.

If your display has removable items, a manila envelope with a closing clasp, attached out of sight on the back (along one side only, so that it hangs when standing), makes transport easier.

CAUTION: If you tape around more than two sides of the envelope, it won't open.

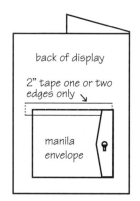

Elements of a Successful Display

Displays are meant to attract attention. It is important to use imaginative ploys to grab and hold the viewer's interest. While eye-catching (and appropriate) fonts are a good tool, and color can demand "Look at me!" there are other ways to catch the attention of the passing crowd.

One good way to make your display stand out is to add a third dimension — in other words, make the display 3-dimensional by attaching to the surface:

- **actual items**
- **decorative elements that enhance the display**
- **miniature models of items — or same-size lightweight models of too-heavy or valuable items**
- **selected items extending past the edge of the display or overlapping other items**

The 12' wide Fish & Wildlife Service Forensics Lab standing display shown below, was designed and assembled for the World CITES Conference in Japan in 1992. It had a header with the laboratory name, function and logo, and the main part of the display featured taut, pithy text (with an easily read selection of about 60 words).

Wrapped around the ends were photos showing people at work in the lab, and center-front sported a colorful mounted map of the world to represent the lab's reach. A selection of poached-then-confiscated ivory items (securely fastened) were within reach for people to touch. A freeform panel featuring a montage of wildlife from alligator to eagle showed the wide scope of the lab's efforts, and plastic holders held brochures in three languages if people wanted to find out more. As a graceful finale, a pink and red flock of flying origami birds (symbolizing goodwill toward the Japanese hosts of the conference) soared from the center toward the upper right.

This proved to be an irresistible combination of elements: a simple message about people doing vital things; touchable, valuable and fascinating items; goodwill symbols; and materials for the viewer to take home.

Because of the valuable ivory, the display had a guard and a constant crowd of viewers during the conference. After the conference, the display was taken to the Washington office to serve as their headquarters display.

display by Irene Brady for USFWS, 1992

Step-by Step Instructions for Creating a Small Display

Sometimes, the scientific illustrator may need to create table displays to showcase illustrations or projects. The following information shows how to make a multipurpose fomecore table display and to exercise imagination in designing attachments.

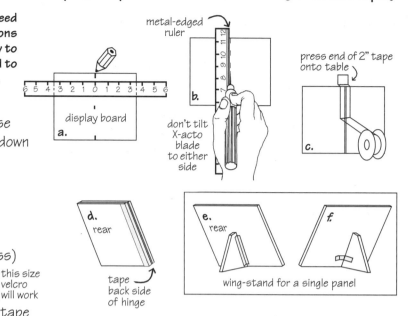

For this process you need:

1. cutting surface: for small items use 11" x 14" sketchbook turned face-down
2. X-acto knife with new blade
3. 5" x 7" fomecore display board
4. plastic C-thru ruler
5. metal-edged ruler
6. low-tack tape
7. small metal jar lid (about 2" across)
8. scissors
9. velcro strip, both surfaces   _this size velcro will work_
10. white glue and/or 2-sided poster tape
11. .5 mechanical pencil and erasers
12. 2"-wide clear tape

1. Prepare work area. Use your 11" x 14" sketchbook face down as a cutting surface to avoid cutting the table.

2. Determine the center. Set your display board piece horizontally on the pad. To use the C-thru ruler to determine the center, place the zero at the ruler's center roughly on the center of the board, then slide it from side to side until the numbers on left and right edges of the ruler match (see **a.**). Mark the display board at top, bottom and center.

CAUTION: Keep both sides of the display clean.

3. Cut (practice on a scrap first). Using a metal-edged ruler (ONLY) and a pencil, draw a line to connect the points. Hold the ruler down firmly (but not heavily enough to dent the fomecore), and pull the (new) X-acto blade down the line along the edge of the ruler, being careful not to tilt to either side, to make a square-edged cut (see **b.**). Don't try to cut all the way through on the first cut. Pull the blade through twice or more until the cut is complete. A dull blade will snag the edges.

4. Prepare to make a hinge. On what will be the **back** side, fit the two pieces exactly back together and tape them together lightly with a couple of pieces of **low-tack** tape. Turn the fastened pieces **right side up** on a smooth tabletop.

5. Tape hinge. Press the end of the 2" wide tape onto the **table** just above the center of the joined display pieces, then stretch it straight down over the joined line (see **c.**). Smooth with a finger down from the top as you go, keeping the tape centered as you smooth. Trim off the excess tape. Remove the low-tack tape on the back. The display will now stand open.

6. Strengthen the hinge. With the display folded shut, press tape down the length of the raw rear edges of the hinge. Smooth the tape around the sides (see **d.**) and burnish down firmly with a fingernail.

7. Single-panel displays need wing-stands. With an X-acto blade, cut a triangle of display board, as shown in **e.** (cut the top point off if desired). The wing stand should extend more than halfway up the back and out no farther than necessary.

Adjust the total length and the slant of the front edge as needed. Attach as shown in **e.** A tabbed piece of tape on the side opposite the hinge, as shown in **f.**, will keep the stand from folding up unexpectedly. Wide displays need two wing-stands.

8. Fomecore corners tend to get crushed easily. To forestall this, cut them off using a small metal jar lid or can (see **g.**). Practice on scraps until you are confident enough to do it with smooth, firm strokes.

Neatly cut rounded corners give displays a professional look. But badly cut rounded corners look worse than crushed ones, so practice first.

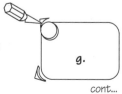

cont...

9. Apply text and materials. Attach a 3-D visual to the display with velcro. You may photocopy and use the skull graphic and text provided (**see c., d. and e. below**) or use your own illustration and text. This tiny display would be appropriate in a museum cabinet or small-scale exhibit protected from curious hands.

Before beginning the next part, review pages 145-148.

10. Prepare the graphic. Photocopy the graphic you plan to use as your 3-D visual onto an appropriate paper. Choose a medium- or light-weight paper because heavy paper makes sculpting more difficult. If you want to avoid gluing, photocopy an image onto label paper, then just cut, peel and stick. Experiment with the next step on a scrap first.

11. Photocopy the graphic onto label paper and cut out the graphic with a ¼" margin around it. If you're not using label paper, completely cover the back with diluted white glue or cut 2-sided poster tape to fit. Press firmly to a scrap of fomecore larger than the graphic. When dry, place it face up on a cutting surface (not the table) and with your X-acto blade cut around the graphic through both the paper and the fomecore **(a.)**, very cleanly (practice on a scrap first). This requires concentration and a very sharp blade held perfectly vertically. If the blade slants to one side or the other, the cutout will have a slanted edge and won't look quite as good.

When finished, use the side of a pencil or pen to press down and bevel or "sculpt" the edges (see **b.** below). Additionally, you can indent the face of the piece slightly for a *bas relief* sculptured effect.

12. Create text blocks. On the computer, create text blocks with the title and the text in box frames **d.** at right). Measure your display and make the text blocks the correct size to fit on the display. Or, create the text blocks without

a.

b.

↖
edge being
pressed

box frames — cut them out cleanly (that's important) — and place them on a slightly larger piece of colored paper so that the color forms a frame **(c.)**. Don't try to create text in a graphics program (see page 99) unless the program produces high quality text. *Don't hand-letter unless you're an* **expert** *calligrapher*.

13. Facing. Since this display is small, if you want a background other than white, you could face the entire front with an attractive paper attached with white glue (spread on diluted white glue with a paintbrush). Choose a subdued paper that will not compete with your message or graphics.

14. Pasteup. Arrange the text blocks and your 3-D cutout on the display (pay attention to design rules). Use your imagination. Design something unique if possible — but remember the most important thing is that the arrangement makes the message easy to grasp. Line up the pieces with a ruler and attach them to the display, first with low-tack tape, then when things looks good, glue or poster-tape them down.

15. Attach 3-D stuff (e.). Squeeze two stick-on velcro pieces together with the backings still on. Next, remove the backing from the hook side and press it to the back of the graphic. Decide exactly where on the display you want the 3-D graphic . Remove the backing from the fuzzy velcro (which is still meshed with the hooked piece) and press the graphic firmly where you are SURE it should go. Later, when you fold up your display, remove the 3-D piece so it won't dent the facing display panel — that's why it's detachable.

Don't attach the HOOKED velcro piece to the display — the rough hooks will indent the opposite panel when you fold it shut.

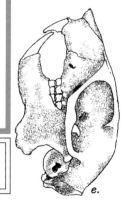

A gray squirrel's skull is a marvel of engineering. The large orange incisors grow continually, but are kept the right length and sharpness by daily grinding, as the squirrel gnaws its way through the shells of nuts and seeds. The rugged molars are well-designed to crush green buds and nutmeats.

The entire skull is sturdily built to survive an occasional fall from high branches which might kill a more fragile climber.

c.

Western Gray Squirrel
Sciurus griseus

d.

e.

Make business cards available on your display or poster. It adds a professional touch and allows interested people to contact you. To make a business card holder, photocopy the template (**a.**) onto heavy paper (card stock) which matches or complements the display. Cut, then fold with dotted lines to the **outside** to facilitate folding. Then refold with the dotted lines to the inside so that they are hidden. Glue together, clamping with paperclips until dry (**b.**). Secure one business card to the inside so it can't be removed (**c.**). Hang with pushpins, tape or velcro and insert your cards.

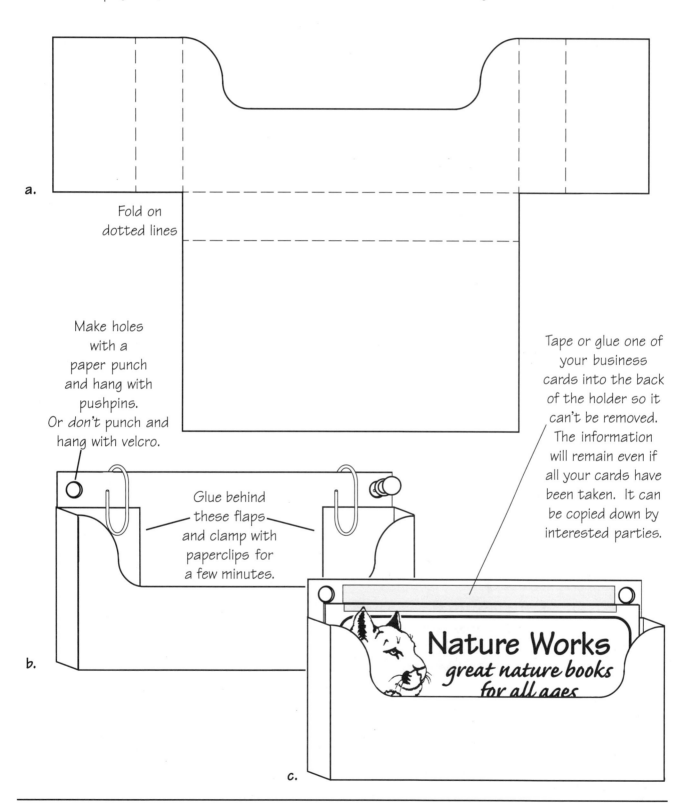

a.

Fold on
dotted lines

Make holes
with a
paper punch
and hang with
pushpins.
Or *don't* punch and
hang with velcro.

Tape or glue one of
your business
cards into the back
of the holder so it
can't be removed.
The information
will remain even if
all your cards have
been taken. It can
be copied down by
interested parties.

Glue behind
these flaps
and clamp with
paperclips for
a few minutes.

b.

Nature Works
*great nature books
for all ages*

c.

Extra Credit – Your Computer-Generated Business Card – 5 pts

Every professional needs a business card. Collect and analyze some business card examples to see what you do (or don't) want your card to say about you. You can use an existing card as a template – just replace their info and art with yours.

BUSINESS CARD REQUIREMENTS:

- your name and skill (most important info) largest
- phone # (with area code), email, fax, and website, if any
- a small piece of your original art as motif or logo
- leave a ⅛" margin between non-bleeding art and the edge
- computer-generated text; correct capitalization, punctuation, and abbreviations; and spell-check it (butt dew knot deep end awn you're spill check her)
- no pixels should be evident on art
- no text should be smaller than 8pt.
- use no more than two fonts on card
- put no information or illustration in the zone that may be perforated by a rolodex punch

For Extra Credit, do this exercise entirely on the computer (except for artwork).

If you have needed the impetus to learn a desktop publishing, graphics, or illustration program, this exercise might be the perfect encouragement.

If you intend to make cards for yourself, one of the easier methods (if you know the program) is to create one perfect card, 1x, in a desktop publishing program, then within the program, copy and paste it into two columns of five cards each. Print them on cardstock with an inkjet printer. Laserjet and photocopied cards tend to stick to plastic wallet inserts, leaving a "bad impression."

If you plan to have cards done from hardcopy by a printer, create a single card layout, at 200%, which they will then manage to their own specs for reproduction. The following instructions will help you make one card, and you can take it from there. This makes sense if you need more than about fifty cards.

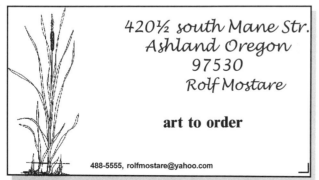

How many things can you find wrong with this card?
(answer and discussion on page 156 – but see how many you can find before peeking!)

A business card measures 2" x 3½." Design and render your card at 200% (twice as large as it will be when printed) or 4" x 7."

Since it is not possible to cut **on** a line, don't outline your card. Instead, use crop marks to show where the card is to be cropped (cut or limited). Crop marks **within** the outline of your design would show on your printed piece. So place crop marks like these.

NOTE: to make crop marks: end both lines exactly on the corner, then erase the ends that touch the corner, back about one-eighth inch.

Put one piece of your own art on the card. It's okay (but more <u>expensive</u>) if **art** bleeds off the edge, but don't let it just touch the edge. (see below left). Keep a ³⁄₁₆" margin between any **text** and the edge of the card. **Center the text or line up edges of art and text, or line up text blocks with each other.**

Business cards may be punched for storage in Rolodexes, so put your name and what you offer in the top third or half of the card (see below). Everything else can go below – but leave room for the Rolodex punch! A card with a vertical layout either won't get put into someone's Rolodex, or it won't show your information once it is in. Do you care?

uh oh!

IF THIS WENT TO A PRINTER, THEY'D WANT:

- the card design on CD or floppy
- **OR** a camera-ready business card layout at 200%
- **AND** two computer printout or photocopy samples at 100%, the way you expect them to look.

POSSIBLE JOB SCENARIOS – AND HOW TO PROCEED

You learn of a natural history journal that is soliciting artwork for a project.
You are asked to produce natural history artwork for a local conservancy group.
You volunteer to help produce materials for a local nature center.

GET DETAILED INFORMATION FROM THE PROJECT DIRECTOR:

- Is it clear what is requested or required?
- Can you handle the subject matter?
- Has enough time been allocated for you to do it? Can you meet the deadline?
- Are they paying anything for it? If not, and you want to do it anyway, tell them you'll expect three to five free copies of the reproduced item for your portfolio (*unless it's an expensive display*).

IF THE JOB HAS POSSIBILITIES:

Make an appointment to see the person you will be working with. TAKE YOUR PORTFOLIO, with examples of what you think that particular job might involve. If you have previously produced similar work, provide examples, photos, good reviews and quotes, or other information about it.

Discuss the assignment. Decide whether you can work with that person. If you are fairly sure you can, get full information (take a notebook and pen, and write detailed notes) about the project, including:

- exactly what subject/s is wanted (*can you find research material about it?*)
- what kind of treatment is expected (*scientific detail, artsy, cartoon, etc. – and can you do that? If you aren't sure, be honest and proceed cautiously.*)
- what is its purpose (*to entertain, to teach, to create interest, etc.*)
- what techniques – halftone, line art or color – are expected (*and can you handle them?*)
- what will be the published size (*get exact dimensions*)
- when do they expect to see roughs (*get a date and write it down*)
- when is the absolute deadline for finished art (*get a date and write it down*)

CAN YOU DO IT?:

- do you have ability, time, and persistence to meet their needs? Be realistic and honest with yourself.
- if you have any doubts, be open and forthright – don't just say yes and hope for the best.

AND THEN:

If they like your looks and you like theirs; if the job looks pretty good to you, and you think it is something you could handle; if it pays well and/or would look good in your portfolio (plus give you more experience)...............Hey! **GO FOR IT!**   **(but first, read the next page)**

Prep List for a <u>Real</u> Illustration Job

BEFORE YOU DO ANY WORK AT ALL:

First, write out a contract or a "memo of understanding" outlining what you plan to do and what you expect your client to do, and review it with them. Reach an agreement on payment at this point. This will avoid misunderstandings and disappointment on both sides. Get it in writing.

GATHER MATERIALS:

Collect written and photo research material.

TAP RESOURCES:

Try the library, the internet, magazines, and your own scrap files if you have any yet (if you plan to be a biological illustrator, start collecting wildlife, botanical and habitat-oriented photos and articles ASAP).

DON'T TRY TO FAKE IT:

You <u>need</u> research materials. Even for cartoons (especially for cartoons), so start collecting.

DESIGN THE ROUGHS:

Create two or more different designs for the client's approval. For best results, do more/better than they expect.

MEET WITH THE CLIENT:

Go over the roughs together, give suggestions and get feedback. Make sure you understand their feedback and what is needed. Follow **their** agenda.

MAKE A SCHEDULE AND STICK TO IT:

Begin right away, work steadily, allow extra time for mishaps and delays.

CHOOSE THE CORRECT ENLARGEMENT:

While line art illustrations are usually done at 150%, halftone illustrations are often done at 100% or actual final size. Find out what is needed.

DON'T WAIT FOR INSPIRATION:

There is no such thing as a "Muse," so don't waste your time "waiting for it." If you are apprehensive, just make yourself sit down and begin, and the art will come. Those awful doubts assail even seasoned artists, so don't be too hard on yourself.

PACE YOURSELF:

If your time is half gone, you should be at least (if not more than) half finished.

PRESENT ARTWORK PROPERLY PREPARED:

Present it to the client before the deadline. Then if there is anything to be changed, you'll have time to correct it. If they ask for changes on something they previously okayed, they should pay you extra. Don't be embarrassed to tell them so. If they give you a hard time about it, you can make the decision as to whether or not you want to continue.

PAYMENT:

Before you hand over the artwork, remind them about what you expect in return (conversationally, if possible, but very matter-of-factly). **<u>Don't agree to let them pay all or part of it later.</u>**

PORTFOLIO:

Keep copies and examples of work you've done for others. You may need them in case they lose or ruin the originals. You'll be paid to do them all over again, but it will be easier because you can just work from your photocopies.

You also need copies for your portfolio. Make the copies of as high quality as you can afford. Sometimes a laserjet printout is sufficient. Inkjet printouts tend to produce fuzzy artwork, so avoid them. Sometimes a photocopy will do. But a really hot piece may rate more expensive treatment. You decide if the extra expense is worth it. See page 155.

UPDATE YOUR PORTFOLIO REGULARLY:

Your portfolio will engender new assignments. Keep adding new pieces to it and sending updates to prospective clients so they won't forget you.

BACK UP YOUR PORTFOLIO

If possible, scan all of your artwork and keep one or more backup copies of the graphic files on CDs, one of which you can store safely elsewhere.

If you want to be an illustrator, you need a comprehensive portfolio. To create your initial resumé/portfolio, assemble everything you have done, and list everything you can do, then put them all together to figure out what kind of job you might be good at. Work on your portfolio first. Review pages 135-136 before you begin.

YOUR PORTFOLIO: First, assemble your best artwork of the types and styles you think you could and would like to do more of. Don't select anything you didn't enjoy, or found particularly scary and wouldn't want to try again. Also omit anything that isn't representative of the work you can now do.

Jot down a review of what you see. Be critical but fair. Try to see it through someone else's eyes. Your list might look a bit like this:

✓This collection is mostly animal drawings, some people, a self-portrait, landscape paintings and some montages from high school, – plus pictures I did in Scientific Illustration class (some are good enough to put in a portfolio).

✓The media I used are pencil, colored pencil, ink, acrylics, photocopy/pen&ink, felt-tip markers, and computer art. I don't think I want to do colored pencils again.

✓My style is realistic, but I am better at animals than people at this point, and my plants are my best pieces.

✓I have samples of two business cards and a cartoon announcement I designed for my friend's graduation.

✓I have printouts of pages I designed for a friend's website.

✓My computer graphics experience is limited, but I've played with some word processing and graphics programs and know how to use a scanner. I can apply computer lettering and flow text, and I'm interested in improving and learning how to do more.

Need some pieces to fill out your repertoire? List subject matter and media that are missing. Combine missing media with missing subject matter — such as an *ink drawing of a mammal*. Now DO it.

Working as a volunteer at a local nature center or some other place that needs artwork will not only increase the scope of your portfolio, but foster sources who will be willing to write you a reference.

Do your best work at all times – a good portfolio piece and a referral to go with it are priceless. A careless or bad job can ruin your reputation.

Take your artwork to a copy shop and make b/w 8½" x 11" photocopies of line drawings and 8½" x 11" color or digital photocopies of halftone and color pieces. Get clean color printouts of your website. Create business cards. Make your portfolio as perfect as possible.

Invest in a presentation book (in the $3–$15 range) with clear pocket pages. In the better presentation books you can add or remove pages to accommodate the exact number of pieces you want to display. Insert your art pieces. Artistically arrange small pieces like business cards, and stick them onto a sheet of neutral-color paper with poster tape. If you do presentations, include some sample printouts.

Now you can now see what you have to offer a potential employer and get a realistic look at what a prospective employer will see. Make representative copies to leave with possible clients, and note down what you leave with them. Also create a set for yourself and add to it regularly.

YOUR RESUMÉ: Make a list of careers you might enjoy. Now, visualize an imaginary job you would like to apply for. Write a practice resumé for that job. Be realistic about your goals and capabilities. Go online for examples of how to write a good resumé.

Before starting:

• List all the things you do well and feel you could do day after day without getting bored, maxxed out or unduly stressed. Then list all the things you don't do well, don't enjoy, or need training or practice in.

• List your personality traits that would make you a good person for that job.

• Don't promote some aspect of yourself or your skills that you aren't prepared to do every day:

– If you aren't familiar with some aspect of a job, admit or omit it.

– If you don't enjoy something, don't promote your ability to do it.

• Ask someone whose opinion you respect to read over your resumé and point out any weak areas. If they'll look over your portfolio and critique it, as well, even better. Then pay attention to what they tell you and make any improvements you can.

Everyone has skills and strong points. Find out what yours are, then go for your dream. Good luck! ☺

(answers to the question on page 152)

In the box below are guidelines for a good business card. A number of other requirements for good card design were also noted as requirements on page 152. The "Bad" Card (below and on page 152) is not an actual card, but a composite from numerous cards containing the many errors that can cause a design/layout to fall short of its goal of presenting its bearer in the best possible light.

A remake, using the same information but adhering to the guidelines, is shown at the bottom of this page. Please inspect both cards carefully. The remake shows only one way the card could be greatly improved. Different solutions, utilizing other font choices and sizes, placement of graphic/s, alignment, etcetera, would also be possible.

By following these guidelines, you should be able to create an attractive, useful, professional-looking card.

BUSINESS CARD REQUIREMENTS:
- your name and skill (most important info) largest
- phone # (with area code), e-mail, fax, and website, if any
- a small piece of your original art as motif or logo
- leave a $1/8$" margin between non-bleeding art and the edge
- computer-generated text; correct capitalization, punctuation, and abbreviations; and spell-check it (butt dew knot deep end awn you're spill check her)
- no pixels should be evident on art
- no text should be smaller than 8pt.
- use no more than two fonts on card
- put no information or illustration in the zone that may be perforated with a rolodex punch

Note: the information above may also be found on page 152.

A. "BAD" CARD. This card shows common mistakes made in business card design.

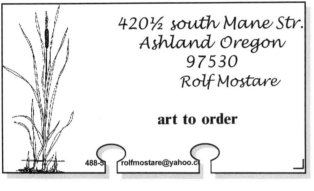

DISCUSSION OF DESIGN/LAYOUT A. PROBLEMS AT LEFT
- the name is smaller than the address
- the phone number has no area code
- Rolf's scanned art is coarse and pixelly at 100dpi resolution
- graphic is not level, tips of cattail just touch the edge – the graphic should either bleed or stay inside margin at least $1/8$"
- incorrect abbreviation for Street; Mane should be Main, but it passed the spell-check; South should be capitalized; 97520 is the zipcode, and a comma goes between Ashland and Oregon
- the text at the bottom (phone and e-mail) is smaller than 8pt
- there are three fonts on this card (two is maximum)
- the card may be in their Rolodex – but they'll never call...
- the card is only 1¾" x 3¼" (should be 2" x 3½")
- the bottom edge is cut crooked
- there must be a $3/16$" margin between text and edge of card
- text elements are placed without plan, they're not lined up with themselves, the edge, the margin, or the art
- incorrect crop marks show on the card (lower right corner)
- while not specifically mentioned on page 152, the elements on this card are not balanced – notice the large empty space
- both name and skill are not in top half of card

B. "GOOD" CARD. Here is a remake using the same information. Possibilities are limitless.

DISCUSSION OF DESIGN/LAYOUT B. IMPROVEMENTS AT LEFT
- text sizes for all subjects are proportionally correct
- all info is spelled, punctuated, and capitalized correctly
- art was scanned at a higher resolution (300 dpi) and leveled; pulled back $1/8$" at top and allowed to bleed on left
- three fonts were replaced by a single, more integrating font
- contact info was enlarged and moved out of Rolodex zone
- card was given the correct measurements, and cut straight
- a $3/16$ +" margin was left between text and edge of card
- text was lined up with itself, and centered in non-art area
- correctly-made crop marks disappeared when card was cut
- both name and skill are in the top half of the card

Index

a list of
STUDENT ART CONTRIBUTORS
and the pages on which their
art appears may be found on
next page.

STUDENT ART CONTRIBUTORS

Jerry Aikins 36, 68, 131
Steve Ballew 13
Aubrey Bayley 50
Mudra Bergan 20, 36
Allison Dew 95
Kyle Emry 86
Andrea Fraga 121
Jamie Heinzelmann 118
Hillary Hulen 43, 133
Nicolaj Imhof 38, 118
Lea Johnson 98
Noelle Jordan 122
Vera Kirkpatrick 89, 121
Andrew Marohl 38
Allyson McCauley 16
Zoë Magnolia McLean 50
Deanna Moore 36
Lisa Sanchez Navarro 133
Megan O'Donnell 25, 133
Michelle Olson 36
Wendy Olson 70, 121
Matt Paroulek 121
Julie Proctor 50
Lin Roden 118
Christian Runge 58
Mary Schnur 16
Peter Schroeder 58, 88, 121
Theresa Selvy 36, 82
Rachel Showalter 66, 118, 136
Holly Smith 86
Heidi Soroken 58, 88, 121, 128
Robert Sweeney 117
Ilona Sweeten 126, 132
Bianca Tapia 123
Sara Trakselis 18, 47, 50, 70
Shannon Troy 126
Elizabeth Wasserman 95
Melinda Whipple-Smith 16, 77
Eugene Wier 133
Dylan Zodrow 43, 132